BIOTOPES
OF THE WESTERN
ARABIAN GULF

MARINE LIFE AND ENVIRONMENTS OF SAUDI ARABIA

BIOTOPES

OF THE WESTERN ARABIAN GULF

MARINE LIFE AND ENVIRONMENTS OF SAUDI ARABIA

Philip W. Basson
John E. Burchard, Jr.
John T. Hardy
Andrew R. G. Price

illustrated and designed by
Lisa Bobrowski

Published by the Aramco Department of Loss Prevention
and Environmental Affairs, Dhahran, Saudi Arabia

U.S. LIBRARY OF CONGRESS NO. 77 71593
ISBN 0-9601164-1-9

Second Edition, 1981

Printed in Great Britain by Shenval '80', Harlow

Frontispiece (preceding page). Two male crabs (Grapsidae sp. 7) fighting. This crab, typical of the Macrophthalmus *zone of tidal mud flats, is a predator on small* Ocypodidae, *especially* Scopimera *spp. and juvenile* Macrophthalmus. *[Tarut Island]*
(Photo by John Hardy)

FOREWORD

A prime function of a biotope handbook is to provide a thorough description of different habitats and the main organisms inhabiting them. The authors have achieved this goal in their description of beaches, tidal flats, hard and soft subtidal bottoms, subtidal grassbeds, coral reefs, artificial or man-made structures, plankton, nekton and hypersaline lagoons – all biotopes of the Western Arabian Gulf.

The authors take particular care to determine the factors of the environment that are responsible for the growth and maintenance of a given biotope and they explain the special adaptations of organisms to each. These two sets of information add a natural history dimension to this book.

Special sections treat the sea grasses and their role in the ecosystem. Added attention is given to the sea turtle and the life history of the commercial shrimp and pearl oyster. The book is alive with first rate photographs and illustrations that tell the story of the habits of many of the species of marine life in Saudi Arabia.

A species list is provided in the appendix, although many of the entries have not yet been given a scientific name. Cataloging all the plants and animals remains a task for future biologists and trained systematists. A species when correctly named scientifically becomes a biological standard permitting the scientist to measure its presence or absence with time and events such as pollution or construction. Fortunately the animals and plants listed in the appendix are preserved in the Aramco biology collections.

The authors are to be commended for having been able to synthesize a wealth of diverse information. This is a first and pioneering effort and it will likely remain a standard reference to Arabian Gulf marine biology for many years to come.

R. J. Menzies
Tallahassee, Florida
October 12, 1976

PREFACE

Comparatively little is known about the natural history of the Arabian Gulf. As early as 1762 the Arabian peninsula was visited by a Danish survey expedition, including the zoologist P. Forsskål, whose findings were published posthumously in 1775 and contain the first scientific descriptions of many marine animals and plants subsequently found in the Arabian Gulf. In the two hundred years since then, several scientific expeditions have worked in the Gulf. The most important of these include the Danish fishery investigations of 1937–38, the visit of the German oceanographic vessel *Meteor* in 1965, and that of the Japanese fisheries training ship *Umitaka Maru* in 1968. Important contributions have also been made by scientific teams working on sedimentary processes along the coast of the United Arab Emirates (Purser, 1973), by biologists at Kuwait University, and by fishery scientists in several countries bordering the Gulf. Few of these studies, however, have been primarily ecological, and most of them have concentrated on the eastern part of the Gulf. As a result, the marine biology of the western Arabian Gulf has remained very incompletely known. Aramco, as an oil company operating in eastern Saudi Arabia and in the Saudi Arabian waters of the Arabian Gulf, began ecological studies of this region as part of its environmental studies program in 1971. In 1974 Dr R. J. Menzies (December 2, 1923–December 18, 1976), acting as a consultant to the Aramco program, suggested that the findings be published in a generally accessible form. This book is the tangible result of his suggestion.

This book makes no claim to being truly comprehensive; rather it should be seen as a first step in the direction of a fully detailed, scientific account of the western Arabian Gulf. With this in mind, we have attempted to fulfill two objectives. Our main purpose has been to present a general picture of, and an appreciation for, the environments and biological communities occurring in the western Arabian Gulf, an account which we hope will be of interest to biologists and the general reader alike. Secondly, we have endeavored to summarize the present state of biological and oceanographic knowledge of the region, hoping that our photographs, drawings, and species lists will provide at least a partial reference base for future researchers. Realizing that the non-specialist may be deterred by a text cluttered with footnotes and bristling with technical terms, we have reduced both to a reasonable minimum, and provided an additional aid in the form of a glossary of specialized scientific terms. Those in search of additional information, such as species lists for particular biotopes, should refer to Section IV (Appendices) of the book. These lists more than double the number of species previously identified from the Arabian Gulf.

Chapter 1 provides the reader with an introduction to the concept of biotopes. Then, in sequence from the shore to the open sea, the book contains three sections – Intertidal Biotopes, Subtidal Biotopes and Water Column Biotopes. Each section is further subdivided in accordance with the dominant species or characteristics of the biotope under discussion.

Though the authors assume that most of their readers will have a special interest in marine biology, they hope also to appeal to general readers, awakening them to the complex interrelationships that exist among all organisms in a biological community, and helping them to appreciate why respect and understanding of the earth's environment are essential to man's well-being.

The authors wish to thank the Engineering/Consulting Services/Environmental Unit of Aramco for help in initiating this project, and for their interest and financial support in developing it. Their help in placing the facilities of Aramco at the authors' disposal is keenly appreciated, for without their continuing assistance the time-consuming processes of data gathering, classification and analysis would have proceeded less smoothly than they did. Most directly involved were C. J. Walters, D. G. Barbee and R. A. Ebner.

For making publication of this volume possible, special thanks are also due to the Department of Loss Prevention and Environmental Affairs, especially W. L. Johnston, Director of Loss Prevention and Environmental Affairs, and to R. A. Ebner, Chief Environmental Affairs Engineer.

The authors also wish to thank the following for various specialized services – Dr Priscilla Basson for statistical analyses; Saroj Britto, Ailsa Clark (British Museum), Lorraine Johansen and Kay Taylor for assistance with invertebrate identifications; Dr George F. Papenfuss for discussions and references on algal identifications, Nasim Maluf and Amal Murad for meiofauna analyses, Sheila Hardy for seawater chemical analyses, Dr Willis B. Hayes for library research, Dr Sami Lakkis for zooplankton identifications, Mary Jane Altebarmakian for phytoplankton analyses, James P. Mandaville Jr for assistance in identification of flowering plants, and Dr J. M. Munro for editorial assistance.

We also wish to acknowledge the contributions made by Saleh M. Redaini, Sarah Kochinski, Dr Martin Giesen, and Mohammed Ayub in the early stages of the development of this book. In addition, thanks are also due to Zafar Malik for efficient logistical support, and to the helicopter pilots of Petroleum Helicopters, Inc, and to the crews of the *Gulf Princess* and *Qatif 7* for their care and patience during sampling trips; and to Noreen Franco – a hearty thanks for typing the manuscript. We are deeply appreciative of the efforts of all persons who have helped us.

The Authors

CONTENTS

1
ORGANISMS AND ENVIRONMENT-
AN INTRODUCTION

THE BIOTOPE CONCEPT

Along the shores of Saudi Arabia, in the western Arabian Gulf, are found a variety of different habitats for marine life. These habitats, together with the animals and plants that live in them, form a series of recognizable entities called **biotopes.**

The dictionary defines a biotope as a "region uniform in environmental conditions and in its populations of animals and plants for which it is the habitat" (Webster's New Collegiate Dictionary, 1973).

In actual fact, however, there is no such thing as a region uniform in environmental conditions. Rather, environmental conditions constantly change in time, and the pattern of these changes varies from one place to another. The biological community found in a given habitat is the combined result of many factors, not least of which are the interactions among the organisms themselves. Such interactions include various types of energy exchange, and competition for resources such as space, food, or in the case of plants, light.

Over a range of environmental conditions, therefore, one combination of species, bound together by complex patterns of energy exchange, will succeed in dominating the competitive relationships. Where environmental conditions are sufficiently different, another combination of species will dominate instead. Such recognizably different biological associations are called communities, and their occurrence normally reflects consistent differences in environmental conditions.

In other words, the endlessly varying habitats of a major biological province or region, such as the Arabian Gulf, can be classified into a limited number of fairly easily distinguishable biotopes, according to the plant and animal communities which inhabit them. Although this "biotope concept" tends to over-simplify the nature of the organism-environment relationships which form the subject of ecology, it does provide a convenient framework on which to arrange what would otherwise be a confusing mass of detailed information, and for that reason has been used as the organizing principle of this book.

Biologists group communities of marine plants and animals into categories according to their habitat. Organisms and communities living in or on the bottom are called benthos (adjective: benthic). Plankton are small or microscopic plants and animals which drift around more or less passively suspended in the water, while nekton are larger animals such as fish and sea turtles, whose distribution is determined primarily by their own powerful locomotor capabilities rather than by the movement of water masses. Neuston is a term applied to specialized organisms living on or at the air-water interface at the surface of the sea.

Within these large categories, it is convenient to make some further subdivisions. Benthic communities are usually classified according to depth, since the depth of water directly affects important variables of the physical environment, such as light, temperature and wave energy. The most important such subdivision is into intertidal communities, which are intermittently exposed to air and direct sunlight by the rise and fall of the tide, and subtidal ones which are always covered by water. Further subdivisions based on depth occur within the subtidal benthos. Another important factor affecting benthic communities is the physical nature of the

Fig 1. The starfish Pentaceraster mammillatus, *one of the most conspicuous inhabitants of deeper sand bottoms, is 20 to 25 cm across, and bright red or orange in color. This individual was brought up from the bottom at 15 m and photographed on the beach. [Jana Island]*

bottom, and particularly whether it consists of hard rocky material, or of softer sediment into which animals can burrow.

Communities of the plankton and nekton also show a well-marked depth zonation, related primarily to the penetration of light into the sea. Because the Arabian Gulf is extremely shallow, however, depth zonation of the open-water biotopes is of relatively minor importance within the Gulf, except where summer density stratification of the water can lead to vertical differences in plankton density. Well-defined changes do occur, especially in plankton communities, depending upon their distance from the shore.

Using this principle, the biotopes described in this book are arranged under three main headings: **intertidal benthos** (Chapters 2 and 3), **subtidal benthos** (Chapters 4, 5, 6 and 7) and **water column biotopes** including both plankton and nekton (Chapters 8, 9 and 10). The fact that benthic biotopes take up the greater part of the book, reflects a universal tendency for benthic habitats to be more varied in physical character than those of the open water, and therefore to include a greater variety of biological communities. Because of the shallowness of the Gulf, benthic biotopes play an even greater role in the overall ecological picture here than elsewhere.

LEVELS OF BIOLOGICAL ORGANIZATION

Organisms interact with one another and with their environment in many different ways, and to understand these relationships it is convenient to classify them according to the "level of organization" at which they occur. This concept, which is used in all branches of biology, considers every living system in terms of a hierarchical series of levels of organization or integration. For instance, the human body is made up of organ systems composed of organs, which in turn are made up of tissues; the tissues are composed of cells and cell products, the cells of various subcellular structures, these in turn of molecules, and so on.

In the ecological context, which concerns us here, the lowest level of organization is that of the individual organism. Finding and consuming food, escaping from predators, migration, mating and other activities are all performed by individual animals; photosynthesis, uptake of nutrients, growth and reproduction are the corresponding plant functions. The next higher level is that of a whole population of organisms all belonging to the same species. The dynamics of single-species populations is a study in its own right, and can have great practical importance, for example in the management of fishery resources. The population dynamics of the human species is a subject of urgent concern for everyone, because of the continuing uncontrolled expansion of the human population, a phenomenon without real parallels in the ecology of other species.

Populations of several different species, occurring together in the same environment and interacting by way of energy transfers, symbiotic relationships, etc., can be considered collectively as a biological community. Several communities interacting with each other and with a particular physical environment are called an ecosystem. All the ecosystems of the world are sometimes referred to collectively as the biosphere.

These concepts can be illustrated by using the common Gulf shrimp *Penaeus semisulcatus* as an example. An individual shrimp is adapted to its environment by innumerable details of structure and behavior. For example, shrimp have a "physiological clock" which regulates their activity so that they move and feed at night and hide during the daytime, a pattern which favors escape from predators. They are able to change color to match the bottom on which they rest, a feature which also helps to protect them from enemies. They dig, walk, swim, and capture and manipulate food by means of incredibly complicated coordination patterns involving six pairs of swimming paddles, five pairs of walking legs, six pairs of appendages serving as mouth parts, and two pairs of feelers or antennae. The neurological programs controlling all these activities are the outcome of a long process of evolution and are almost entirely under genetic control; the learning capacity of a shrimp is extremely limited. Furthermore, larval and juvenile shrimp occupy quite different habitats from the adults, and both their structure and their behavior are adapted to their respective ways of life.

Commercial shrimp fishermen are concerned, in an empirical sort of way, with a few aspects of individual shrimp behavior. Fishing is conducted at night when shrimp are active; and the nets must be towed faster than a shrimp can swim to prevent shrimp from simply escaping out the open front of the net. The fishermen's main concern, however, is with features of the shrimp population, and in particular with its density which determines how many shrimp can be caught, and its reproductive capacity which determines the rate of recovery of a depleted stock.

These features must be studied at the population level, since they cannot be derived from information about individual shrimp. The dynamics of a shrimp fishery resource can, to a considerable extent, be treated as a self-contained subject at the species population level, by means of formulae relating the existing population size, the rate of removal of shrimp by fishing, natural mortality, or other factors, and the recruitment or rate of addition of young shrimp to the population.

To understand the effects of changing environmental conditions, however, it is not sufficient to consider only their direct effects on the shrimp. A change in temperature, salinity, or the concentration of dissolved nutrients might not affect shrimp directly at all, but could still make the difference between their survival and their disappearance in a given area (for instance by affecting the food supply of some other animals which in turn are eaten by shrimp). Questions of this sort must, therefore, be studied in terms of the entire community of which the shrimp form a part.

For some questions, however, even a community-level analysis may not suffice. This is partly because communities themselves interact; an increase in the extent of one community in a region is likely to occur at the expense of a decrease in the extent of one or more others. Furthermore, shrimp belong to several different communities at different stages in their life cycle, and so participate in a very wide range of ecological interactions. Larval shrimp belong to the plankton; juveniles inhabit shallow beds of sea grass; and adults shift about, in ways as yet poorly understood, among several types of subtidal sedimentary biotopes. Some of the problems of shrimp biology, therefore, can be dealt with adequately only by understanding the entire ecosystem of which these communities form a part.

KINDS AND NUMBERS OF ORGANISMS

When any new habitat or region is investigated, the first biological information to be gathered is usually a list of the kinds of plants and animals to be found there. Such lists are never exhaustive, since more species are still being found even in well-studied habitats, but even at an early stage they serve to identify the most important actors in community events. Knowing the name of a plant or animal is, in most cases, likely to provide a good deal of information about its life history, food habits, etc., since many of the common species will have been studied in one or more of these respects by biologists elsewhere.

In most environments a few species of organisms are abundant, while the great majority are rare. Measuring the abundance of the important species in a community is an obvious step toward the quantitative analysis of community structure. In practice this usually involves counting the numbers of individuals collected within some standard area or volume.

In studies of community metabolism, however, it is often desirable to compare the contribution or activity of organisms of very different sizes, for instance whales and the plankton on which they feed. For such purposes, numbers of individuals would not be a useful unit of measurement. It is more informative to compare the populations of such disparate organisms in terms of biomass, which is simply the weight or mass, expressed in appropriate standard units, of all the organisms in the species population.

Biomass units can also be used to express the abundance of organisms in a unit area or volume of the habitat, or in samples of defined size taken from the habitat. The units of biomass are the same as those in which primary production is measured, so that it is possible to compare the amount of energy flowing through a system with the amount stored in any component population or in the system as a whole.

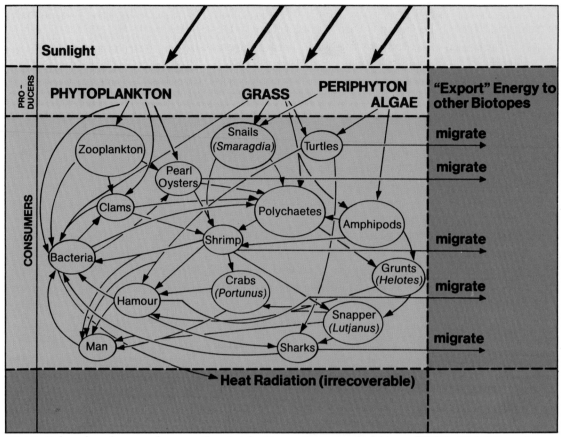

Fig 2. Selected pathways of energy flow in the Tarut Bay grassbed biotope, with special attention to shrimp and hamour. The diagram also shows how a highly productive biotope, such as the grassbed, can provide surplus energy which becomes available to organisms in other biotopes.

PRODUCTION RATES OF ECOSYSTEMS

Living organisms require a continuous supply of energy in order to carry on their activities. With some insignificant exceptions, all of the energy that fuels biological processes is derived from sunlight. Green plants, by means of chlorophyll and a few other pigments, convert the energy of sunlight into energy-rich organic compounds, especially glucose, using carbon dioxide and water as raw materials. This process is called photosynthesis. The energy-rich compounds serve as fuel not only for the growth and metabolism of the plants, but also for any animals that may eat them; a portion of this energy may be passed on to a second animal that eats the first, or acquired by decay bacteria when a plant or animal dies. Such energy transfers can be summarized in a food web or energy flow diagram (Fig 2).

Two kinds of information are required to construct a working model of community energy dynamics. To make a map of the pathways along which energy is transferred from one population to another, qualitative data on "who eats whom" are required. To give quantitative meaning to such a map, however, it is also necessary to know how much energy is available to the system, how much is tied up in each population, and how much moves along the various pathways in a given time period.

Quantitative measurements of this kind are particularly important for evaluating how much exploitation – for instance, the harvest of shrimp by fishermen – an ecosystem can sustain without damage. Unfortunately, such measurements are very difficult and time-consuming, and only a few of the world's ecosystems have so far been studied with sufficient thoroughness to provide adequate data for exact quantitative models.

A great deal of useful information, however, especially for purposes of comparison, can be obtained by measuring the "primary production" or "primary productivity," which is the rate of production of organic matter due to photosynthesis by the producer organisms. This

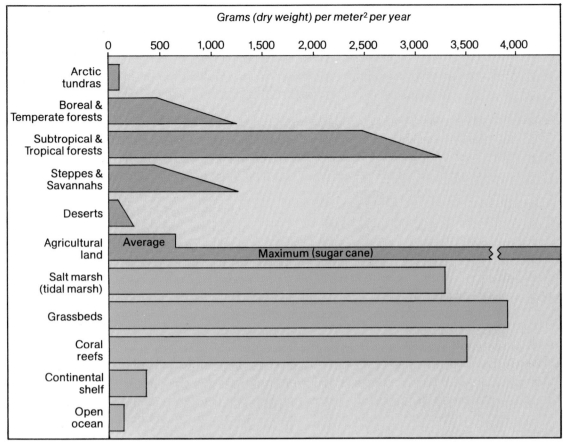

Fig 3. Comparative production rates of terrestrial and aquatic ecosystems. Grassbeds, coral reefs and tidal marshes are the most productive marine biotopes, and constitute a valuable resource. The numbers in this figure are only approximations, derived by combining results obtained by various methods and expressed in units for which only rough conversion factors are applicable. Based on Krebs (1972) and Yentsch (1963).

represents the total energy available to a specific community or ecosystem. Many conclusions can be drawn on the basis of such measurements, even without detailed knowledge of how the energy is distributed within the system under consideration. Losses occur as an inevitable feature of all energy transfers within the community, and also by the "export" of energy in various forms to other parts of the ecosystem. Normally the losses balance the net primary production, and the community biomass remains approximately constant. Cyclic seasonal changes in biomass are, however, a common feature of many biotopes; and natural or artificial changes in environmental conditions may result in a more permanent increase or decrease of biomass. Such changes are regularly accompanied by changes in the community structure, since what is really involved is the establishment of a new and different state of equilibrium.

Ecosystems differ greatly in their relative productivity (Fig. 3). Marine ecosystems are generally less productive than terrestrial ones; but the productivity of the most productive marine ecosystems – coral reefs, tidal marshes and grassbeds – can approach or exceed that of intensively managed agricultural land.[1]

All three of the most productive marine ecosystem types occur in the western Arabian Gulf, where they play an important role in the regional ecosystem; but they could be seriously threatened by land development involving the filling and dredging of coastal areas. Such development patterns can cause a serious and permanent reduction in the marine productivity of an entire region.

1 Certain spectacular claims for agricultural production rates, far exceeding those measured for any natural ecosystem, are apparently based on extrapolation of short-term daily or hourly rate measurements, which could not possibly be sustained for an entire growing season.

FACTORS LIMITING PRODUCTIVITY

Photosynthesis requires light, water and carbon dioxide, and also small amounts of certain other substances, known as nutrients, which are essential for the growth or metabolism of the photosynthetic organisms. In the sea, water is always available, and carbon dioxide is not normally a limiting factor. The energy production of marine ecosystems is limited by the availability of light, and frequently also by the availability of certain nutrients, of which the most important are phosphates, nitrogen compounds and silicates.

Light sufficient to sustain useful primary production penetrates even the clearest sea water to a maximum depth of only about 100m. Where plankton or sediment is abundant, the depth of effective penetration (euphotic zone) is much less. This means that all the energy which sustains marine ecosystems is produced in a thin surface layer amounting to only about 1/300 of the volume of the sea. The deeper layers make no contribution to total production, though they do play a large role in the conversion of this production into forms of direct interest to man, such as edible fish.

Much of the open ocean is a "biological desert" of low productivity. Coastal waters are usually much more productive. Intertidal biotopes, whose area in comparison with that of the ocean is insignificant, can be extremely productive. The energy input from some intertidal plants such as mangroves can be of great importance on a local or regional scale, as in Saudi Arabia.

Whole volumes have been written on the distribution of nutrients in sea water and the way in which they control production rates. Nitrogen compounds, phosphates, and sometimes silicates can occur in sea water in such low concentrations that their availability limits the rate of photosynthesis. In deep oceanic waters nutrients are constantly being removed from the surface layer because many plankton organisms (with the nutrients bound in organic form within their tissues) die and sink below the euphotic layer before they are eaten. This "rain" of organic matter sustains the animals living in the deeper parts of the sea; but it also removes nutrients from the surface layers, and may severely restrict productivity as a consequence.

Large areas of the open sea are actually among the world's least productive ecosystems (Fig 3), and in this respect they are strictly comparable with the arctic tundra or arid desert. In certain geographical areas, however, the natural circulation of the oceans brings nutrient-laden deep water masses to the surface in a phenomenon known as "up-welling." Such areas are immensely productive, and support dense populations of plankton and plankton-eating fish, as well as most of the world's richest fisheries.

The most famous up-welling area is probably the Humboldt Current off the coast of South America; but similar if less spectacular phenomena occur in many parts of the world. Up-welling occurs in the Arabian Sea adjacent to the southern coast of the Arabian peninsula, and contributes to the rich fishery resources of that area. Within the Arabian Gulf, however, the water is far too shallow for up-welling to occur.

In continental shelf areas generally, including the Arabian Gulf, nutrient distribution follows a somewhat different pattern. Plankton organisms sink not into the depths of the sea, from which their contained nutrients can be recovered only by up-welling, but onto the shallow bottom, where they support densely populated benthic communities of various types. In some areas the bottom may actually lie within the euphotic zone, and sustain high rates of primary production by benthic algae, sea grasses or coral reefs.

In any case, vertical mixing by wind and tide is usually sufficient to bring about effective recycling of the nutrients, which are therefore not lost from the euphotic zone to the same degree as in oceanic areas. Nutrients are, furthermore, constantly being added to the system from nearby land areas, since run-off and river waters generally contain much higher nutrient concentrations than the sea. As a result there is a general tendency for nutrient levels, and primary production rates, to be higher in coastal and continental shelf areas than in the open sea, except for the up-welling areas already mentioned. A gradation of nutrient concentrations, as a function of distance from the land, has even been recorded within the confines of the Arabian Gulf.

SPECIES INTERACTIONS

Like the biology of a single species, the interactions between organisms of different species can be investigated at several different levels. Shrimp, for example, are a favorite prey of the common Arabian Gulf grouper known as hamour, *Epinephelus tauvina*. At the individual level, this prey-predator interaction involves hunting and swallowing behavior on the part of the hamour, and hiding and escape behavior on the part of the shrimp. At the population level, predation by hamour is one of many items making up the "natural mortality" part of the shrimp population equation. At the community level, shrimp are one of many food resources available to hamour. That a thriving shrimp population is of benefit to hamour is fairly obvious. What is much less obvious is that predation by hamour has a beneficial effect on the shrimp population, since predation helps to keep shrimp from increasing to the point of depleting their own food supply, and even more importantly tends to remove sick or unfit individuals from the population, thereby maintaining the overall standard of adaptation or fitness. The individual shrimp caught by a hamour cannot be expected to appreciate these benefits, but they are perfectly real nevertheless.[2]

The prey-predator relationship between shrimp and hamour is an example of a trophic interaction.[3] It is important to realize that relationships of this kind are not in any sense examples of "competition." Prey populations are essential to the survival of predators, and predators are probably equally essential to the survival of the prey populations. This is, incidentally, a particularly graphic illustration of the fact that population survival does not necessarily imply the survival of any particular individual! True competition exists, however, between populations of different prey species exposed to the same predators, and likewise between different predator species exploiting the same prey resources. The outcome of this sort of competition is normally increased adaptation or fitness of all the participants, or in other words, evolutionary progress. Extinction (of some species in some places) is an incidental consequence of the process, but by no means an essential feature.[4] When two similar species compete for the same resource, one will usually displace the other on a strictly local scale. Over a range of habitat conditions, however, the advantage will seldom be all one way, and the usual outcome is for each species to become specialized for exploiting a different part or feature of the habitat. This specialized role or function of a species in the overall community is termed its "niche."

Special relationships between organisms of different species, involving more or less intimate association of the partners, are called by the general term symbiosis, meaning living together. Such relationships may be mutualistic, or beneficial to both partners, as in the case of reef corals and their photosynthetic flagellates or zooxanthellae. More commonly, however, most of the benefit accrues to one of the partners, as in the case of the numerous commensal relationships in which one species takes advantage of the food-gathering or house-building activities of another, without actually causing it any harm. When one of the partners obtains a benefit, usually in the form of food or energy, at the direct expense of the other, the relationship is called parasitic. Tropical, shallow-water marine habitats feature a bewildering variety of symbiotic relationships among different species of organisms, and many examples are described in this book.

2 The same benefits cannot, unfortunately, be claimed for most cases of human predation on populations of wild animals, since the means of capture – a trawl net in the case of shrimp – are generally much less selective than any nonhuman predator. The response of human predation levels to changes in prey population size is also much less sensitive than that of typical nonhuman predators, which shift their prey selection to match changes in the relative availability of different prey species.

3 Trophic interactions involve the transfer of energy from one organism to another, as for instance when one eats the other. Such relationships always imply dependence, in that one organism population forms a "resource" for another which obtains energy from it. These relationships are usually portrayed in a "food web" diagram (Fig 2), depicting the flow of energy through a community or ecosystem.

4 Interactions of man with other species are leading with ever-increasing frequency to the extinction of the latter, even in cases where the relationship is obviously not competitive. This is yet another aspect in which human ecology differs radically from that of other species.

DIVERSITY AND STABILITY

An outstanding feature of most naturally occurring communities and ecosystems is their stability. Small changes or disturbances, including those caused by human activities, tend to be repaired or restored in the course of time, so that the community persists over a considerable period. Although the details are a subject of some controversy among ecologists of different opinions, such stability is generally regarded as being closely related to the diversity of the community or ecosystem concerned. Many of the interactions among different species have the property of "negative feedback," which is to say they tend to compensate for minor changes in the system. It follows that systems with many such interlocking relationships should be more stable and less prone to spontaneous fluctuations than systems with very few pathways of interaction. The principle can be illustrated by a hypothetical example based on the interaction of shrimp and hamour. If shrimp are only one out of 100 species available to hamour as food, a sudden decline in shrimp populations, caused by some extraneous factor or perhaps by unusual weather conditions, will simply result in hamour eating fewer shrimp and marginally more of the other 99 species available to them. The predator pressure exerted by hamour on the shrimp population will decrease, improving the survival chances of individual shrimp and leading to an early recovery of the shrimp population.

If on the other hand shrimp are the only species available as food to hamour, a sudden decline in the shrimp population will probably cause starvation of many hamour, and an eventual decline in their number. Before starving, however, the hamour will make substantial inroads on the remaining shrimp population, driving shrimp abundance to a very low level. Once the hamour have starved, the remaining shrimp, if any, will have a chance to recover. Because there are now few hamour, the shrimp will suffer little predation and will probably multiply inordinately – the result: a shrimp "population explosion." Hamour, because of their much longer life cycle, will take several years to catch up. When they do, however, their population will probably continue to increase until limited by the availability of shrimp. At this point over-predation by hamour will cause a catastrophic collapse of the shrimp population, followed by starvation of most of the hamour, and so on. This type of interaction is called a prey-predator cycle, and is obviously an unstable condition likely to lead to the extinction of one or both of the participants.

A crude but useful comparison of the quantitative aspect of energy flow and accumulation in different communities is possible using the concepts of biomass and primary production, quantities which can be measured – in spite of certain practical difficulties – much more easily than making a complete analysis of all the energy exchanges within a community. It would obviously be useful if similar measures could be developed for the short-hand description of qualitative community features as well. What is needed is some way of estimating the number of different kinds of pathways available for energy flow in a given community or biotope. While this is in some respects a much more difficult problem, due to the extreme complexity of any adequate description of all the interactions taking place in a community, an approach is possible through what is called the species diversity concept.

Several different methods of expressing diversity are in common use among ecologists, and there is no general agreement as to which is the best, nor indeed as to precisely what is meant by "diversity." If, however, the main use of a diversity index is to compare the variety of metabolic pathways available in different communities, or in different occurrences of the same community, it is possible to state some of the requirements such an index must meet. Since each additional species in a community necessarily adds several metabolic pathways, a useful diversity index must increase (other things being equal) as the number of species in the community or sample increases. It must also be responsive to the relative abundance of species within the community. If 99% of the biomass of a given community consists of a single species, most of the community energy supply will flow through the relatively few pathways involving that species, and the other pathways will be quantitatively insignificant. A good diversity index should, therefore, increase (other things being equal) in proportion to the evenness of distribution of the biomass among the species in the community. In other words, it should be maximal when all species are equally abundant, and minimal when one species completely dominates the community. One index meeting these requirements, as well as being independent of the size of the sample for which it is computed, has been used in the study of Arabian Gulf biotopes, and is described in detail in the Appendix (p 203). This index expresses the probability that two organisms, drawn at random from the biotope or a sample of it, will belong to different species. Its value ranges from 0, when all the individuals belong to the same species, to a maximum of 1, when each individual belongs to a different species.

Although ecologists are by no means unanimous as to what controls the diversity of biological communities, it is fairly clear that environmental stress of many kinds tends to lower diversity. Spectacular population cycles, such as the prey-predator oscillation just described, are well known from laboratory experiments with artificial communities containing only a few species. A well-known natural example is that of the lemmings, which live in a low-diversity community in a highly stressed Arctic environment. A highly stressed, species-poor, hypersaline environment is described in this book, and spectacular population fluctuations of the main organism, the flagellate *Dunaliella salina,* occur there. On a more modest scale, the constant impact of waves on a beach is also a stress factor, and open coast beaches actually do have a measurably less diverse biota than similar beaches located within protected bays.

Human intervention is, almost without exception, a stress factor in this sense, and causes reduced diversity in the affected communities. Conversely, diversity measurements on different occurrences of a given community type are a very useful indicator of the extent of human impact on the biological system. The reduction of diversity is obvious when, for example, a species is hunted to extinction, or when accumulation of poisonous chemicals such as DDT causes the disappearance of key predators, such as the peregrine falcon, from large areas of the earth's surface. Less obvious, but in some respects more instructive, is diversity reduction brought about by changes in the trophic status of whole communities. Paradoxically, an increase in the energy supply to a community, by way of excessive nutrient enrichment, can be a potent cause of ecological decline or even collapse.

The production rates of different marine biotopes, generally speaking, seem to depend more or less directly on the availability of nutrients. From this observation, it is tempting to conclude that it should be possible to increase the productivity of any particular community of interest to man, for example the grassbeds supporting a shrimp fishery, by simply adding more nutrients, in a manner similar to the use of chemical fertilizers in agriculture.[5] Such expectations are misleading, however, and production enhancement by nutrient addition is possible only within fairly narrow limits. Nutrient addition beyond these limits typically brings about qualitative degradation of the ecosystem, and is therefore usually called pollution. This is because any major change in nutrient availability or production rate does not benefit all members of the community equally; such changes affect not only the amount of energy flowing through the community, but also the way in which it is distributed. While large nutrient additions commonly do result in increased productivity as measured by energy flow through the system, the amount of energy ending up in the form of "desirable" species, such as commercially valuable fish, generally declines, while that going into the production of "undesirable" species, such as bacteria or algae, increases. The biomass of such an over-fertilized community increases, but its diversity markedly decreases. If nutrient addition is continued beyond this point, a situation is likely to result in which the decomposition necessary for recycling of the large biomass consumes all of the available oxygen, and the whole community collapses into a condition of very low biomass and near zero diversity, with a large residue of unused energy in the form of un-oxidized organic matter. This sequence of events is called eutrophication, and a well-known illustration is a sewage collection pond.

5 This comparison ignores the all-important fact that the artificially simplified communities of terrestrial agriculture require continuous, intensive manipulation to ensure that a significant part of the fertilizer input is channeled into products useful to man. Without seeding, cultivating, spraying and the input of vast quantities of energy – typically several times the energy yield of the crops obtained – modern intensive agriculture would be unthinkable.

Fig 4. Ras al-Mish'ab, seen from the air, exhibits many characteristic features of the Saudi Arabian coastline, including a typical hook-shaped sand spit, lagoons, and tidal channels. Submerged grassbeds show clearly through the water as dark patches.
(Photograph by John Hardy)

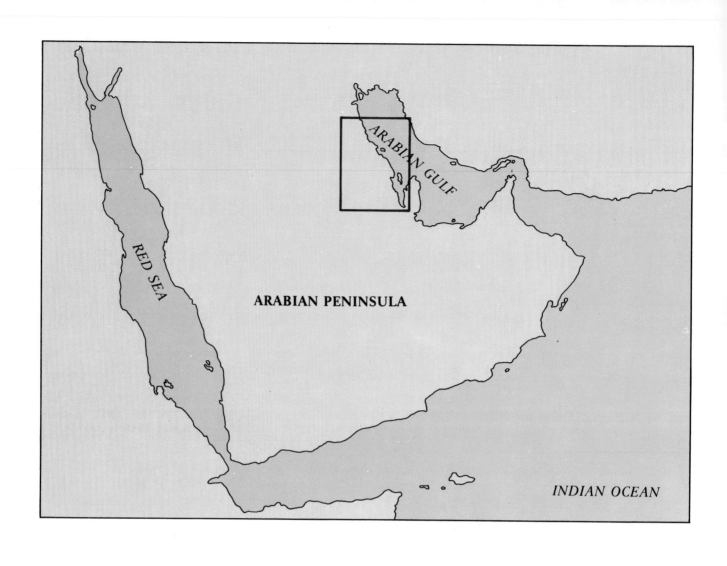

Fig 5. The Arabian peninsula. The study area from Ras al-Mish'ab to Salwah is enclosed in the blue rectangle and is shown in detail in Fig 6.

THE PHYSICAL ENVIRONMENT

Geologically speaking, the Arabian Gulf is a relatively recent addition to the world's seas. It was formed by movements of the earth's crust when the land mass of Arabia broke away from the African continent, leaving a gap today filled by the Red Sea. The other edge of the Arabian plate was forced up against the continent of Asia, forming the Zagros mountain range in the compression zone where the two plates met. A further result of this movement was a gentle downward warping of the eastern part of the Arabian plate, which was eventually forced below sea level to form the present floor of the Gulf.

The eastward migration of the Arabian plate began in the Miocene period, but the Arabian Gulf itself probably formed in late Pliocene times, only three or four million years ago. Later, during each of the Pleistocene glacial periods, large amounts of water were locked up on land in the form of ice, and a world-wide lowering of sea level took place. At their maximum these lowerings amounted to about 120m and completely emptied the Gulf basin, which at these times amounted to a wide shallow valley with the combined waters of the Tigris and Euphrates rivers flowing along its bottom, to reach the sea near the present-day location of the Strait of Hormuz. The Gulf has thus been reduced to the status of an estuary several times during its relatively short history. The most recent such episode ended less than 20,000 years ago and was followed by a progressive rise in sea level known as the "Flandrian Transgression," which filled the Gulf again. The sea reached approximately its present level only about 5,000 years ago (Kassler, 1973).

The Gulf has three important features. It is, in the first place, an extremely shallow sea, with an average depth of only 35m and a maximum reaching only 100m. The floor of the Gulf thus lies entirely within the depth range normally considered as belonging to the continental shelf. The surface waters and coastal shallows undergo wide rapid temperature changes in response to daily and seasonal cycles of heating and cooling. These fluctuations are not damped, as they are in most seas, by the thermal inertia of a large mass of deeper water. On the contrary, strong winds result in frequent and thorough mixing of the entire water column, and vertical temperature gradients are usually small, except in late summer when some density stratification can occur. Most Gulf biotopes are therefore subjected to far greater temperature fluctuations, especially on a seasonal basis, than similar marine environments elsewhere in the world. Surface temperature in Saudi Arabian coastal waters can range from 10°C in winter to 35°C in summer, and even well offshore the range is from 15° to 33°C.

Secondly, the land masses surrounding the Gulf are very arid. Rainfall is low throughout the region, and as a result the loss of water from the Gulf by evaporation far exceeds the input from rivers and run-off. The Gulf, therefore, is considerably more saline than other seas. Further increases in salinity occur locally wherever areas of shallow water occur in partially enclosed bays and lagoons. By far the largest such enclosure is the Gulf of Salwah, lying between Saudi Arabia and the Qatar Peninsula, and nearly cut off from the Arabian Gulf proper by the island of Bahrain and the shallows on either side of it. High salinity is one of the most important environmental factors controlling and limiting the occurrence and distribution of marine life in the Gulf.

Thirdly, the Gulf is connected with the adjacent Indian Ocean only by a narrow passage at the Strait of Hormuz. Consequently, the high salinities and wide temperature fluctuations of Gulf waters are not damped to any great extent by exchange of waters with neighboring seas. The Gulf has a so-called Mediterranean circulation pattern, in which heavy, salty Gulf water flows out through the bottom of the Strait of Hormuz, while a compensating quantity of lighter and less saline Indian Ocean water flows inward at the surface. The volume of this exchange is modest, however, and the resulting "steady state" conditions within the Gulf continue to differ drastically from those of the ocean at large.

Arabian Gulf marine life therefore inhabits a stressful environment, characterized by temperature extremes and by high, often fluctuating salinities. As a result the biota is said to be "restricted"; that is, many kinds of organisms are unable to exist at all, and the diversity of biological communities in the Gulf is thought to be low compared with that of similar

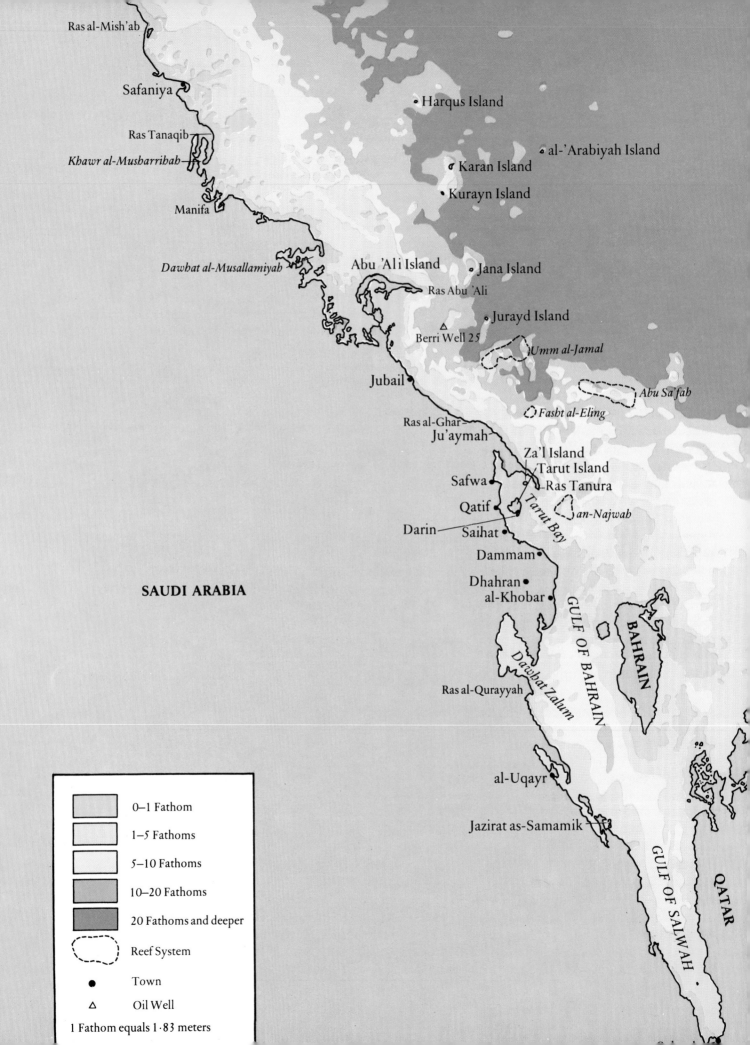

Ras al-Mish'ab

Safaniya

Ras Tanaqib

Khawr al-Musharribah

Manifa

Dawhat al-Musallamiyah

Abu 'Ali Island

Ras Abu 'Ali

Berri Well 25

Jubail

Ras al-Ghar
Ju'aymah

Safwa

Qatif

Darin

Saihat

Dammam

Dhahran

al-Khobar

SAUDI ARABIA

Harqus Island

al-'Arabiyah Island

Karan Island

Kurayn Island

Jana Island

Jurayd Island

Umm al-Jamal

Abu Sa'fah

Fasht al-Eling

Za'l Island
Tarut Island
Ras Tanura

an-Najwah

Tarut Bay

GULF OF BAHRAIN

BAHRAIN

Dawhat Zalum

Ras al-Qurayyah

al-Uqayr

Jazirat as-Samamik

GULF OF SALWAH

QATAR

	0–1 Fathom
	1–5 Fathoms
	5–10 Fathoms
	10–20 Fathoms
	20 Fathoms and deeper
	Reef System
●	Town
△	Oil Well

1 Fathom equals 1·83 meters

communities living under more equable conditions elsewhere. As a general proposition this is undoubtedly true, and it is clear that many groups of organisms are either absent from the Gulf, or of very limited distribution there. During the preparation of this book, however, it has become apparent that Arabian Gulf marine life is considerably richer than was expected, and that many of the animals and plants are able to tolerate remarkable extremes of temperature and salinity. The dynamics of some of these communities, living at the very limits of their capability to adapt to a harsh environment, should form a fascinating and fruitful study for future biologists in this area.

The Saudi Arabian Coastal Zone

The Arabian Gulf coastline of Saudi Arabia extends for an airline distance of a little more than 450km, from Ras al-Khafji in the northwest to Salwah in the southeast. On both physical and biological grounds this stretch of coast can be divided into two distinct sections of nearly equal length (Fig 6).

The northern section, from Ras al-Mish'ab to Ras Tanura, forms part of a gentle arc which continues across the Bahrain islands to the northern tip of the Qatar Peninsula. This part of the coastline trends roughly northwest-southeast, and is exposed to waves generated by the prevailing northerly winds of the Gulf.

Salinities along the open coast are those typical of the western part of the Gulf in general, and range according to place and season from about $38.5^0/_{00}$ to about $41^0/_{00}$. Salinities are lowest at the northern end, and highest at the southern end of this section. Regular diurnal or semi-diurnal tides occur all along this part of the coast, and the maximum tidal range is a little over 2m.

From Dammam southwards, the coastline has a more southerly trend and lies nearly parallel to the direction of prevailing winds. Almost all of this southern section of the coastline lies within the Gulf of Salwah, and is protected from wave action not only by its orientation, but also by the stretch of extremely shallow water lying between Saudi Arabia and Bahrain. These shallows also form a barrier to tidal water movements, and the tidal amplitude within the Gulf of Salwah is much reduced.

Salinities are high throughout this region, ranging from about $55^0/_{00}$ at the entrance to the Gulf of Salwah to upwards of $70^0/_{00}$ at its southern extremity. The biological character of this part of the coast is much affected by the high salinities and the extremely limited tidal circulation.

Between Dammam and Ras Tanura, at the junction between the northern and the southern sections of the Saudi Arabian coastline, lies Tarut Bay. Though sharing many features of the numerous other bays along the coast, Tarut Bay is in some respects unique, particularly in the high productivity of its tidal flats and grassbeds which make it a major shrimp nursery. At the same time, Tarut Bay has been a center of human activity for millennia, and is now the site of major ports, oil facilities and residential communities. In fact, there is reason to believe that the high productivity of Tarut Bay is in part the result of human activity, particularly the long-standing irrigated agriculture of the Qatif oasis. For these various reasons Tarut Bay has been of special interest to Aramco marine biologists.

Fig 6. On a large scale map, the eastern coast of Saudi Arabia appears as a nearly straight line. Closer examination, however, reveals the presence of extensive systems of bays and lagoons. These are low energy environments, in which tidal mud and rock flats, and subtidal grassbeds or other soft bottoms predominate. Higher energy, predominantly sandy beaches are found along the straighter portions of coastline, for example between Ras Tanura and Jubail. The color coding on the map also clearly shows the great extent of shallow water near the coast. In these coastal shallows, grassbeds are a widespread feature of soft bottoms, from low tide mark to depths of about 10m. On hard bottoms, coral reefs are of widespread occurrence in the depth range from 4m to 15m or 20m. Some larger reef structures reach the surface, and are topped by coral islands, whose location can be seen on the map and are also listed on page 116.

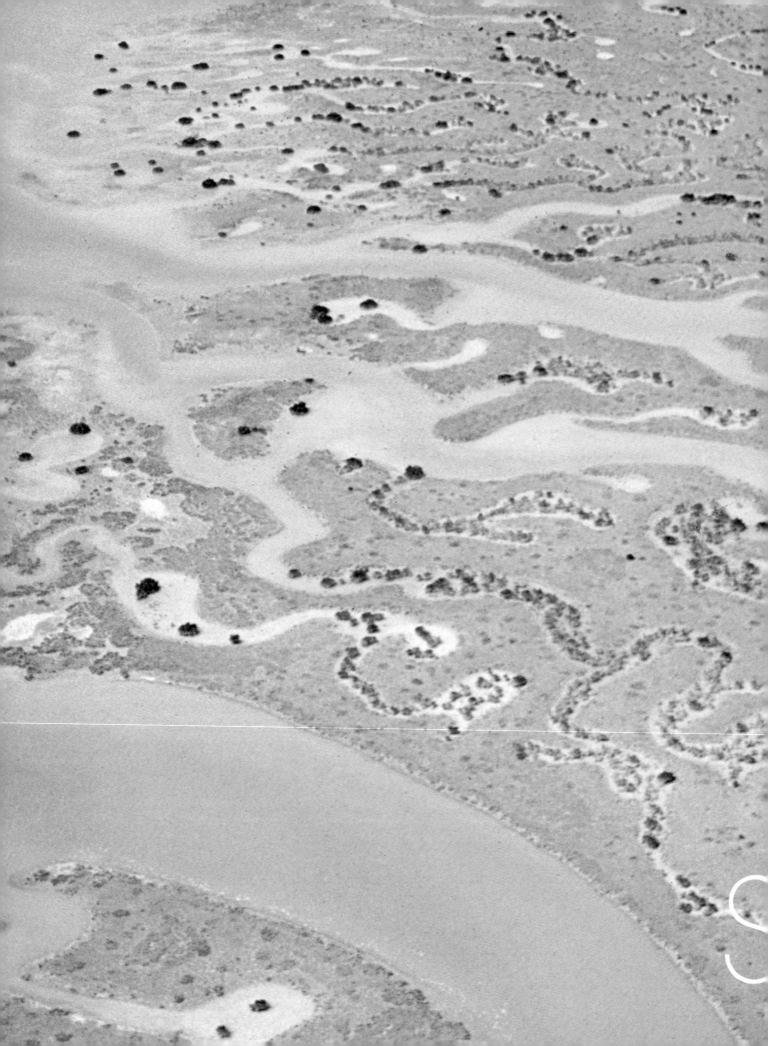

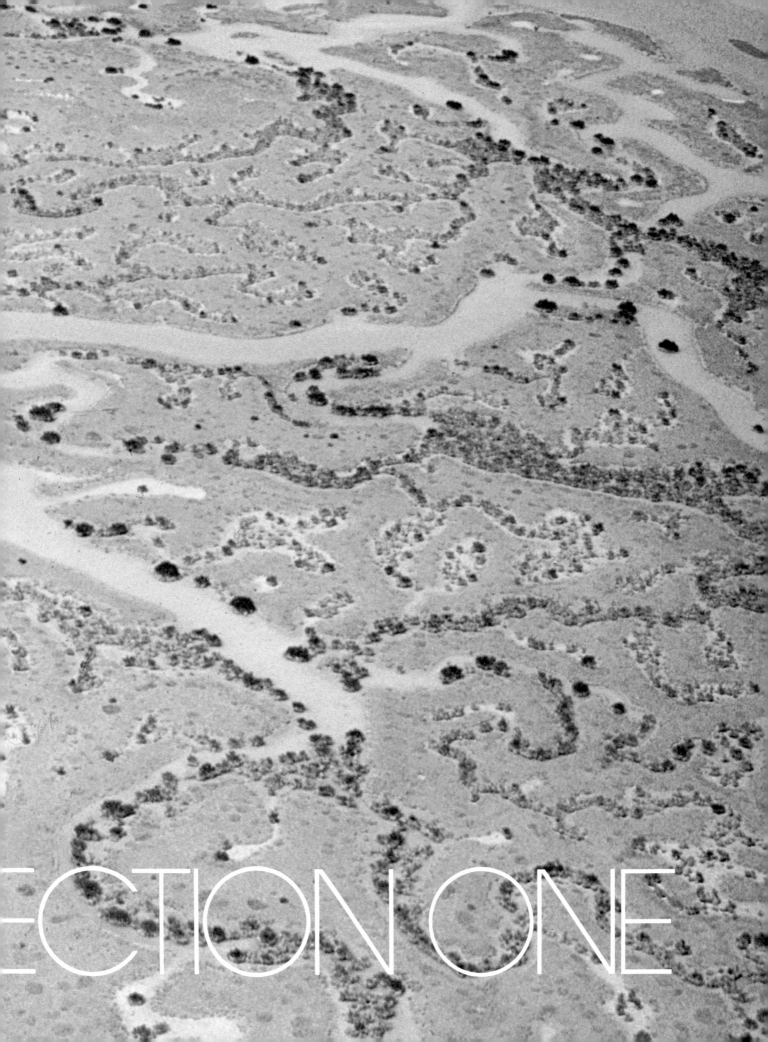

ECTION ONE

INTERTIDAL BIOTOPES

At the edge of the sea lies the intertidal zone, a narrow ribbon of land which is alternately exposed to air and sunlight, and covered by sea water, as a result of the rhythmic changes of sea level called tides.

PHYSICAL FEATURES

The dominant environmental factor controlling the occurrence of plants and animals in the intertidal zone is the alternate exposure and submergence of the habitat, which subjects organisms living there to drastic and sudden changes in temperature, salinity and the availability of oxygen and nutrients. At low tide, surface living organisms undergo intense heating and drying by the sun, and are sometimes exposed to catastrophic salinity reduction during periods of rainfall. These fluctuations are particularly extreme in a hot, arid climate such as that of Saudi Arabia, and play a major part in establishing the distinctive character of the Arabian intertidal communities.

The duration of emersion is greatest at the upper edge of the intertidal zone, which may be covered with water only on one or two of the highest tides in each lunar month, and least at the lower edge, which may be exposed to air only on infrequent occasions. Between these limits, a regular gradation of the duration and frequency of emersion is found. As a result, communities of intertidal organisms show a well-marked zonation. In general, communities at the upper edge of the intertidal usually contain only a few species particularly resistant to environmental extremes, and may include some organisms from primarily terrestrial groups. Communities near the lower limit of the intertidal, in contrast, are much richer in species and include many organisms also found in the adjacent subtidal regions.

Water movements, especially the action of waves, are an important feature of the intertidal zone, and their varying intensity is a major factor controlling the occurrence of different communities there. Organisms on a wave-beaten shore are better provided with food and oxygen than those on shores sheltered from the waves; but they must also withstand the powerful pounding of waves. Water movements also play an important part in determining the type and distribution of intertidal sediments. In general, coarse sediments are deposited in high energy areas of vigorous water movement, whereas the finer particles remain in suspension until they can settle out in low energy environments, where water movements are limited to the gentle ebb and flow of the tides. As a result, beaches on the open coast are generally composed of relatively coarse sand, while extensive tidal mudflats form in sheltered bay areas.

Another important environmental factor is the physical nature of the material on or in which the organisms live. This may be either hard or soft, consisting either of some sort of rock, or of unconsolidated sediment ranging in consistency from coarse gravel to soft mud. Successful colonization of these differing substrates requires very different types of adaptation, and as a result they are occupied by quite distinct communities.

Fig 7 (preceding page). Aerial view of a tidal mud flat at the north end of Tarut Bay, showing the meandering tidal channels typical of this biotope. Light green halophyte vegetation and dark green mangrove bushes show up clearly in the photograph. (Photograph by John Hardy)

On rock substrates, most organisms are either permanently attached and sessile or else able to cling firmly to avoid being washed away. Many have special adaptations for making use of holes or cracks in the rock as shelters. On sandy or muddy substrata, most animals adopt burrowing habits, and the grain size of the sediment is a major environmental factor controlling the occurrence of different communities. Coarse grained sediments, such as beach sand, are relatively porous, and interstitial water circulates freely among the grains, bringing oxygen to the organisms that live there. Such sediments are generally deposited in areas of strong water movement, and animals living in them must be capable of active movement, to avoid being either buried or washed out of the sediment. Fine grained sediments such as those of tidal mud flats, on the other hand, have poor internal circulation, and their interstitial water is usually deficient in oxygen. Organisms colonizing such sediments tend to have special adaptations of behavior or physiology for obtaining oxygen, or for enduring the lack of it. Since fine-grained sediments are deposited only in sites protected from violent water movements, however, their inhabitants do not have the same need for mobility as those of coarser sediments.

INTERTIDAL HABITATS IN SAUDI ARABIA

The outstanding feature of the coastline is its extremely low relief. The average slope of the sea bed on the Arabian side of the Gulf is only about 35cm per kilometer. One result of this flat coastal topography is an unusually extensive intertidal zone, whose width in many places can be measured in kilometers. Since the same gentle slope continues below low tide mark, even the exposed beaches are generally fronted by a wide belt of subtidal shallows, which modify the character of the beaches.

On a large scale map of the Middle Eastern region, the eastern coastline of Saudi Arabia appears as a more or less straight line, extending from Ras al-Mish'ab in the north, in a generally south-easterly direction, to Salwah at the southern end of the Gulf of Salwah (Fig 5). Viewed at closer range, however, much of the coastline is seen to be highly convoluted, with extensive and complex systems of mostly shallow bays (Fig 6). Since with few exceptions no significant amounts of fresh water flow into these bays, they tend to be more or less hypersaline, in contrast to the estuarine, brackish-water conditions normally associated with this kind of topography elsewhere. These bays contain large areas of **intertidal flats,** protected from wave action, which become sites of mud deposition and frequently also of beach-rock formation. In spite of high salinities and extremes of temperature, these intertidal flats are among the most productive of Saudi Arabian marine biotopes (Chapter 3).

The other main subdivision of the Saudi Arabian intertidal is the **exposed coastal beach.** These beaches are protected from heavy wave action by the wide subtidal shallows that usually occur in front of them. They therefore tend to consist of somewhat finer-grained sand than that found on similarly situated beaches elsewhere. Rocky substrata are of limited occurrence in the Saudi Arabian intertidal zone, and mostly take the form of more or less fragmented, soft sedimentary rock, often intermixed with sand (Chapter 2).

Fig 8. A typical exposed sandy beach at low tide. A prominent berm is visible as a ridge of sand extending into the background from the right-hand edge of the picture, and behind it a nearly level beach platform can be seen. In the center, a Lesser Crested Tern Sterna bengalensis *feeds its young. [Karan Island]*

2
EXPOSED COASTAL BEACHES

The Gulf shore of Saudi Arabia includes a total of about 350 km of exposed coastal beaches. These are mostly sandy beaches and generally fit the familiar pattern of sand beaches anywhere (Fig 8). Because the average slope of the Saudi Arabian landmass, and of the sea bed on the Arabian side of the Gulf, is only about 35 cm per km, the beach is normally fronted by a wide belt of subtidal shallows. This expanse of shallow water absorbs much of the energy of the larger waves. Small waves less than a meter in height break incessantly on the beach, but it is rarely if ever pounded by heavy surf.

Most of these beaches are composed largely of carbonate sand. Microscopic examination reveals that the bulk of this material is of biological origin: it consists of small but still recognizable fragments of shells and coral broken by the waves and finally washed up on to the beach (Fig 9). Thus the extensive subtidal shallows of the Arabian shore furnish a rich supply of coarse-grained carbonate sediment to the beach.

Quartz grains of terrestrial origin also occur mingled with the carbonate particles. These are derived from the aeolian or wind-blown sands which form desert dunes on the arid Arabian land mass. Such aeolian sand is generally yellowish or reddish in color, due to a coating of iron oxide on the surface of the individual grains. The origin of beach dunes can thus usually be determined by color alone. Yellowish or reddish dunes, such as those along the shores of Dawhat Zalum, consist mainly of aeolian sand; while pure white or greyish dunes, such as those found immediately behind the beach front at Ju'aymah, consist mostly of carbonate material derived from the sea. Carbonate dunes are the prevailing type along most of the exposed beaches of Saudi Arabia.

Subtidal sand bars, running parallel to the shore, are a typical feature of most sandy beach environments. They are formed by wave action, as part of a continuous cycle in which sand is removed from the beach by wave backwash, shifted about in the subtidal shallows, and eventually redeposited on the beach by other waves. Heavy waves, especially during storms, favor removal of sand from the beach, while gentle wave action favors redeposition; but both processes are con-

Fig 9. Tiger beetle Cicindela *sp., on a beach berm. The nature of the beach sand, consisting largely of broken shell fragments, is typical for Gulf beaches and shows clearly in the photograph. [Tarut Island]*

Fig 10. Outcrops of recently formed beach rock occur on the lower part of many Saudi Arabian sand beaches. [Karan Island]

stantly operating, and the status of the beach at any given time is a function of the balance between them. In consequence, any change leading to an increase or decrease in the sand supply of the subtidal shallows, will lead to growth or recession of the beach front. Because of the very wide, subtidal shallow zone fronting most Saudi Arabian beaches, multiple sand bars are usually formed, running parallel to the coastline and separated by deeper troughs. Where sand is abundant, the troughs serve as traps for finer particles, and grassbeds often form there. Where sand is less abundant, rocky bottom is often exposed in the troughs, and serves as a base for belts of algal or coral growth. Where the sand supply is severely limited, most of the lower intertidal and the subtidal shallows may consist of flat sheets of exposed rock, and nearly all the sand may be accumulated on the upper part of the beach.

On the eastern coast of Saudi Arabia, the prevailing northerly winds blow at an acute angle to the coastline, and the surf strikes the beach at an angle. Therefore, there is a constant, wave-driven movement of water along the shore in a southeasterly direction, and sand grains washed off the beach by one wave will be deposited a little farther to the southeast by the next. This "longshore transport" of beach sediment is a nearly universal feature of beach coastlines. In Saudi Arabia, because of the low relief of the coast and the large proportion of sand beach, such sand movements have a major influence on the coastal landforms as well as on the ecological characteristics of the beach. Long, often hook-shaped sand spits, running southeasterly from the major headlands or coastal projections, are the most conspicuous manifestation of longshore sand transport (Fig 4). The Ras Tanura sand spit is a particularly fine example of this type.

Along most of this coastline, the sand deposits form a relatively thin layer overlying soft sedimentary rocks of fairly recent formation. These are either Neogene sandstones, siltstones or soft limestones, or various types of beach rock formed by contemporaneous *in situ* cementation of the sediment.[1] These rocks are exposed at many points along the coast, forming rocky beach areas of varying size. Except for a few prominent headlands such as Ras al-Ghar[2] where low sandstone cliffs face the sea, these outcrops are flat and shelving, and largely confined to the lower intertidal and immediate subtidal regions. In sand-rich areas, which include most of the more exposed stretches of beach, rock outcrops form a very minor portion of the beach habitat and consist of isolated patches of broken, much sand-scoured rock in the lower half of the intertidal zone. Sand pockets occur between and under the flat rock plates, and these areas show an intimate mingling of the rock and sand habitat types. On somewhat less wave-exposed stretches of shoreline, sand is generally less abundant, and rock outcrops or beachrock frequently occur in the form of extensive "rock flats" in the lower part of the intertidal zone.[3]

1 The processes of sedimentation and rock formation in the Arabian Gulf are very fully described and analyzed in Purser (1973).

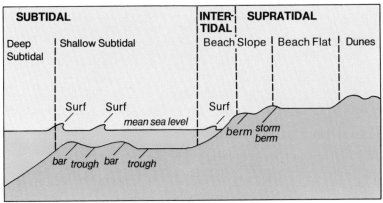

Fig 11. The main topographic features of a Saudi Arabian sand beach. Plants and animals inhabiting the beach show a well-marked zonation from the uppermost beach levels to the subtidal zone, reflecting the changing physical conditions at different levels on the beach. The beach is a meeting place of land and sea, and forms a transition between strictly terrestrial environments above, and strictly marine environments below the intertidal zone.

TOPOGRAPHIC FEATURES OF THE BEACH

The entire beach complex includes subtidal and supratidal regions of almost flat topography, separated by the short relatively steep slope of the beach itself. Although beaches are usually classified as intertidal biotopes, the influence of the land and the sea on each other extends both above and below the strict limits of the intertidal zone. Below low tide mark, extensive shallows occur whose physical and biological character is strongly influenced by the adjacent beach and by cycles of sand transport, nutrient exchange, etc. in which both participate. Above high tide mark, in a similar way, occurs a coastal strip of terrestrial environment, modified by the proximity of the sea, in which distinctive communities of plants and animals are found. The main topographic features of a typical Saudi Arabian sand beach are shown in Fig. 11.

The main features of the supratidal zone include a belt of low dunes in back of the beach, more or less overgrown with grass. This dune belt is separated from the beach front by a "beach flat" of varying width, consisting of coarse, loose sand together with debris thrown over the top of the beach slope by storm waves. At the top of the beach slope is a low sand ridge or berm, slightly higher than the beach flat behind it. This berm, which forms the highest point or crest of the beach slope, is formed largely by storm waves during the highest spring tides, and is sometimes called a storm berm. Often, other smaller berms, formed by the most recent set of spring tides or by a storm, are seen at lower levels on the beach. These are rather transitory structures, however, whose appearance and disappearance is a visible reminder of the constantly shifting nature of the beach environment.

2 26°51.5′N, 49°52′E

3 Similar, even more extensive rock flats occur in the intertidal zone of sheltered bay and lagoon areas, and are described in Chapter 3.

Fig 12. Mixed sand and rock beach. [Ju'aymah]

Fig 13. The tall beach grass Halopyrum mucronatum *is a dominant plant of the dune belt of exposed sand beaches along the Saudi Arabian coastline. [Ju'aymah]*

BEACH AS HABITAT

Like other intertidal environments, exposed beaches are subject to alternate wetting and drying with the rise and fall of the tide, and consequently to fluctuating conditions which amount to considerable environmental stress for organisms living there. At low tide the surface of sand and rocks is heated by the sun and dried by the combined action of sun and wind. In Saudi Arabia the surface of dry sand exposed to summer sun can reach temperatures exceeding 70°C. Such temperatures are rapidly lethal to nearly all forms of life except certain plant seeds and spores. In the intertidal zone, retained moisture cools the sand and considerably lessens the impact of temperature extremes; but even here, the surface temperature still reaches values detrimental or lethal to many organisms. During low tide periods, furthermore, the circulation of interstitial water is minimal, and very little oxygen is available to buried or burrowing organisms at that time.

In contrast, when the tide is high, wave action is the major source of environmental stress. The surface layers of sand are shifted about with each wave that strikes the beach, and considerable build-up or removal of sand can take place on the beach slope during a single tidal cycle. Sand-dwelling organisms must, therefore, be able to move about rapidly to avoid being either washed out of the beach, or buried out of reach of their oxygen and food supply. On rocky sections of beach, conditions are more stable, but organisms living there must permanently attach themselves to the rock, cling temporarily to its surface, or hide in rock cavities to avoid being washed away. Where rock and sand occur intermingled, as is the case in most rocky sections of the Saudi Arabian exposed beaches, rock-dwelling organisms are subjected also to the scouring action of wave-driven, shifting sand.

SAND BEACH COMMUNITIES

The distinctive biota of the sandy beach actually begins in the supratidal zone. The dune belt, which in places may be as much as 100m wide, has several characteristic species of land plants, in particular the tall beachgrass *Halopyrum mucronatum* (Fig 13) and peculiar animals, such as the sand-dune gecko *Stenodactylus khobarensis*, belonging to terrestrial groups. Two of the most distinctive supratidal inhabitants, however, are semi-terrestrial representatives of definitely marine animal types. These are the beach fleas or sandhoppers, and the ghost crab *Ocypode saratan*. Both of these animals move freely up and down the beach, and enter the water on occasion, but their most typical habitat is just above high water mark. Sandhoppers are small whitish amphipod crustaceans, which derive their common names from their habit of leaping erratically about when disturbed. During the daytime they dig into the loose sand or hide under objects on the beach, and may be uncovered in hundreds by lifting up piles of rotting seaweed which forms their principal food. At night they scurry about the beach. Because of their great abundance, sandhoppers are

Fig 14. Sand towers up to 30cm high are built by males of the ghost crab Ocypode saratan. *The towers, a territorial signal, advertise the crab's presence to rivals or potential mates. [Jana Island]*

an important factor in converting the energy content of dead seaweed and other flotsam washed up on the beach, into forms available to other community members such as birds.

Ghost crabs, which are among the largest beach invertebrates, have a body up to 6cm wide and legs spanning up to 20cm. They are a pale, whitish color similar to sandhoppers. This ghostly color gives them their popular name, and also helps to make then inconspicuous on the beach — a fact of great importance in their lives, since at least the smaller individuals are eagerly sought after as food by various seabirds. Ghost crabs are long-legged, alert, extremely active and difficult to catch. During the daytime, however, they generally remain out of sight, hiding in burrows which they excavate on the upper levels of the beach. At night, and sometimes also during low-tide periods in the daytime, they emerge to forage for food. Their food preferences are remarkably versatile. As scavengers, they feed on dead fish, picnic remnants and almost any other form of dead animal matter on the beach. As predators, they may capture and eat almost any other beach animal smaller than themselves, especially young sea turtles at hatching time. They may enter the surf to capture various subtidal or intertidal animals, especially the mole crab *Hippa* sp. At least one population of ghost crabs has been seen to make regular excursions to a nearby mud flat, where they dig the mud crab *Macrophthalmus depressus* out of its burrow as prey. Ghost crabs may also resort to deposit feeding, in which they pick up damp sand, extract the microscopic plants and animals, and discard the cleaned sand in a series of neat pellets. Male ghost crabs frequently erect conspicuous sand towers, up to 30cm high, in front of the entrance to their burrows (Fig 14). These towers apparently act as a form of territorial signal, advertising the crab's presence to rivals or potential mates even when the crab is out of sight in its burrow.

Fig 15. Some species of sea birds, such as the terns and cormorants shown here, use the beach mainly as a resting place, and obtain their food at sea. [Karan Island]

The upper levels of the sand beach are also frequented by a variety of sea birds. Some species, such as the terns *Hydroprogne caspica* and *Sterna bengalensis* and the cormorants *Phalacrocorax carbo* and *P. nigrogularis*, use the beach mainly as a resting place, and obtain their diet of small fish by diving in shallow waters nearby. Several species of seagulls,[4] however, obtain much of their food from the beach, and may be seen diligently patrolling in search of cast up remains of animal life. They also eat ghost crabs whenever they can catch them. Of the many species of shore birds or waders that frequent the Saudi Arabian coast, certain species of plover[5] are especially characteristic of the exposed beach. These birds feed on sandhoppers, young crabs and other small beach life. While most are migrants, and breed in summer on Arctic or subarctic shores far from the Arabian Gulf, some of them, and especially the Kentish Plover *Charadrius alexandrinus*, nest on the beach flat or in the dune belt of Saudi Arabian beaches in spring.

Lower down the beach, in the intertidal zone proper, there are few visible signs of animal life. This barren impression is rather misleading, however, since over 200 species of macroscopic animals have been collected by Aramco biologists from exposed sand beaches, and an even larger number from beaches of mixed sand and rock. Almost all of these animals burrow beneath the sand, at least when the tide is out. Marine snails are the dominant group, with 48 recorded species. Four other well-represented groups of roughly equal rank, with over 20 species each, are the pelecypods (clams and cockles), the polychaete worms, the peracaridans, and the decapod Crustacea. Sand beach peracaridans include mainly isopods and amphipods; besides sandhoppers, more than 20 species of amphipods have been collected on these beaches. The beach decapods are mostly crabs, including of course *Ocypode saratan*.

One of the most typical sand-beach animals is the mole shrimp or mole crab *Hippa* sp. This peculiar decapod is not really a true crab, but rather a distant relative of the hermit crabs. Its 2cm long, egg-shaped body is smooth and slippery, ideally adapted for penetrating loose sand. Mole crabs lie buried in the sand in the wave-wash zone facing out to sea. When a wave breaks they emerge from the sand, swim rapidly up or down the beach, and then dig themselves backward into the sand again as the wave recedes. In this way they move up and down the beach with the rise and fall of the tide.

Meiofauna: Denizens of the Interstitial Spaces

In contrast to the relatively limited numbers of large animals or macrofauna, are the numerous tiny organisms which spend their lives in the interstitial spaces among the sand grains. This habitat is colonized by a few microscopic algae and bacteria, and by a large and varied assemblage of specialized small

4 *Larus argentatus, L. genei, L. ridibundus,* and the large predatory *L. ichthyaetus.*

5 *Charadrius hiaticula, Ch. alexandrinus, Ch. leschenaultii,* and *Pluvialis squatarola.*

animals, collectively known as meiofauna. These are the most numerous and in some ways the most interesting denizens of the beach.

The composition of the sand beach meiofauna community is controlled largely by the outcome of competition for a limited food supply, a competition in which the specialized feeding habits of the various members of the community play an important role. According to the way they obtain their food, meiofauna animals generally fall into one of three main groups:

Active burrowers, including most of the worms, pass beach material through their digestive systems, digesting the organic portion and discharging the remainder unchanged.

Scrapers, including many small Crustacea such as copepods and ostracods, obtain nourishment in the form of small organic particles scraped from the surface of the sand grains.

Sorters and filterers, of which bivalve mollusks are the most important, derive their sustenance from small organic particles such as detritus or plankton, which they filter or sort out of the water.

As in other highly stressed environments, meiofauna communities generally have a low diversity, but often show a high abundance of individual species. Abundance and diversity also vary widely on a very local scale. For example, the uppermost 5cm of sand on the beach at Ju'aymah, sampled in February, 1975 at the low tide level, contained 9,504 nematodes per liter. Similar samples, taken at the same time at the upper edge of the wave wash zone, contained only 352 nematodes per liter. The meiofauna of sand pockets on rocky sections of beach is, generally speaking, both more abundant and more diverse than that found in pure sand beaches. Probably these sand pockets benefit from an increased food supply because of their proximity to the rock beach biotope. Samples taken of the layer 20 to 25cm below the surface of the sand beach, in contrast, showed greatly reduced abundance and diversity of meiofauna as compared with surface samples at the same location. This probably reflects a shortage of available oxygen in the sediment. A grayish layer, due to the presence of free sulfides and indicating very low levels of oxygen, commonly occurs at 25 to 30cm depth in these beaches.

Nematodes are by far the most abundant members of the meiofauna of the Saudi Arabian sand beaches and are followed in importance by harpacticoid copepods, polychaete worms, and turbellarians. Occasionally, however, these numerical relationships are upset by adverse environmental conditions. One particular meiofauna animal, known world-wide as an indicator of such conditions, is the archiannelid polychaete *Protodrilus*. This animal is an opportunistic species, which thrives under adverse conditions and excludes weaker organisms by using up available oxygen and food. In sand samples from one area, more than 6,000 individuals of this species were found per liter of sand.

Fig 16. Saudi Arabian rocky beaches generally lack a covering of seaweed, since the hot sun effectively prevents the growth of large algae above the low tide mark. As a result these beaches appear much less productive than the weed-covered rocky shores of temperate regions.

Bacteria

The sand beach is also the home of countless bacteria. In other parts of the world, conservative estimates of 200,000 per gram of sand have been recorded (Hedgpeth, 1957). Organic debris such as algae, sea grass blades and various kinds of dead animal life are thrown up onto the beach and often buried by sand or shell fragments. Large quantities of buried organic matter may thus accumulate, especially on the berm at the top of the beach, and this material forms the energy source for bacteria which decompose it. Additional organic matter is delivered to the beach in the form of fine particles, which percolate into the sand as each wave recedes. Bacteria play an essential role in almost all energy cycles and transfers of the sand beach community. The greyish sulfide layer encountered at depths of 20 to 30cm in most of the beaches so far studied along the Saudi Arabian coast, results from the action of bacteria on organic matter in the absence of oxygen, and indicates the presence of excess organic matter in the sediment.

Plants

The plant life of sand beaches in Saudi Arabia is largely confined to microscopic algae. Two main types are present. The so-called mucilaginous algae, which are probably diatoms, form thin, fragile, semi-transparent yellowish sheets on the sand surface. They occur particularly in environments with low wave energy, and help to stabilize and lithify the sediments in these environments. Unicellular green algae, the other main type, inhabit the surface of most carbonate sands, often giving a greenish tint to the sediment. Both these types of algae are characteristic of intertidal and shallow subtidal marine sediments. Attached or rooted vegetation is generally absent on Saudi Arabian sand beaches, except for occasional patches of sea grass exposed at extreme low tide. On the windward beach at Karan Island, however, which consists of particularly coarse sediment, green filamentous algae have been found attached to small pebbles just below the wave wash zone.

Fig 17. The filamentous green alga Cladophora *sp. often forms clumps of dense growth on rocky beaches. [Ju'aymah]*

ROCK BEACH COMMUNITIES

In spite of the harsh environmental factors typical of intertidal zones, the rocky intertidal is a highly productive biotope in many parts of the world. The rocks provide a firm attachment for the holdfasts of many species of large algae or seaweed which are the key to the productivity of rocky beaches, since they provide both shelter and food supply for large animal populations. On rock beaches with large tidal amplitudes, an extensive surface is often available for plant and animal colonization of this kind. On these beaches it is usually possible to recognize several distinct horizontal zones, characterized by different populations of plants and animals. Such zonation is a reliable indicator of height in the intertidal region, and can often be followed along many kilometers of the shoreline. Productive rocky shores of this type are common in the temperate regions of both northern and southern hemispheres. Well-studied examples occur on the coasts of England, Japan and the United States, to name only a few places.

Rocky beaches along the Saudi Arabian coast, in contrast, cannot be considered highly productive. The main reason is that at low tide, especially in summer, the rock surface is subjected to intense heating and desiccation by the sun, which effectively prevents the establishment of a vigorous growth of large algae (Fig 16). Due to the absence of algal shelter in this harsh environment, the fauna of Saudi Arabian rocky beaches is limited to animals which inhabit crevices, holes and the underside of boulders, or else are mobile forms capable of retreating to shelter when the tide is out.

The permanently attached, **sessile animals** are almost all plankton feeders, and obtain their nourishment while covered with water at high tide. A majority are filter feeders, and capture plankton by straining the water through various kinds of sieve apparatus. Bivalve mollusks use their gills for this purpose, whereas tunicates make use of their greatly modified pharynx, the anterior portion of the digestive tract. Sponges trap plankton in tiny chambers lined with flagellated "collar cells." Barnacles and porcelain crabs "fish" for plankton with sweeping movements of their net-like body appendages. Sea anemones catch plankton organisms individually, using tentacles studded with stinging capsules, while tube-dwelling polychaetes, ophiuroids and some others make use of mucus and cilia to trap the plankton. All of these types of animals can be found on Saudi Arabian rock beaches, especially in crevices and on the undersides of flat pieces of rock (Figs 19 & 20).

Although all the bivalves are filter feeders, the rock-dwelling kinds show a great variety in their method of attachment to the substrate. Oysters *Crassostrea*, jingle-shells *Anomia* and jewel-boxes *Chama* are cemented to the rock by one valve. Ark-shells *Arca* and *Barbatia*, mussels *Mytilus* and pearl oysters *Pinctada* are attached by a bundle of tough byssus threads; these animals can, if necessary, release their attachment and spin new threads to another point of support. The hammer oysters *Malleus* and *Isognomon* live wedged into crevices in the rock, and as they

Fig 18. Chitons are flattened mollusks protected by an armor of eight overlapping calcareous plates. They are usually found clinging tightly to rocks in the intertidal zone, where they creep slowly about grazing on algae. [laboratory photograph of living animal]

LORRAINE JOHANSEN

43

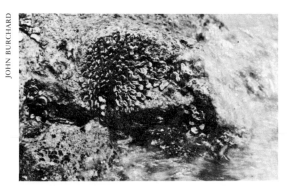

Fig 19. The calcareous tubes of serpulid worms usually occur in dense clusters attached to rocks on beaches and tidal flats. When the tide is in these polychaetes extend their tentacle-crowned heads from the tubes in order to feed on plankton. [Ju'aymah]

grow their shells take on the irregular shape of the cavity in which they live. Date mussels *Botula* and *Lithophaga*, and piddocks *Gastrochaena*, actually bore into the soft rock, and live enclosed in a chamber of their own making, from which only their siphons protrude to the outside. This is similar to the habits of sand beach bivalves, which in contrast to the variety found among rock dwellers all live buried in the sand, with their siphons extending to the surface to obtain plankton and oxygen.

One of the common polychaetes of the rock beach is a serpulid or feather duster worm, which lives permanently cemented to the rock surface in a limestone tube of its own making (Fig 19). When the tide is in this animal protrudes its head end from the tube in order to feed. The head is provided with two tufts of cilated tentacles, which spread out in the water like a pair of fans or feather dusters, and serve to trap plankton as well as to obtain oxygen from the water. One of the tentacles is much enlarged and at its end bears a hard limestone knob, which acts as a "stopper" or operculum and seals the tube tightly when the animal withdraws inside. This is an effective defense against most enemies, and also serves to prevent the worm from drying out at low tide. This tubeworm occurs in densely packed clusters attached to rocks on the lower part of the beach, usually in places where the shape of the rocks provides some shelter from the summer sun. Each tube, which is usually·3 to 4mm in diameter at its open end, is furnished with an overhanging "roof" above the opening. Although it is tempting to think of this structure as a sun-shade, its true function is not yet known.

Another common rock-encrusting animal is a small barnacle,[6] less than 1cm in maximum diameter. Like the tubeworms, these animals are usually found in dense clusters in particular spots where conditions are favorable, rather than being evenly distributed all over the beach (Fig 20).

Other sessile animals commonly found on Saudi Arabian rock beaches include several species of tunicates and sponges. Both of these types of animal are found only in sites where they are well protected from the sun, most usually on the underside of loose plates or sheets of rock. Where the rock is less fragmented, as for example on the cliffs at Ras al-Ghar, these animals are uncommon or absent.

In contrast to the sessile forms are the many species of **vagile animals,** able to move about freely on the rock surface. The most important group in this category is that of the gastropods, or snails. Rock beach snails are generally heavily built, thick-shelled species able to cling firmly to the rock surface and so resist being washed off by waves. A majority of them are herbivorous and graze on algae. On the Saudi Arabian rock beaches their food supply consists mainly of blue-green algae, which are noted for their resistance to adverse environmental conditions. The dark or blackish color (Fig 21) so typical of intertidal rocks along the Saudi Arabian shore is largely due to

Fig 20. Small barnacles Balanus *sp., like the serpulid worms, are usually found attached to intertidal rocks in dense clusters, wherever conditions are particularly favorable. [Tarut Island]*

6 Probably *Balanus amphitrite.*

Fig 21. Rocks in the upper intertidal zone are blackened by the growth of blue-green algae. Some of these algae form a coating on the rock, while others actually bore into the rock surface.

Fig 22. Eriphia sebana smithii *is a predatory crab common on rocky island beaches. [laboratory photograph of specimen from Jana Island]*

the growth of various species of blue-greens,[7] which either form a mat on the surface or actually bore into the outermost layers of rock. The same species of algae also colonize shallow subtidal rocks, and even the shells of living animals such as the conch *Strombus decorus persicus*, which abounds on sandy bottoms just below low tide mark.

Important grazing gastropods on the Saudi Arabian rocky shore include top-shells *Trochus erythraeus*, turbans *Turbo coronatus*, the limpet-like pulmonate *Siphonaria rosea*, the slug-like *Onchidium peronii* (Fig 23), and several others such as *Euchelis asper*, *Monodonta canalifera*, *Nodilittorina subnodosa* and *Planaxis sulcatus*. A few common snails such as *Thais* spp. and *Drupa margariticola* are carnivorous, however, and feed on sessile animals such as barnacles.

Among the more active animal types, crabs are especially noteworthy. Some, such as spider crabs and the ubiquitous *Metopograpsus messor*, are partially or wholly herbivorous, and graze on the algae. Related to *Metopograpsus* and with similar habits is the much larger *Grapsus tenuicrustatus*, a rare species on the mainland beaches, but very common and conspicuous on certain offshore islands. In contrast, the numerous species of portunid and xanthid crabs[8] are generally predatory, feeding on other crustaceans or on snails which they crush in their powerful chelae (Fig 22). Another striking rocky beach predator is the stomatopod or mantis shrimp *Gonodactylus demanii*. This animal is able to stun passing animals, and to break the shells of small mollusks, by the impact of a blow from its greatly enlarged raptorial legs (Caldwell and Dingle, 1976). Somewhat similar tactics are also used by the pistol shrimp *Alpheus* spp., which have one chela enormously developed and modified so as to produce an underwater shock wave capable of stunning or killing small fish and other animals on which the shrimp then feeds. *Alpheus* and *Gonodactylus* are both commonly found hiding under rocks in the intertidal zone, though both also occur subtidally in hard bottom biotopes.

Tide pools on the rocks have their own typical fauna including many animals which are actually not able to withstand exposure to the air. The most prominent members of this group include the extraordinary variegated, greenish shrimp *Saron marmoratus*, several small shrimps of the family Palaemonidae, and small blennies and gobies of many species.

Rock and sand beaches are highly stressed environments. The structure and behavior of their inhabitants are marked by traits enabling them to avoid or withstand adverse conditions. Compared with most other biotopes, exposed beaches are poor in both quantity and variety of life. Nowhere is the intimate relationship between biological features and the physical environment more clearly seen, however, than in the animals and plants of exposed beach biotopes.

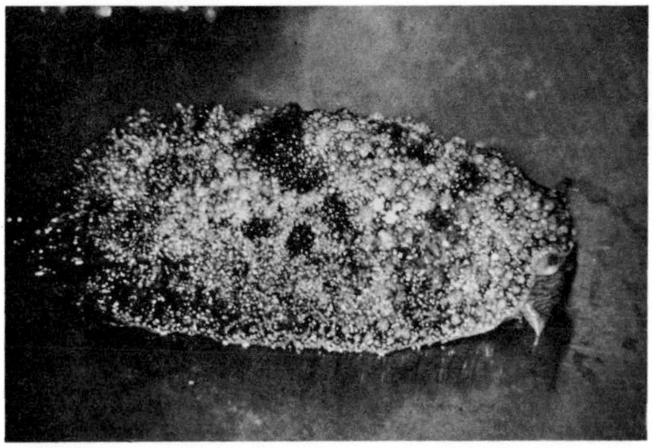

Fig 23. The shell-less, air-breathing gastropod Onchidium peronii *is a common inhabitant of the rocky intertidal both on exposed beaches and on tidal flats. [laboratory photograph]*

7 *Lyngbya aestuarii, L. majuscula, Oscillatoria princeps* and *Phormidium* sp.

8 *Portunus* spp., *Thalamita admete, T. crenata, Pilumnus longicornis, Xantho exaratus, Eriphia sebana smithii* on the islands, and many others.

Fig 24. Three specimens of the very common mud snail Cerithidea cingulata *on the lower mud flat, with filamentous green algae* Enteromorpha *sp. growing on their shells. [Two and a half times life size; Tarut Island]*

3
TIDAL FLATS

Tidal flats are the most important type of intertidal environment, in terms of area, along the Gulf coast of Saudi Arabia. In contrast to the relatively narrow strip of intertidal along the exposed beaches, tidal flats occupy 30 to 40% of the area of the numerous large and small bays along the coastline. Extensive tidal flats also occur on the sheltered southeast side of each of the major headlands or coastal projections. The total area of tidal flat along this coastline can be roughly estimated at between 500 and 1,000 sq km. The greater part of these flats consists of mud or very fine sand, deposited in bays and other sheltered locations where wave energies are low. Extensive stretches of rocky tidal flat also occur both in hypersaline bays and along relatively sheltered stretches of the open coast. In the bays these rock flats generally consist of mud, sand and shell fragments, cemented by limestone precipitation into a form of beach-rock locally known as faroush. Along the open coast they may consist of beach rock or of Neogene sedimentary rock of very similar nature and origin (Figs 21 & 26). Flats of coarser sand are uncommon, but occur in certain sheltered places on the open coast and also in bays, where waves or tidal streams have accumulated sediments of this type.

The outstanding feature common to all types of tidal flats is a very low relief. The width of the intertidal zone in the Saudi Arabian tidal flat areas is usually more than a kilometer. One result of the flat topography is poor drainage, and at ebb tide thin sheets of trapped water form extensive and very shallow

Fig 25. Tidal channel in the halophyte zone of a Tarut Bay tide flat. At high tide these channels are navigable by local fishing boats such as the one shown. [Safwa]

JOHN BURCHARD

Fig 26. Tidal flat near Dammam, consisting of beach rock thinly covered with sand. The sand is full of Cerithidea cingulata *and, at higher levels, of* Scopimera scabricauda. *Broken blocks of beach rock harbor many hard-bottom organisms such as barnacles and crabs. Tiny mysid "shrimp" swarm in the shallow tide pools.*

tide pools, especially on the rocky type of tidal flat. On softer tide flats the ebbing tide cuts complex systems of tidal drainage channels, and water trapped in the deeper portions of these channels forms a different type of tide pool, in which larger animals such as fish can find shelter.

Tidal flats are known to be among the most productive of all natural ecosystems (Odum, 1971), and those of the western Arabian Gulf are no exception to the rule. Although direct measurements of production rates on local tidal flats are not yet available, it is clear from the animal biomass they support that mud flats are the most productive type. Rock flats are probably significantly less productive, though still high on the overall scale. The high productivity of Saudi Arabian tidal flats is most apparent at low tide, both from the vast numbers of small animals visible to the careful observer (Figs 24 & 40), and especially from the large flocks of shore birds which visit them to feed in winter. At high tide the bounty of the tidal flats is exploited in a similar way by many species of fish. A considerable part of the production of the tidal flats is therefore "exported" to other parts of the coastal zone ecosystem by the animals which visit them to feed.

Another aspect of the high productivity of tidal flats is the accumulation of excess organic matter trapped in the sediment. This undergoes degradation by bacteria and provides an energy source for burrowing animals, and particularly for meiofauna. In the fine-grained sediments typical of tidal flats, oxygen can penetrate only slowly from the atmosphere into the interstitial spaces. On a productive mud flat this does not suffice to oxidize all the organic matter, and an excess of incompletely oxidized material accumulates in the sediment. Except for a thin surface layer, therefore, the sediment is mostly anaerobic and contains free sulfides, as evidenced by the characteristic rotten-egg smell of hydrogen sulfide.

MUD FLATS

Mud flats in the Tarut Bay area have been studied by Aramco biologists at several sites. One of these sites, on the southwestern side of Tarut Island, was selected for a year-long study in 1975. Eleven sampling stations were established along a transect line extending from the upper level of the tidal flat down to the low tide mark more than 700m distant. The difference in elevation between the top and the bottom of this transect is a little less than 1.4m (Fig 28). At this location on the leeward sheltered side of Tarut Island the tidal flat consists mainly of very fine, silty sediments. The finest-grained sediment is found at the lower, seaward end of the transect, and the grain size increases progressively at the more landward stations. At any given location along the transect, grain size is finest at the surface and increases with depth in the sediment (Fig 27). The tide flat is cut by extensive, meandering tidal channels through which the ebb tide drains (Fig 7). Tide pools of varying size occur all along these channels. The interstitial water of the mud flat sediments contains, on the average, about ten times the concentrations of dissolved nutrient salts — phosphate, nitrate/nitrite and ammonia — as found in nearshore waters sampled during the same period.

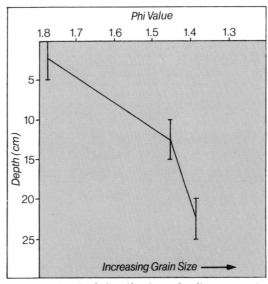

Fig 27. Vertical distribution of sediment grain size in the Cerithidea *zone of the mud flat transect.*

Zonation of Mud Flat Communities

Tidal mud flats in the Tarut Bay area are characterized by a series of well defined zones, each occupied by a different community of organisms and each appearing different to the eye. Most of these zones are well represented at the 1975 study site. Arranged in order from the landward to the seaward edge of the mud flat, these zones include the marsh grass zone, the halophyte zone, the mangrove zone, the algal mat zone, the *Macrophthalmus* zone and the *Cerithidea* zone.

Fig 28. Diagram of the tidal mud flat transect line on Tarut Island, showing major life zones. Dots and elevation of actual sampling sites indicate the surveyed position. The zonation shown here is typical for mud flats in the region, though the relative development of different zones varies locally.

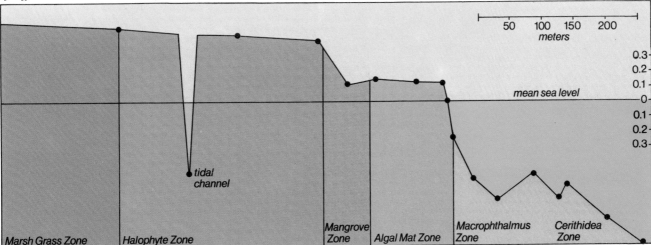

51

Fig 29. The tall reed Phragmites communis *is a dominant plant in the marsh grass zone of Tarut Bay tidal flats. [Tarut Island]*

THE MARSH GRASS ZONE: This zone actually belongs to the supratidal region, since most of it lies above the average high tide level. Like the beach supratidal region, it represents a zone in which the terrestrial habitat has been modified (and in this case greatly enriched) by proximity to the sea. In appearance this zone is a luxuriant meadow of salt-tolerant grass and grass-like plants. The growth is often dominated by the reed *Phragmites communis* (Fig 29); *Aeluropus lagopoides* and *Bienertia cycloptera* are other important members of the association. The marsh grass zone is particularly extensive and luxuriant in the Tarut Bay area, probably because both the ground water level and the availability of nutrients have been increased by centuries of irrigated agriculture in the Qatif oasis. The marsh grass shelters dense populations of insects and small birds, especially during the cooler months. A conspicuous, typical inhabitant is the Marsh Harrier *Circus aeruginosus,* usually seen flying low over the grass in the hope of surprising some small mammal or bird.

THE HALOPHYTE ZONE: This, the uppermost portion of the true intertidal region, forms a wide flat platform which is covered by only a few centimeters of water at high tide. It is a horizontal expanse of light grey mud, densely or sparsely overgrown with salt-tolerant flowering plants or halophytes. These include both perennial and annual species, but none grow higher than about 20cm so that the overall effect is of a low mat of vegetation on the mud surface. In this association *Arthrocnemon macrostachyum* (Fig 31) is often dominant; another important species is *Halocnemon strobilaceum*. The desert candle *Cistanche lutea* blooms here and there in spring. Patches of algal mat are scattered about among the vegetation.

Fig 30. Halophyte vegetation (foreground) covers large areas of the tidal mud flat. The halophyte zone is the uppermost portion of the true intertidal region. Also visible are tide pools and scattered mangroves, and in the background a road embankment and the date palms of the Qatif oasis.

The mud in this zone, being covered with water during only a brief portion of each tidal cycle, is of a moist but rather firm consistency, and one can walk across it without sinking in deeply. No doubt the interlacing root systems of the halophytes also contribute to this stability. The mud surface is riddled with small round holes, the burrows of the ocypodid crab *Cleistostoma dotilliforme*, which is the dominant animal species in this zone. This small grey and white crab, up to 2cm in body width, excavates vertical burrows to a considerable depth in the mud, and piles up the excavated material around the entrance to form a distinctive tower or turret (Fig 32). These burrows occur at a high density, on the order of 20 to 100 per sq m throughout the halophyte zone. Another crab, *Metopograpsus messor*, is much less abundant, but is sometimes more conspicuous because of its dark coloration and habit of running about in the open rather than hiding in holes. Unlike *Cleistostoma*, which is strictly confined to the halophyte zone of tidal mud flats and does not occur elsewhere, *Metopograpsus* is extremely versatile and occurs in virtually all intertidal habitats in the Gulf. It is most abundant on or around rocky substrates, however, and on the mud flats occurs where the mud is relatively dry and firm, especially along the banks of tidal channels.

THE MANGROVE ZONE: The seaward edge of the halophyte zone is marked by an abrupt "step" or drop in the level of the mud, at the transition from the firm halophyte "turf" to wet mud of a much softer consistency. A person walking here may often sink up to his knees. The uppermost levels of this wetter sediment are usually occupied by a belt of black mangroves *Avicennia marina*, forming a thicket of dark

Fig 31. The halophytic plant, Arthrocnemon macrostachyum, *one of the dominant forms of the "halophyte zone." [Tarut Island]*

Fig 32. The mud surface of the halophyte zone is riddled with small round holes, burrows of the crab Cleistostoma dotilliforme. *This small crab is the dominant animal species at this level on the tidal flat. Each burrow is surrounded by a mound and turret built from the excavated mud. [Safwa]*

53

Fig 33. Black mangrove Avicennia marina *on a tidal mud flat. The radiating root system is indicated by lines of upright pneumatophores, which project above the surface of the mud and provide ventilation to the buried roots. Behind the mangrove are halophytes growing on slightly higher ground, and in the background a large tidal channel. [Tarut Island]*

green bushes one or two meters high. Mangroves trap sediment and bind it together with an extensive root system, thus gradually extending the tidal flat seaward. The wet, fine-grained mud is rich in organic matter and devoid of oxygen below the surface; and the mangrove roots are able to survive only by means of pneumatophores which project above the mud surface at regular intervals and conduct oxygen to the buried portions of the root system (Fig 33). This is only one of several interesting adaptations of mangroves for life on the tidal mud flat. Another concerns their system of reproduction. Plant seeds of the usual type require oxygen and would be unable to germinate if buried in the black, anaerobic mud. If exposed on the surface they would be washed away by the tide before having a chance to take root. Mangrove seeds are not dropped from the parent plant as soon as they are formed, but remain attached until they have germinated and grown to a considerable size. Local mangroves drop their seedlings only after these have grown into young plants neatly wrapped in their seedling leaves, and about the size and shape of small plums. These seedlings are able to take root quickly on any mud surface onto which they may fall or be carried by the tide (Fig 34).

THE ALGAL MAT ZONE: Seaward of the mangrove belt, a zone of algal mat is often present. At the study site this zone was about 130m wide (Fig 28). The sediment surface in this region is cemented together by a mat, several centimeters thick, composed of blue-green algae[1] and associated diatoms. Tide pool water in this region had a relatively high oxygen concentration, undoubtedly as a result of vigorous photosynthesis in the algal mat, and a low pH. Many small and microscopic animals inhabit the mat, including gastropods, ostracods, nematodes, flatworms, copepods and oligochaete worms. Larger animal life, such as the burrowing crab *Macrophthalmus*,

Fig 34. Mangrove pneumatophores on a tidal mud flat. Among the pneumatophores may be seen several young mangrove seedlings, some still bearing the large "seed leaves" or cotyledons which provide a food store for the initial growth spurt of the young plant. [Tarut Island]

Fig 35. The black mangrove Avicennia marina *blooms in July. [Tarut Island]*

1 *Microcoleus chthonoplastes* and *Chroococcus membraninus.*

55

Fig 36. Blue-green algal mat, composed primarily of Chroococcus membraninus *and* Microcoleus chthonoplastes *along with several species of pennate diatoms. Algal mats of this type are an important feature of tidal flat environments in the Arabian Gulf. [Tarut Island]*

which is otherwise extremely abundant at this level on the mud flats, is conspicuously absent from the algal mat areas.

The algal mat zone is a variable feature rather than a universal or regular part of the sequence of zones on the tidal mud flat. In certain areas which had previously been dominated by mangroves or by *Macrophthalmus*, algal mats have been observed to form as a result of disturbance of the habitat by man. In other algal mat areas, no evidence of such disturbance could be found. The available evidence does suggest, though, that algal mats and thriving populations of crabs and snails are mutually exclusive. Normal population densities of *Macrophthalmus, Cerithidea* and the other associated crab and snail species keep the mud surface constantly churned up and prevent the algae from forming a mat. Once established, however, an algal mat consolidates the sediment surface to such an extent that small juvenile crabs are unable to tunnel there and so fail to become established. Adult *Macrophthalmus* crabs seem to be very sedentary and invade an algal mat, if at all, only at its edges. This may, therefore, be a case of competition between two different community types for the same substrate, with the outcome determined by factors that still remain to be studied. At any rate, algal mats are a widespread feature of intertidal environments in the Gulf (Fig 36), and have aroused some interest because of their role in sedimentary processes (Kendall and Skipwith, 1968).

THE *MACROPHTHALMUS* ZONE: Between the mangrove belt and the extreme low tide level, which marks the seaward limit of the intertidal mud flat, extends a broad expanse of very wet liquid mud, whose surface even at low tide is always covered by a thin film of adherent water. The upper portion of this region is occupied by a community dominated by several species of burrowing, deposit-feeding crabs. The most conspicuously abundant of these is *Macrophthalmus depressus*, after which the community is named. This crab, up to 3 cm in body width, occupies a more or less permanent burrow in the mud, and at low tide is usually seen just outside the entrance, where it feeds on minute organic particles sifted out of the sediment. Particularly in summer, the males also spend much of their time threatening each other by waving their large blue chelae (Fig 37) and trying to attract nearby females. Commonly a male and a female share the same burrow, and both may be seen feeding outside. The female has smaller chelae, and is much less aggressive than her mate. Densities of this species are difficult to determine, but probably reach or exceed 50 adult individuals per square meter of sediment.

The very distinctive crab community of the *Macrophthalmus* zone also includes several other species. Three of these,[2] like *Macrophthalmus depressus*, are deposit feeders belonging to the family Ocypodidae (along with *Ocypode saratan, Scopimera scabricauda,* and *Cleistostoma dotilliforme*); but they are very much smaller and therefore inconspicuous, even though at

2 *Paracleistostoma* sp., and two small species of *Scopimera*.

Fig 37. The male of Macrophthalmus depressus, *a dominant crab of the intertidal mud flats, assumes this defensive attitude if disturbed. The blue chelae and contrasting orange patches on the crab's body make the threat signal more conspicuous. [Tarut Island]*

Fig 38. Large mud crab Eurycarcinus *sp. (family Xanthidae) in a defensive posture. This crab, here shown on wet mud in the* Macrophthalmus *zone, is a predator found at all levels on the tidal mud flat. [Tarut Island]*

Fig 39. The large echiuran worm Ikeda taenioides *extends its "tongue" or proboscis over the surface of the mud flat, and picks up microscopic food particles by ciliary action. The proboscis, which is mud-colored and inconspicuous, may extend for more than a meter before being drawn back into the burrow with its load of food. The deep red body of the worm always remains hidden below the surface of the mud. [Tarut Island]*

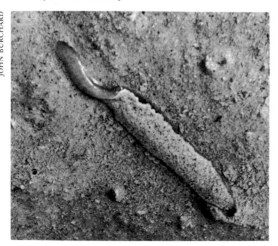

least one of them is probably more abundant than *Macrophthalmus* itself. The purplish and white *Eurycarcinus* sp. is a predator in spite of its clumsy build, apparently feeding on any other crab it can catch (Fig 38). This is the largest of the mud flat crabs, reaching a body width of over 5cm, but it is relatively uncommon. It occurs at all levels on the mud flat, though perhaps most abundantly in the *Macrophthalmus* zone. The most striking of the mud flat crabs, however, is an unidentified grapsid. The males of this species have greatly elongated, purple-tipped white chelae with which they fight ritual battles (see Frontispiece). The females are similar but have much smaller chelae. Both sexes are extremely fast-moving and agile and prey largely on the little *Scopimera* crabs. They capture them in a sudden dash before the smaller crabs can disappear down their holes.

THE *CERITHIDEA* ZONE: Below the *Macrophthalmus* zone, and down to the level of the lowest spring tides, is found a community dominated by the snail *Cerithidea cingulata* (Figs 24 & 40), which occurs at densities up to 2,100 individuals per square meter; but *Cerithidea* is fairly abundant in the *Macrophthalmus* zone as well. There is a gradual transition between these two zones, rather than a sharp demarcation. Other typical animals of the *Cerithidea* zone include the predatory snail *Murex kusterianus*, which is also abundant in several other biotopes, and the curious worm *Ikeda taenioides*, which lives buried deep in the sediment, but extends its ribbon-like proboscis out over the mud surface to feed (Fig 39). The proboscis is sometimes well over 1m long when extended. Numerous species of burrowing pelecypod mollusks also inhabit this zone, but owing to difficulties of sampling have not yet been systematically studied.

Variations in Mud Flat Zonation

The zonation pattern just described is typical of tidal mud flats in Tarut Bay, as well as in several other areas examined by Aramco biologists. Considerable variation occurs, however, in response to local factors, especially the topography of the shoreline, the properties of the sediment, and the nature of the adjacent terrestrial and marine environments. Generally speaking these variations amount to the reduction or suppression of one or another of the zones, rather than any real change in the sequence. For example, mangroves are abundant in Tarut Bay, but are not known to occur further north. Tidal mud flats further north than Tarut Bay, therefore, lack a mangrove zone. Similarly, the width and luxuriance of the marsh grass zone vary widely according to the nature of the adjacent terrestrial habitat, and in many places this zone is virtually absent. The most consistent features of tidal mud flats are the halophyte, *Macrophthalmus* and *Cerithidea* zones. Especially in the latter two, however, the biological community is strongly influenced by the character of the sediment, which may range from extremely soft mud (as in the Tarut Bay examples) to a rather

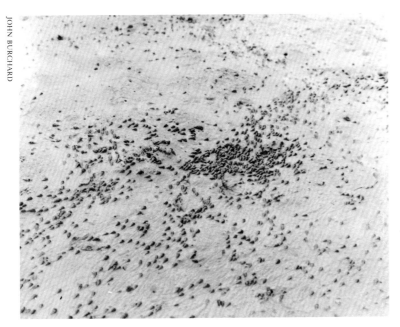

Fig 40. *The snail* Cerithidea cingulata *frequently attains population densities of more than 1,000 individuals per square meter on the tidal mud flat. The curious tendency of these snails to move along parallel lines, as shown by the feeding tracks in the photograph, is not understood; it may have something to do with the direction taken by the ebb tide streaming off the tidal flat. A few crab holes* (Macrophthalmus depressus) *are also visible in the photograph.* [Tarut Island]

muddy, fine sand. All these sediments will be colonized, at the appropriate tidal level, by *Macrophthalmus depressus*, but the associated fauna may differ somewhat. On coarser sand sediments, *Macrophthalmus* will be absent, and *Scopimera scabricauda* will take its place. These animals have such diagnostic habitat preferences that it seems justified to classify any intertidal area inhabited by *Macrophthalmus depressus* as a mud flat by definition, and any area inhabited by *Scopimera scabricauda* as a sand flat, even without further investigation of the matter. This is a particularly clear-cut example of the usefulness of the "biotope principle" in categorizing the endlessly varying natural environment.

SAND FLATS

Large, flat areas of intertidal sand occur in many locations where wave or current energies are higher than those prevailing in the mud flat areas, but less than those found on exposed beaches. For example, extensive tidal sand flats occur on the windward northern side of Tarut Island, while on the leeward side the tidal flats consist almost entirely of mud. Generally, the sand on tidal flats is finer-grained than the sand of exposed beaches, and has a considerably higher content of organic matter, which frequently gives it a greyish coloration. At low tide the exposed sand flats almost always show distinct ripple marks, produced by the receding waters of the ebbing tide. Often the sand is only a thin layer overlying a rock or beach-rock substratum. Tidal channels occur on sandy tidal flats, but because of the more compact nature of the sediment they are much less elaborate and extensive than on mud flats. In many areas the local patterns of wave and current result in an intimate intermingling of sections of tidal flat with different characteristics, so that mud flats, sand flats and even rock flats occur in immediate contact. A good example is the northwestern corner of Tarut Island, where all three types occur within a few meters of one another.

Fig 41. Tidal sand flat with burrows of the small crab Scopimera scabricauda, *surrounded by typical feeding tracks and piles of "pseudofaecal" sand pellets. A feeding crab moves slowly sideways away from its burrow, scooping up food-containing sand beneath itself and throwing the pellets of cleaned sand backwards between its legs. In this way a shallow trench is formed, with pellets piled to one side of it. [Tarut Island]*

Zonation on sand flats is much less obvious than on mud; the uppermost part of the shore profile is usually a normal sandy beach. Ghost crabs *Ocypode saratan* prefer exposed beaches to sheltered ones, but in some locations, such as the southern side of Abu 'Ali Island, they inhabit sand beaches whose lower levels fall into the mud flat category. At the Abu 'Ali site *Ocypode* feeds mainly on *Macrophthalmus depressus*, which they dig out of their burrows in the mud at low tide.

The middle levels of tidal sand flats are characterized by populations of the small crab *Scopimera scabricauda*, at densities averaging 25 and sometimes exceeding 100 individuals per sq m. Like most of its relatives this is a deposit feeder and is active when the tide is out. It picks up a mouthful of sand, extracts the organic particles by flushing them out with a stream of water, and discards the cleaned sand as a compact "pseudofaecal" pellet. A feeding crab produces such pellets at the rate of 2 to 4 per minute, so that the sand surface soon becomes littered with them, betraying the presence of the crabs (Fig 41). *Scopimera* are extremely shy, and dart back into their holes at the slightest disturbance.

Lower down the sand flat, especially where some water is retained in tide pools or shallow depressions, *Ikeda taenioides* is abundant. Large tide pools and the bottoms of tidal channels are the home of the strange crab *Macrophthalmus grandidieri*, whose body is more than twice as wide as it is long.

Yet another distinctive subdivision of the sand flat biotope consists of patches of very loose, rather wet, coarse sand, near the low tide level. These are inhabited by a variety of larger burrowing animals including sea cucumbers, several species of bivalves[3] and the extraordinary *Macrophthalmus telescopicus*, a small crab usually found hiding beneath the loose sand, with only one of its enormously elongated eyestalks protruding above the surface.

Juveniles of many subtidal animals, such as the large swimming crab *Portunus pelagicus*, show a strong preference for tidepools and other areas of permanent water in the intertidal, where they are probably more sheltered from predation than in the subtidal region.

ROCK FLATS

Intertidal rock flats occur extensively along the Saudi Arabian coast, especially in the Gulf of Salwah and other bay areas where conditions favor the formation of beach rock. Tidal rock flats in the form of faroush, a soft greyish limestone made up of broken shells, sand and mud particles cemented together, occupy large areas in Tarut Bay, in spite of the fact that this material has been systematically harvested for centuries as building stone. Faroush is apparently a form of beachrock and occurs in flat, more or less jointed sheets. The rock layer is usually 10 to 20cm thick, and the underlying sediments, which consist of coarse shell sand with a silt or mud admixture, are often anaerobic.

Wide expanses of intertidal rock flat are also found along

Fig 42. Tidal channel in the halophyte zone of a tidal mud flat. On the right may be seen a steep-cut bank produced by erosion on the outer curve of a bend in the channel; on the left is a mud bank deposited by slowing of the current before the bend. Numerous crab holes are visible in the banks of the channel. [Tarut Island]

relatively sheltered sections of the open coasts. These rocks are often rougher in texture than the faroush flats in bays, and may be partially covered by thin sheets of sand (Fig 26). Their flat topography, however, readily distinguishes them from the rocky beach biotope.

As in the case of subtidal sheet rock, most of the animal life of rock flats is found in the cracks or under loose blocks. The animals of the rocky tidal flat are of the same ecological types as those of the rocky beach, and many of the same species occur in both biotopes; but whereas the rock beach has fewer kinds of animals than the adjacent sand beach, the rocky tidal flat has a greater variety of animal life than any other intertidal biotope in the Gulf. The most important animal types contributing to this diversity are polychaete worms,[4] gastropods,[5] pelecypods,[6] and decapod Crustacea.[7]

Rock flats are also the habitat of several species of algae. For example, the sides of rock-lined tidal channels on the northwest side of Tarut Island were covered with a growth of benthic species.[8]

TIDAL CREEKS

Tidal creeks or drainage channels are a feature especially of the muddy tidal flat, where they form a branching, meandering drainage system arising in the upper levels of the halophyte zone and emptying into the sea at or near the level of the lowest low tides (Fig 7 & 42). They are created mainly as a result of erosion by the receding waters of the ebb tide, and like any river system on land have many small tributaries on the upper part of the flat, which combine into a few large streams in the

3 Especially *Solecurtus australis, Gari occidens* and *Paphia sulcaria.*

4 Mostly crevice dwellers, but also including rock-boring and tube-dwelling types.

5 *Thais* spp., *Monilea* spp., *Trochus* sp., *Littorina* sp., *Onchidium peronii*, etc.

6 *Pinctada* spp., *Isognomon* spp., *Malleus* spp., *Anomia* sp., *Lithophaga* spp., *Botula* sp., *Barbatia* sp., etc.

7 *Alpheus* spp., Xanthidae of the genera *Actumnus, Chlorodiella, Etisus, Pilumnopeus, Pilumnus, Xantho*, etc., and many others including *Metopograpsus messor* which is most abundant in this biotope.

8 *Enteromorpha* sp., *Rhizoclonium kochianum, Chondria dasyphylla* and *Achnanthes* sp.

61

Fig 43. Metopograpsus messor, *a ubiquitous crab of intertidal biotopes, shown here among dead sea grass on a sandy tidal flat. [Saihat]*

lower part. Also like river systems on land, they have conspicuous meanders with steeply cut banks on the outer side of each bend. The coarser particles of the eroded sediment soon settle out to form a sand bar just downstream of the bend, while the finer particles are carried down to be deposited as a bank of soft mud where the current slows on the inner, upstream side of the next following bend. These bars and banks function as dams when the tide is out, and retain large permanent tide pools all along the course of the creeks. These pools are typically 2 to 3m wide, 10 to 30m long and up to 50cm deep. Especially in the upper parts of the creek bed, which are cut off from the sea for a large part of the tidal cycle, the pools are subject to large fluctuations of temperature and salinity. Where the large creeks empty out onto the lower tide flat, an alluvial fan of relatively coarse sediment is usually formed, often slightly elevated above the surrounding mud flat.

Along the banks of tidal creeks, the various levels of the mud flat biotope occur in a nearly vertical sequence with little horizontal separation. The resulting zonation is basically similar to that already described for this biotope, with a few special features resulting from the creek topography. The upper part of the creek banks, which form an abrupt miniature cliff 30 to 50cm high, are riddled with cracks and holes inhabited by numerous crabs, especially *Metopograpsus messor* (Fig 43). Sand bars in the creek bed, thrown up by selective deposition of coarse sediment, are inhabited by typical sand flat organisms, notably *Scopimera scabricauda*, while the soft mud banks occurring elsewhere as a result of the same sorting action are inhabited by a typical *Macrophthalmus* zone community.

The permanent tide pools of the creek bed are inhabited by young and partly grown individuals of a great variety of subtidal animals, which evidently find here a rich food supply and relative freedom from predators. The most abundant of these are shrimp,[9] swimming crabs,[10] and many kinds of fish.[11] Certain other species of animals seem to find in the tidal creek a preferred or even exclusive habitat at all stages in their life history. One of these is a small transparent carid shrimp *Palaemon (Palaeander)* sp., found by hundreds in certain tide pools along the creeks. Another is *Macrophthalmus grandidieri*, which has so far been found only in large tidal creeks draining sand flat areas, where it is common. Others with a less exclusive preference include the shrimp *Metapenaeus stebbingi*, which though found in other biotopes is vastly more numerous in the creek beds than elsewhere; and the gaily colored killifish or top-minnow *Aphanius dispar*, which is also found in freshwater springs and is apparently capable of swimming back and forth between tidal creeks and irrigation ditches without suffering from the drastic changes in salinity!

9 *Metapenaeus affinis* and *M. stebbingi.*
10 *Portunus pelagicus*
11 *Acanthopagrus* sp., *Gerres* sp., *Hemirhamphus far*, *Mugil dussumieri*, *Nematalosa nasus*, *Platycephalus* sp., *Pseudorhombus* sp., *Sardinella* sp., *Therapon jarbua, etc.*

SECTION TWO

SUBTIDAL BIOTOPES

Subtidal benthic biotopes include all assemblages of organisms found below the low tide level and occurring on, in, or associated with the bottom. Obviously, this category includes a great variety of habitats and many different community types, so for the sake of convenience some subdivision is necessary.

The most important factor determining which organisms occur in these habitats is undoubtedly the physical nature of the sea bed, which may consist either of rock or rock-like materials such as coral (hard bottoms), or of unconsolidated sediments of various kinds (soft bottoms). The next most important physical variable is the depth at which the habitat is located, as this directly controls the amount of light, the intensity of water movement, and other important factors, resulting most commonly in well-marked depth zonation of the biological communities. For present purposes, therefore, it is convenient to consider subtidal benthos under the two main headings of hard bottoms and soft bottoms, each of which is further divided into sub-categories.

Hard Bottom Biotopes

The main biotopes in the hard bottom division include **coral reefs, rocky bottoms** of a variety of types, and **artificial structures.**

The Arabian Gulf coral reefs occur in two main forms: as patch or platform reefs in shallow water, and as fringing reefs surrounding offshore islands. These two types of reefs have many similarities, and are here considered together. Offshore islands play an indispensable role in the ecology of several important marine organisms, especially sea turtles and sea birds, and these also will be discussed in connection with the coral reef biotope (Chapter 6).

Rocky bottoms occur in a variety of forms with differing biological characteristics. The most important in the western Arabian Gulf include: rocky patches in the immediate subtidal adjacent to exposed beaches and along the banks of tidal channels; patches or banks of exposed rock of a rough and fragmented texture including varying amounts of coral debris, found at depths of approximately 5 to 15m and located offshore from exposed beaches; and expanses of flat, beachrock-like material, almost featureless except for regular joints or cracks and occurring over considerable areas at depths from the immediately subtidal to 12 or 15m (Chapter 4).

Artificial structures include any man-made object occupying a permanent location on the sea bed. The most important such structures in the Arabian Gulf are the platforms used in offshore oil production. These structures offer a rich habitat for many forms of marine life (Chapter 7).

Soft Bottom Biotopes

The main biotopes in the soft bottom division are more difficult to classify convincingly, since the nature of the sediment and its associated marine life changes from one aspect to another without sharp discontinuities, according to depth, water

Fig 44 (preceding page). When disturbed, Lesser Crested Terns rise from their nests in a cloud and noisily protest the intrusion. [Karan Island] (Photo by John Burchard)

movement and other factors. The sediment characteristics range from coarse coral gravels and shell sands through sand, silty sand and muds with and without sandy admixture, to fine clays. For the sake of convenience, these habitats have been somewhat arbitrarily classified into **grassbeds, subtidal sands** and **subtidal muds,** in accordance with the gross physical appearance of the sea bed sediments on which the organisms live.

Grassbeds are turf-like growths of marine angiosperms – sea grasses, as they are sometimes called – which occupy large areas of sandy and silty-sand substrates from the immediate subtidal levels down to depths of 10 or 12m. They form a distinctive and highly productive biological entity, and occupy a key position in the life cycles of various commercially important marine animals in the area, notably the shrimp (Chapter 5).

Subtidal sands and subtidal muds include at least four or five different biological communities (Chapter 4). Here, as in the case of tidal flats, it is often easier to recognize a particular biotope by the distinctive plant and animal community inhabiting it, than it is to specify the exact physical conditions defining its occurrence.

Productivity of Benthic Biotopes

Much of the fishery effort in the Arabian Gulf is directed toward shallow water "demersal" or bottom-living fish species, and toward shrimp; in other words, toward the exploitation of benthic biotopes. The productivity of these biotopes is therefore a matter of practical as well as theoretical interest.

As a general rule, the productivity of benthic biotopes is "secondary"; that is to say, the primary production which sustains benthic communities is carried out by phytoplankton in the overlying water column, and exploited by benthic animals either through filter-feeding or through picking up planktonic organisms which have settled to the bottom.

In shallow, tropical waters, however, two very important exceptions to this general rule occur. These are coral reefs on hard bottoms, and grassbeds on soft bottoms. The essential feature of both these biotopes is that very high rates of primary production are maintained by benthic organisms: in one case the sea-grass plants, and in the other the coral polyps with their associated, symbiotic algae or zooxanthellae. In both cases a large energy surplus results, which not only supports a rich assortment of animal life within the grassbed and coral reef biotopes, but also contributes significant amounts of energy to other, neighboring biotopes (Fig 2).

Because of the extremely gradual slope of the sea bed in the western Arabian Gulf, a large proportion of the bottom lies within the range of effective light penetration, and so is able to support coral reefs or grassbeds. These two biotopes, therefore, play a particularly important role in the overall biological economy of the Gulf.

Fig 45. The long-spined sea urchin Diadema setosum *is a common inhabitant of subtidal mixed and rocky bottoms in the Arabian Gulf, especially on and around coral reefs [Jurayd Island]*

4
HARD AND SOFT
BOTTOMS

ROCKY BOTTOM BIOTOPES

Rocky bottoms in the western Gulf may be broadly divided into two types according to their physical structure. The first category, **rough rock bottoms,** includes various types of rocks with an irregular and highly dissected surface texture, which provide many projections, corners, crevices and holes utilized by various kinds of marine organisms as points of attachment and/or living spaces (Fig 45). Such rocks typically support a heavy growth of algae, and are inhabited by a great variety of animal life. The main adaptive types in this biotope include sessile animals permanently attached to the rock; rock-boring animals living inside the rock; creeping animals moving about over the rock surface, and usually capable of clinging firmly to it as a means of self-protection; and hole or crevice dwellers, usually actively moving species such as crabs or stomatopods, which shelter in holes and crannies of the rock, but emerge to feed. The sessile and rock-boring species, which include many bivalves, usually feed on plankton by filtering or by some other means of capture, such as the stinging tentacles of hydroids and sea anemones. Creeping animals, among which snails are prominent, often live by grazing on algae, while many of the crevice-dwellers are predatory. These adaptive types are similar to those of the rocky intertidal zone, though the actual species of animals are usually different.

On the other hand, **smooth rock bottoms** consist mainly of flat, shelf-like rock with few surface irregularities. Such rock is typically divided, by a network of joints or fissures, into large polygonal plates measuring several meters across (Fig 46). Most of the organisms live in or around the fissures, and the

Fig 46. Smooth rock bottoms are often divided into polygonal plates, several meters across, as shown in this aerial view. Most of the organisms in this environment live on or around the fissures between the plates, and the bare rock itself is conspicuously poor in life. [Near Ras al-Qurayyah]

bare rock surface is conspicuously poor in life. The surface is frequently covered by a thin layer of sand or silt, which may harbor a limited selection of animals more typical of unconsolidated sediments. Extensive burrow systems occur on this type of bottom, obviously made and inhabited by sizeable active animals, possibly shrimp or stomatopods. Unfortunately, all attempts to collect and identify the occupants of these burrows have so far proved fruitless.

Rough rock bottoms are found at depths ranging from the wave-wash zone of rocky beaches, where they usually take the form of boulders or outcroppings interspersed with sand patches, down to a depth of at least 15m, and probably deeper. Rock outcroppings occurring around offshore islands below the zone of coral growth, at depths of 20 to 50m, should also be included under this heading. The main forms of this biotope which have been examined during field work so far include: boulders and outcrops occurring in the immediate subtidal zone of many or most exposed beaches (Fig 47); the beds and sides of tidal channels in Tarut Bay, with a depth range and biota essentially similar to the previous category; and extensive tracts of rough rocky outcrop in depths of about 5 to 15m, which occur in the sublittoral zone of many exposed beaches.

Smooth rock bottoms have so far been encountered mainly in two situations. In one of these, subtidal extensions of intertidal beachrock (faroush) platforms cover large areas of shallow bottom near the shore. These expanses of bare rock are especially extensive in bay areas with limited water movement and increased salinities, and are probably the result of contemporaneous cementation of sediments or submarine lithification, in which the precipitation of carbonates is partly a consequence of photosynthetic activity of microscopic algae on the sediment surface (Chapter 10). Under somewhat different conditions, extensive areas of flat rock bottom also occur at depths of 5 to 15m in and adjacent to Tarut Bay and elsewhere, especially in areas where strong currents minimize sedimentation. Flat rock at these depths is frequently covered by a thin layer of silt or sand, inhabited by soft-bottom organisms. Where the sediment layer is thicker, the rock-bottom biotope merges into one or another of the soft bottom communities. Patches of sediment often alternate with patches or bands of exposed rock, and in these areas the biological communities include a mixture of hard-bottom and soft-bottom organisms.

Biological Features of Rock Bottoms

Because of the wide variation in rock bottom habitats, it was not possible to select a single model site for study as representative of the whole biotope. Instead, the main biological features of different types of rock bottoms will be described briefly. Because of the dominant role that light penetration plays in determining the type of biota encountered, the shallower and deeper zones will be considered separately.

Fig 47. Mixed sand and rock bottom in the subtidal shallows of an exposed beach. The sand supports a growth of the sea grass Halodule uninervis, *while the rock surface is entirely covered by competing growths of small algae, sponges, and the colonial tunicate* Botryllus sp. [Ju'aymah]

Fig 48. On shallow subtidal rocks, corals (in this case Cyphastrea *sp., center) compete for space with small algae (covering most of the rock surface), large algae (*Sargassum *sp., extreme right) and a variety of sessile invertebrates. [Ju'aymah]*

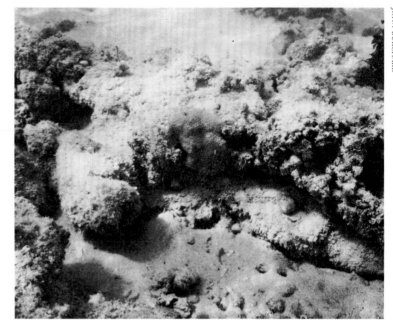

SHALLOW SUBTIDAL ROCKS: Patches, bands and boulders of more or less rough textured rock are a common feature of the immediate subtidal region of most exposed beaches, usually alternating with sand belts. The outstanding features of this environment are vigorous water movement due to wave action, and strong light due to the shallow depth. The same combination of conditions is also characteristic of rocks exposed at the sides and bottoms of the shallower tidal channels in Tarut Bay, among other places, and their biological features are therefore quite similar.

Plentiful light favors the growth of algae, which densely cover the surface of the rock. Most of these are small species[1] (Fig 49), giving rise to a surface texture resembling fine fur or felt. Larger species[2] (Fig 50) also occur forming dense thickets, sometimes over a meter high, on subtidal rocks just below the wave-wash zone, as well as in the tidal channels. Both types of growth are shown in Fig 51.

Another group of hard-bottom organisms whose growth is favored by light is that of the reef corals (Chapter 6). In fact, wherever rock bottoms occur in well-lighted regions, there is a competition for space between corals and algae. Many small colonies of various reef coral species occur on shallow subtidal rocks (Fig 48), but reefs do not form in this zone, apparently because extreme water temperatures and/or sedimentation inhibit coral growth in the shallows close to shore. In a similar way, physical environmental factors probably tip the balance one way or the other in different parts of the habitat, leading to the formation of dense algal growths at one extreme, and coral reefs at the other. Between these two extremes mixed communities occur, in which corals and algae coexist.

1 *Sphacelaria furcigera, Jania rubens, Spyridia filamentosa, Polysiphonia* sp., and many other species.

2 *Sargassum angustifolium, S. binderi, S. boveanum* var. *aterrima, S. latifolium* and *Hormophysa triquetra.* Also *Dictyota dichotoma* var. *intricata, D. divaricata, Padina gymnospora* and *Colpomenia sinuosa.*

Fig 49. A filamentous red alga, Spyridia filamentosa. *The photograph shows the terminal filaments which provide a base for the growth of smaller filamentous algae, diatoms and numerous invertebrate animals.*

Shallow subtidal rocks are usually of the rough category, irregularly shaped and full of holes, due partly to the scouring action of wave-agitated sand and partly to the activities of boring animals. The irregular shape of these rocks may also result partly from coral growth in the recent past, when the sea level was slightly higher than it is now. The hollows and crannies of such rocks provide safe shelter for a great variety of organisms, including mantis shrimp *Gonodactylus demanii*, rock crabs (family Xanthidae) of several species, several kinds of blenniid fish, a variety of gobies, and many different kinds of polychaete worms. All of these are active animals and emerge from their hiding places to feed. Clinging firmly to the surface of the rocks are other mobile animals, especially chitons, limpets and herbivorous snails such as *Turbo* sp., which graze on the dense covering of small algae. Carnivorous snails, such as *Thais pseudohippocastaneum*, prey on other mollusks or on sessile animals such as barnacles.

Another way of exploiting the opportunities offered by the rocky bottom is illustrated by the many bivalves living permanently attached to the rock. These obtain their food by filtering plankton out of the surrounding sea water. Some, such as the rock oyster *Spondylus* sp. or the pearl oysters *Pinctada* spp., are found attached to the exterior surface of the rock. Others, such as the hammer oysters *Malleus* sp. and *Isognomon* sp., inhabit crevices in which they become immovably wedged as they grow. Still others, such as the date mussel *Lithophaga* sp. or the piddock *Gastrochaena* sp., actually bore holes into the rock. The holes are enlarged internally as the animal grows, but remain connected with the outside by a narrow opening. After the death of the original inhabitant, these holes are colonized and often enlarged by other kinds of animals, and are an important factor in producing the porous, Swiss cheese-like texture of the rock in this zone.

Fig 50. Padina gymnospora, *a foliose brown alga whose fronds are prettily marked with concentric dark rings of reproductive structures.*

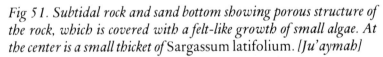

Fig 51. Subtidal rock and sand bottom showing porous structure of the rock, which is covered with a felt-like growth of small algae. At the center is a small thicket of Sargassum latifolium. *[Ju'aymah]*

Fig 52. Sargassum boveanum, *a large brown alga which contributes to the formation of extensive subtidal algal beds. The small "berries" are actually gas-filled bladders which buoy up the plant and so keep it upright in the water.*

Many of the inhabitants of rough subtidal rocks are also found in the lower portions of the adjacent rocky intertidal, where physical environmental conditions are similar except for periodic exposure to the air. Others, especially corals and the larger algae, are strictly subtidal, since they are unable to withstand even short periods of exposure under Saudi Arabian climatic conditions.

Large expanses of intertidal and shallow subtidal rock flat occur in protected areas where wave action is minimal, and especially in bay systems where salinities are high. Typical examples of this type of habitat are found near Dammam, in Dawhat Zalum, and along much of the Saudi Arabian coast of the Gulf of Salwah.

Flat rock bottoms are, in principle, colonized by the same types of organisms that inhabit rough rocks at corresponding depths, but the differing physical nature of the substrate greatly affects the success of such colonization. Species requiring holes or crevices are found only along the joints between rock plates, and their numbers are limited by the availability of hiding places. Organisms such as the algae *Sargassum* spp. (Fig 52) or pearl oysters, which are able to attach to a flat rock surface, generally require a certain amount of water movement. On flat rock bottoms they therefore tend to occur where wave action or tidal currents provide good mixing. They are commonly found just below low tide level along flat, rocky shorelines, and in the vicinity of bay entrances where tidal movements are strong. Over large expanses of rock flat, especially in more or less hypersaline bays, extremes of temperature and salinity occur which severely limit the growth of marine life. Such rock flats often appear barren; but even then they usually support a dense growth of microscopic blue-green algae, which give a blackish coloration to the rock.

DEEPER ROCK BOTTOMS: Below depths of about 3m, light penetration is insufficient to support the growth of large brown algae (e.g. *Sargassum* spp.). Their place is largely taken by red algae, including many calcareous encrusting forms, and by corals. In places, dense aggregations of pearl oysters occur. These habitats vary widely, and are therefore difficult to classify. They range from tide-swept, more or less silt-covered sheets of flat rock, to fully developed coral reefs, and include a range of intermediate types in which the predominance of different life forms is probably controlled by the texture of the rock (itself the result of past environmental conditions), the extent and frequency of wave and current action, and the sediment load. Salinities above approximately $45^o/_{oo}$, which occur generally from Dammam southwards and in enclosed bays throughout the region, limit the occurrence of organisms in this as in other habitats.

Flat rock bottoms in this category were examined by Aramco biologists at five sites within or just outside Tarut Bay, covering a depth range from 5 to 22m. Each site has some peculiarities of its own.

SITE 1 is located approximately halfway between Dammam and Ras Tanura, about 500m seaward of the Dhahran-Ras Tanura pipelines, in water about 5m deep. The bottom consists of flat, smooth rock covered with a few millimeters of silt. Apart from a few pearl oysters and tunicates attached directly to the flat rock surface, most of the animals are found in the crevices or joints between adjacent rock plates. Animals visible in these joints include small xanthid crabs, small sea anemones, gobies, snapping shrimp *Synalpheus* sp. and snails. Sand dollars[3] are found creeping through the silt layer, especially in rock depressions where up to 2cm of silty sand has accumulated. At the intersections of the rock joints occur extensive, deep burrow systems from which the antennae of large shrimp-like crustaceans sometimes protrude. These burrows are apparently also inhabited by a number of other kinds of animals, but attempts to dislodge the residents by injections of irritant or anaesthetic chemicals were unsuccessful, and the hardness of the rock made underwater excavation impossible.

SITE 2 is located at 6m depth, adjacent to the Dhahran-Ras Tanura pipelines, and a little less than 2km from Ras Tanura. The bottom consists of nearly flat rock with occasional sand pockets. Tidal currents of about 1.5 knots sweep the area, but a considerable variety of reef corals occur, growing as small isolated colonies attached to the bare rock surface. Almost all are species of compact growth (e.g. *Favia* spp). One surprise is the occurrence of several small colonies of the coral *Turbinaria* sp., a species normally found only at much greater depths. The very turbid water, which reduces the light intensity, may account for the presence of this species here.

A short distance away from this site there is a small but flourishing coral reef, where physical conditions are not obviously different. The coral reef itself is composed of only three species,[4] but on the immediately adjacent flat rock bottom there are numerous small colonies of at least ten coral species not found in the reef itself.

SITE 3 is located just seaward of the Dammam shipping channel, in 14m of water. The bottom consists of shelving, somewhat broken rock, with a silty covering varying from negligible to several centimeters thick. Loose plates and fragments of rock are scattered over the bottom, perhaps as a result of dredging operations, and provide shelter for a variety of marine life. The most obvious inhabitants include large swimming crabs,[5] mole lobsters *Thenus orientalis,* and many species of fish of all sizes, most notably hamour *Epinephelus tauvina.* Large pelagic and semi-pelagic fish[6] and at least two species of sharks[7] have also been observed.

3 *Clypeaster humilis* and *Echinodiscus auritus.*

4 *Stylophora* sp., *Acropora* sp. and *Platygyra* sp.

5 *Portunus pelagicus* and *Charybdis natator.*

6 Chana'ad *Scomberomorus commersoni,* barracuda *Sphyraena jello,* cobia *Rachycentron canadus,* tuna *Euthynnus affinis,* etc.

7 *Carcharhinus maculipinnis* and *Chiloscyllium griseum.*

Fig 53. Tide-swept rocky bottom at about 6m depth, with a large pearl oyster Pinctada *sp., cocks-comb oysters* Lopha cristagalli, *small corals and coralline algae. The raised rock plate in the background is actually the remains of a long-dead colony of* Acropora. *[Tarut Bay]*

JOHN BURCHARD

Fig 54. The hieroglyphic patterns of brain coral Platygyra *sp. are seen dramatically in this picture. At the center is a giant sea anemone more than 30cm in diameter, with attendant anemone-fish* Amphiprion *sp., and in the background an encrusting layer of the coralline alga* Lithothamnium. *[Jana Island]*

SITE 4 is located several hundred meters south of Ras Tanura South Pier, at 22m depth. The bottom consists of flat rock covered, except for a few outcroppings, by 2 to 4cm of sand. The area is swept by tidal currents of up to two knots, so that the sand is in constant motion and contains few animals. Most of the limited benthic fauna at this site is attached to the rock outcrops, and to various man-made objects on the bottom. The most abundant, relatively large animals are pearl oysters *Pinctada radiata* and several species of sea fans or gorgonians. The sea fans in turn support several commensal animals, notably brittle stars and a highly specialized snail *Primovula rhodia.* Cowries *Cypraea turdus* are also found here, but fish life is not conspicuous, except for numerous small hamour.

SITE 5 : A different type of rock bottom, forming a transition to the coral reef biotope, is found at a depth of 8 to 10m offshore from Ju'aymah. The bottom here consists of irregular rocky ridges, trending parallel to the shore line and alternating with belts of sand. The rock is very rough-textured and includes large amounts of broken coral, cemented together by encrusting algae. Live corals of several species grow here and there, but do not form a reef. In places, heads of brain coral *Platygyra* sp. several meters in diameter occur. The animals of this area include, besides the rock-bottom inhabitants already mentioned, many which are typically associated with corals and considered as coral reef fauna. These include reef fish of various species,[8] giant sea anemones with their commensal anemone-fish *Amphiprion* sp. (Fig 54), and a variety of crabs and shrimp all living in more or less intimate symbiotic relationships with the corals.

At several sites around the bases of offshore coral islands, rock exposures are encountered at depths down to 50m. In the Gulf, coral reef formations extend to depths of only 15 to 20m. Cursory observation indicates that these deeper rocks, which are mostly rough textured, are colonized mainly by gorgonians and sponges, but antipatharians, so-called black coral, have been found at several locations in depths from 25m downwards. These organisms also colonize artificial structures in the same depth range.

SOFT BOTTOM BIOTOPES

Unconsolidated subtidal sediments in the western Gulf can be classified as **sand,** consisting mostly of coarse particles, or **mud,** consisting of finer ones. Deep-sea oozes and clays have not been formed in the shallow continental shelf environment of the Gulf.

Physical Features of Soft Bottoms

The distinction between sand and mud is an arbitrary one, but it reflects a real difference in the biological communities inhabiting these two types of substrates. **Sand bottoms** are

8 *Heniochus acuminatus, Pomacanthus maculosus, Chaetodon* spp., *Gobiodon citrinus,* and many others.

formed and maintained in high energy environments, where vigorous water movements occur as a result of wave action or currents. The sand tends to shift about constantly, and animals living in it must be able to change position rapidly to avoid being either buried or washed out. Sand bottoms are usually porous, with a good circulation of water, oxygen and dissolved nutrients. They contain relatively little excess unoxidized organic matter, and reducing conditions occur only at some distance below the surface of the sediment.

On the other hand, **mud bottoms** are formed in low energy environments, where the water moves more slowly. The fine particles pack tightly, and circulation of water among them is poor. Oxygen can penetrate only slowly into the sediment, and as a result excess organic matter accumulates there unoxidized. Reducing conditions prevail except in a very thin surface layer, and animals living in this environment must either remain in the oxygenated surface layer or develop special adaptations, similar to those of mudflat animals described in Chapter 3, enabling them to inhabit the anaerobic portion of the sediment.

Local Distribution

Subtidal **sand bottoms** occur locally in three main situations: as belts of varying width in the immediate subtidal zone of exposed beaches; as delta-like deposits formed by the action of tidal streams in and near coastal bay systems; and in deeper waters offshore, usually in the vicinity of coral reefs or islands (Fig 55), where an abundant supply of new coarse sediment, together with strong tidal streams, prevents the formation of finer-grained deposits.

The subtidal sand belts bordering exposed beaches represent part of a larger system in which the growth and sediment-stabilizing activity of sea grass beds is dynamically balanced by the erosional forces of wave action and longshore currents (Chapter 5). Both grassbeds and sand bottoms therefore tend to occur alternately in long narrow strips, arranged more or less parallel to the shoreline. Where the sand is not stabilized by grass cover, it is transported along the shore by the prevailing current, which in most locations along the Saudi Arabian coastline sets to the southeast. Sand therefore accumulates on the northwest side of naturally occurring headlands or artificial shoreline extensions, while long hook-shaped sand spits form on the southeast side of the larger headlands. The Ras Tanura spit is a particularly fine example of this process. The depth of the zone of active sand movement is a function of the amount of wave action on a particular beach, and under local conditions ranges from about 2 to 8m, depending on the exposure of the beach. The width of the sand zone depends on the slope of the shoreline, but is usually at least several hundred meters along this coast.

There are tidal deltas in many parts of Tarut Bay, and similar formations occur in most of the other bay systems along the coast. Like the open-coast sand belts, they are the result of a

TOM BOBROWSKI

Fig 55. A male and female Moses sole Pardachirus marmoratus *during courtship on a coral sand bottom. These 20cm fish can give off a chemical that paralyzes the jaws of an attacking shark. [Jana Island]*

dynamic balance between grassbed formation and erosional forces. In bays, however, the main erosional force is provided by tidal streams, and the loose sand deposits take the form of fan-shaped structures around the mouths of major tidal channels. Since tidal streams regularly alternate in direction, there is little net transport of sand, but the strong currents produce large-scale ripple-marks, often amounting to sand ridges several meters high. The structure and dynamics of these ridges are very similar to those of wind-blown aeolian sand dunes on land.

Offshore there are sand deposits at considerable depths – down to at least 30m – especially in the vicinity of coral islands or reefs. Strong currents occur around such reefs and islands, because they obstruct the large-scale tidal water movements in the shallow Gulf; these currents play a major part in sustaining the sand deposits. Another factor is certainly the continuous rain of coarse calcareous particles from the reef. Extensive sand bottom areas are also found interspersed with coral heads on the reef itself, wherever the bottom slope is gradual enough to permit the accumulation of sediment.

Mud bottoms are found in depths of 6m and more, wherever water movement and topography permit the accumulation of sediment. Except for a few rock outcrops, most of the bottom of the Gulf at depths greater than 30m is composed of mud. Between 10 and 30m mud bottoms are widespread, but other habitats also occur. At depths less than 10m mud bottoms occur only under particularly favorable conditions, usually in the vicinity of muddy tidal flats.

Biological Features of Soft Bottoms

The distribution of subtidal **sand bottom** communities in the Gulf is controlled mainly by light penetration, sand grain size, and the mobility or stability of the sand. Well-lighted, relatively stable sand bottoms down to about 10m support considerable photosynthesis, primarily by diatoms and other micro-algae, which form a film on the sand grains. This in turn

JOHN BURCHARD

Fig 56. The common rock-boring sea urchin Echinometra mathaei *sometimes occurs in dense aggregations or swarms, similar to those of the notorious crown-of-thorns starfish* Acanthaster planci. Echinometra *appears to feed on algae and dead coral (with its contained boring organisms) rather than on living coral. Swarms such as the one shown here, by removing algal growth, may actually tip the competitive balance in favor of recolonization by corals. [an-Najwah reef, off Dammam]*

78

JOHN BURCHARD

Fig 57. Lizard fish Parapercis nebulosus *on mixed sand and coral bottom at 5 m depth. In front of the fish is one small colony each of* Favia *and* Goniastrea. *In the background is the base of a large "table" of* Acropora. *[Fasht al-Eling]*

Fig 58. A mixed bottom of sand and coral rubble, with small colonies of at least six species of living corals. Near the center of the picture a large sea cucumber Stichopus *sp. creeps slowly across the bottom. [Abu 'Ali]*

provides nourishment for an abundant meiofauna, and for a variety of larger animals as well. These include large species of polychaetes and burrowing decapod crustaceans such as ghost shrimp *Callianassa* sp., and especially numerous snails. Particularly conspicuous among these is the common conch *Strombus decorus persicus,* which occurs in large numbers on the shallow sand flats during its mating season in late summer. Other typical snails inhabiting this biotope are olive shells *Oliva* spp. and cowries *Cypraea turdus.* Predatory snails, especially moon shells *Natica* spp., plow through the surface layer of sand, feeding on other snails and bivalves. A typical crab, found especially in the shallow sand belts of exposed beaches, is *Matuta planipes.* It swims rapidly, using its oar-like legs, and quickly dives into the sand when disturbed. Several species of small fish also have a habit of diving into the sand to escape enemies. The most characteristic fish of shallow sand bottoms, however, are various species of gobies, inhabiting burrows made by alpheid shrimp. One such commensal association will be described in Chapter 5 and is a widespread feature of shallow subtidal sands. Several other such goby/shrimp species pairs occur, however, in particular situations, such as the sand patches associated with coral reefs.

Another major group of organisms found in abundance on sand bottoms of this type is that of burrowing sea urchins. Two main types occur: the flat, pancake-like ones known as sand dollars, and the rounded forms called heart urchins. Of the former, two species[9] are common locally, especially in somewhat muddy, organic-rich sand. Heart urchins, as their name suggests, are roughly heart-shaped rather than flattened. They live buried underneath the surface of the sand, tunneling slowly along and feeding on small organic particles. Several species occur locally, with distinctly different habitat preferences.[10]

A second distinctive type of sand-bottom community is found in parts of the tidal deltas most strongly swept by currents, where sharp-crested dune-like ridges of coarse sand are built up at right angles to the axis of current flow. These ridges reach a height of 3 to 4m and current velocities across their crests often exceed two knots, causing a rapid shifting of the surface layers of sand. This unstable, extremely coarse-grained sand is inhabited by dense populations of small clams *Ervilia scaliola,* only a few millimeters long. In spite of being no larger than many of the sand grains, this animal is able to move about in the sand with extraordinary rapidity, and so always remains near the surface. Other, equally specialized animals occur in this habitat, but have not yet been studied in detail.

Deeper sand bottoms have been studied on the sand slopes immediately adjacent to the base of the coral reef at Jana Island. Grab samples of very coarse-grained sand consisting largely of

9 *Clypeaster humilis* and *Echinodiscus auritus.*

10 *Metalia townsendi* is the most widespread species. *Metalia sternalis* and *Lovenia elongata* have been found in shallow subtidal sands around coral reefs. *Brissopsis persica* is found on mud bottoms.

shell and/or coral fragments, taken at depths of 15 to 30m at a few other locations, contained communities resembling those found at Jana (Fig 58).

A conspicuous inhabitant of this bottom type, at least in the vicinity of the coral reefs, is the colorful starfish *Pentaceraster mammillatus* (Figs 1 & 61). Less obvious, but perhaps more typical inhabitants, are the burrowing protochordate *Branchiostoma* sp., a tiny fragile sea urchin *Temnotrema siamense* with red-banded spines, and two species of solitary corals[11] whose individual polyps each grow attached to an empty snail shell inhabited by a sipunculid worm *Aspidosiphon* sp. The worm feeds by extending its front end into the sand, thus keeping the coral polyp in the upright position necessary for catching plankton.

A puzzling aspect of sand-bottom biology in the Gulf is the occurrence of "sand volcanoes." These are conical sand mounds, up to a meter high, with a hole at the top from which a vigorous jet of sand and water, lasting for several seconds, is emitted from time to time. Volcanoes typically occur in large numbers, more or less completely covering an expanse of bottom (Fig 59). Small patches of volcanoes occur in the subtidal shallows of Karan Island and off the Ju'aymah beach at depths as shallow as 3m. At greater depths volcanoes may become the dominant feature of the underwater landscape, as for instance at depths of 5 to 10m off Jubail, or at 25 to 30m off Jana Island. Attempts to excavate the animal making these volcanoes have so far been unsuccessful. The most likely candidate, however, is a large ghost shrimp or thalassinid, since animals of this type have been recorded as making volcano-like structures elsewhere (Farrow, 1971).

Two distinct animal communities were found on **mud bottoms** in the limited depth range so far investigated. At present it is not possible to suggest what factors determine the occurrence of one or the other community. The commoner and more widespread of the two has been encountered at depths from 6 to 15m and at locations ranging from Tarut Bay (adjacent to the Sandy Hook Yacht Club) to Safaniya. The dominant species in this community is a cockle *Cardium papyraceum* 5cm long, living partly buried in the mud. This animal is a filter feeder. It has been recorded at densities of up to 50 individuals per square meter, but an average population is 5 to 10 per square meter. Other larger animals abundant in this community include the sea urchin *Temnopleurus toreumaticus*, the burrowing crab *Dorippe dorsipes*, pen shells *Pinna* sp., the snail *Murex kusterianus*, several species of shrimp[12] and several species of fish[13] (Figs 60 & 62). A rich assortment of amphipods, polychaetes and other smaller animals is also charactertistic of this association, which Aramco biologists

Fig 59. "Sand volcanoes," though a common feature of sandy bottoms in many areas of the Gulf and elsewhere, have long puzzled biologists. These conical mounds of sand, up to a meter in height, have a hole at the top from which a jet of sand and water erupts intermittently. No one has yet succeeded in digging out the inhabitants of these "volcanoes." A likely candidate, however, is a ghost shrimp or thalassinid. [Jana Island]

---

11 *Heterocyathus* sp. and *Heteropsammia* sp.

12 *Penaeus semisulcatus* the commercial shrimp, *Metapenaeopsis* spp., and *Trachypenaeus curvirostris*.

13 *Platycephalus indicus*, *Upeneus tragula*, *Lutjanus fulviflamma*, *Epinephelus tauvina*, etc.

Fig 60. A large midshipman or flathead Platycephalus indicus, *about 50cm long, lying buried in the sand among finger corals* Stylophora sp. *This fish, one of the tastiest local species, is a carnivore and emerges suddenly from the sand to snap up small fish, shrimps or crabs which unwittingly wander close to its hiding place. [Tarut Bay]*

83

Fig 61. The large starfish Pentaceraster mammillatus *photographed in its natural habitat on the reef base at about 15m. Typical for this zone of the reef are small, low growing knolls of several species of faviid corals. Corals of this type, which reach large dimensions in shallow water, are here restricted in size by the low light intensity. [Jana Island]*

Fig 62. A group of goatfish or red mullet Upeneus tragula *on a sand bottom at 14m depth. These fish are well camouflaged in life (there are 16 individuals in the picture) but turn red when removed from the water. They reach a length of about 25cm and are highly prized as a culinary delicacy. [Dammam Channel]*

have called the *"Murex/Cardium"* community after the two most abundant large animals found there.

The *Murex/Cardium* community is a "normal" type of benthic community, with a reasonably high diversity and a variety of different types of animals. Organisms belonging to this community commonly occur, along with shrimp, in the nets of commercial shrimp fishermen, and it appears that a considerable part of the Gulf shrimp trawling is conducted over this type of bottom. This is probably the main biotope occupied by adult commercial shrimp *Penaeus semisulcatus* after they leave the grassbeds.

In complete contrast is the second type of mud-bottom community, which Aramco biologists have termed the *"Brissopsis/Amphioplus"* community. This has so far been analyzed fully in only one area, near the port of Manifa, where it appears to occupy many square kilometers of the bottom.[14] It is an extremely low-diversity assemblage completely dominated by two species, the heart urchin *Brissopsis persica* at an average density of 20 to 25 individuals per square meter, and the brittle star *Amphioplus seminudus* at an average density of about 1,200 individuals per square meter. The remaining fauna include only a few polychaetes, a very few small mollusks and a few ostracods, all uncommon or rare. This community has a high biomass, nevertheless, because of the great abundance of its two dominant species.

Both the *Murex/Cardium* association and the *Brissopsis/Amphioplus* association occur at similar depths, and on superficially identical mud. Further analysis will be required to account for the mutually exclusive occurrence of these two associations in different places.

14 *Brissopsis persica*, the dominant animal of this association, has been recovered in shrimp trawls from several other locations, indicating that the *Brissopsis/Amphioplus* community is not confined to the one area.

Fig 63. The important commercial shrimp Penaeus semisulcatus *is one of at least ten species of penaeid shrimp present in the Gulf, and generally accounts for over 90% of trawl catches. These shrimp feed on a variety of organisms including mollusks, polychaete worms and small Crustacea. Individuals commonly grow to a length of more than 15cm but have a life span of only a little more than one year. [Photographed in laboratory]*

5
GRASSBEDS

All along the Saudi Arabian coast, large areas of shallow bottom are covered by beds of sea grass. This is one of the most extensive biotopes in terms of area, as well as one of the most important in terms of its contribution to the overall biological economy of the Gulf. Directly or indirectly, sea grass forms a major food source for many important marine animals. Its interlacing leaves shelter the vulnerable young of many species, especially the commercial shrimp *Penaeus semisulcatus* (Fig 63), and furnish attachment sites for many others, such as the pearl oyster. The grass also plays an important role in stabilizing bottom sediments, and affects the local physical environment by changing bottom topography, absorbing the energy of waves and tidal streams, and removing sediment from the water column. Except for the coral reef, the grassbed is richer, in both numbers and variety of organisms, than any other biotope occupying the same range of depth.

In appearance a grassbed resembles an underwater lawn (Fig 64), denser or sparser according to local environmental conditions. The grass grows rooted in sand, silt or mud, and traps silt and organic detritus from the overlying water, thus in time building up its own substratum. Grassbeds and patches, especially in areas of strong tidal flow, tend therefore to become elevated above their surroundings, to be flat on top and to have sharply defined edges.

So-called sea grasses are actually not true grasses at all, but flowering plants related to the familiar pondweeds. Altogether 49 species are known (den Hartog, 1970), and grassbeds of various kinds are a common feature of shallow, sedimentary marine environments in many parts of the world. Only three species, however, are involved in the formation of grassbeds in the western Arabian Gulf. All three are known to be unusually

Fig 64. A dense stand of Halodule uninervis *is typical of the grass flat region of Tarut Bay grassbeds. The grass blades are overgrown with a fur-like periphyton including many species of small algae, as well as the bright orange, colonial tunicate* Botryllus *sp. The water depth at this site, at low tide, is about 1.5 m.*

JOHN BURCHARD

*Fig 65. Three species of sea grass: Left —
Halodule uninervis, Middle — Halophila
ovalis, Right — Halophila stipulacea. (Drawing by Martin Giesen)*

tolerant of environmental extremes, and in particular of variations of salinity. The commonest and most widespread species found locally is *Halodule uninervis,* which is also the most grass-like, with narrow ribbon-like leaves about 3mm wide and up to 25cm long. *Halophila stipulacea* has much broader, light green leaves up to 10cm long, while *Halophila ovalis* has delicate oval leaves, whose basal portion forms a slender stalk (Fig 65).

All these species grow by means of rhizomes, or buried stems, which extend horizontally just beneath the sediment surface. Every few centimeters the rhizome is thickened to form a node or joint, bearing one or more roots and a tuft or "rosette" of leaves, which emerge above the sediment surface. In *Halodule* a rosette may contain from one to five leaves, and each rosette is borne on the end of a short vertical stem, which arises as a branch from the rhizome. In the two species of *Halophila* the vertical stems are short, in fact barely visible, and each bears a single pair of leaves with their bases enclosed by a pair of bracts or reduced leaves.

In a flourishing grassbed the rhizomes criss-cross and interlace, creating a tough mat or turf-like structure. Vertical elongation of the upright stems, in *Halodule* at least, allows the growth of the grass to keep pace with the accumulation of sediment. Under favorable circumstances a layer of stabilized sediment several meters thick eventually forms, protected from erosion by the fibrous remains of old rhizomes and by the dense turf forming its uppermost layer.

Over 500 species of animals have so far been identified in samples taken from local grassbeds. The great majority of these belong to one or the other of two main adaptive types: animals that burrow in the sediment, or animals with specific adaptations relating directly to the grass itself. The most prominently represented animal groups include about 140 species of polychaete worms, mostly of burrowing habits; nearly 90 species of gastropod mollusks, of many different adaptive types; about 70 species of pelecypods, mostly burrowing forms but including some, like juvenile pearl oysters, which live attached to the grass blades; over 45 species of decapod crustaceans, mostly crabs and shrimp-like forms; and 35 species of amphipods, mainly inhabitants of the grass roots, surface sediment and the periphyton.[1] The great majority of these animals are small, being adapted to make the most of the spaces between and among the grass blades and rhizomes. Almost all of them are inconspicuous, being either buried in the sediment, or colored green, making them almost invisible among the grass. Few of them would be apparent to a casual observer snorkeling over a grassbed, but there are also more conspicuous animals such as the pen shell *Pinna* sp., the large swimming crab *Portunus pelagicus*, large black sea cucumbers and various fish.

Three main factors control the occurrence of grassbeds under local conditions. These are the depth of water, the physical nature of the bottom substrate, and the extent of water movement by wave action, wind and/or tidal streams. Although grassbeds in many parts of the world extend upwards into the intertidal zone, the intense heat and solar radiation of the Arabian summer effectively prevent sea grass from growing above the level of the lowest spring tides. A few exceptions occur on seaward beaches, such as at Ju'aymah, where grass patches occur at a level which is exposed by the lowest spring tides. These patches are probably preserved from desiccation by wave action, and are composed of small, stunted-looking plants.

The maximum depth at which sea grass can grow is controlled by light penetration, and varies at different locations depending on the turbidity of the water. In very turbid areas, such as parts of Tarut Bay, the lower limit is less than 5m. In other parts of the same bay, where the water is only moderately turbid, grass grows vigorously at depths of as much as 10m. In especially clear-water areas grass has been found growing at depths of more than 17m and dense grassbeds occur down to depths of about 15m. These are either open-water locations (for instance offshore Safaniya), or protected from the sediment-stirring effects of waves and currents by topographic features as in the Qurayyah area. Grass growth is densest at depths where abundant light is available: in Tarut Bay between about 1 and 3m, and in clear-water areas down to 8 or 10m. At greater depths the grass growth is noticeably sparser.

By trapping sediment, an established grassbed can extend laterally to some extent over previously unsuitable substrata, but the initial establishment of sea grass in a locality requires a sandy or muddy bottom in which the seedlings can take root. *Halodule uninervis* is a "pioneer" species capable of colonizing a wide variety of substrates, but even it cannot grow on bare rock, coral or other hard bottom forms.

Fig 66. Pen shell Pinna *sp. in a Tarut Bay grassbed. This near relative of pearl oysters lives anchored by byssus and largely buried in sand, with only the open end of the shell protruding. The gape of this large specimen is about 15cm long and the total height, including the pointed, buried portion, is about 40cm. The living* Pinna *is usually inhabited by a pair of commensal shrimp* Anchistus *sp., and after the death of the mollusk the empty valves remain in place and provide shelter for blennies* Petroscirtes *sp., small octopus, or crabs.*

1 Periphyton or "aufwuchs" refers to the dense "fur" of small algae and sessile animals that usually coats the surface of submerged vegetation or other solid objects.

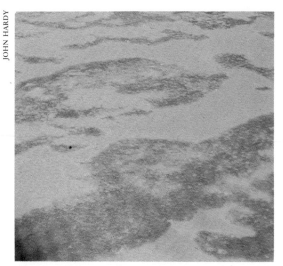

Fig 67. The interplay of grassbed growth with erosional forces, due in this case mainly to wave action, gives rise to an intricate mosaic of grass patches and belts of shifting sand. [offshore from an exposed beach]

Sediment trapping also tends to bring about growth of grassbeds in an upward direction. In sheltered bays this upward growth tends to level off just below the range of the lowest spring tides. The result is a flat platform or terrace of grass. Along exposed shorelines, where the main water movements are due to wave action, the formation of such a shallow platform is largely prevented. The upward extension of grassbeds is here limited by a subtidal zone, narrower or wider according to the degree of wave exposure of the beach, in which wave-induced sediment movement is too vigorous to permit the growth of grass. This upper limit of grass growth is commonly at a depth of 2.5 to 4m, depending on the exposure of the beach. Below this depth, especially on beaches with a very gradual slope, there is a zone in which belts of grass alternate with strips of shifting sand, both aligned nearly parallel to the shoreline. The grass belts are cut at intervals by deeper channels, corresponding to the rip currents by which wave-accumulated water returns seaward. On this type of shore profile continuous grassbeds are found only below a depth of about 6m, and then only if suitable sediments are available.

As a result of the interaction of these controlling factors, grassbeds have an extremely wide but patchy distribution in the nearshore shallows of the Gulf. Sheltered bays are favored sites; extensive grassbeds occur in al-'Uqayr bay, in Dawhat Zalum, in Tarut Bay, in the embayment southeast of Abu 'Ali Island and in the embayment southeast of Safaniya. In Tarut Bay, a random sampling of 50 locations yielded an estimate of 66% grass cover for the bay as a whole. Two other extensive bay systems have as yet only been examined from the air, and their grassbed areas have not been mapped. These are the bay complex between Ras Tanaqib and Manifa, and the bay complex northwest of Abu 'Ali Island.

Grassbeds are also widely distributed in the shallows along the open coast. Extensive grassbeds are known to occur adjacent to Jazirat as-Samamik, south of the entrance to the al-'Uqayr bay system; at Ras al-Qurayyah, an especially rich bed; and scattered along the entire shoreline between Ju'aymah and Jubail. Extensive grassbeds also exist in the shallows between al-Khobar and Bahrain. To the north of Abu 'Ali Island the coast is more exposed, and the nearshore shallows are dotted with small coral reefs. The grassbeds occurring in that area have also not been mapped. The prevalence of very coarse sediments, mainly coral gravel, may make conditions unsuitable for grass growth in many sites there.

GRASSBED TOPOGRAPHY

The topography of a grassbed, especially in shallow areas, is the result of a constantly shifting dynamic balance between erosion caused by water movement, and build-up due to the growth and sediment-trapping properties of the grass itself. In sheltered locations, where wave action is minimal and tidal streams are at most of moderate strength, growth and sediment accumulation predominate. This results in the formation of flat, homogeneous meadows of grass. Where a sufficient supply of sediment is available, upward growth tends to produce a grass flat just below the lowest low tide level, somewhat analogous to the reef flat typical of coral islands and patch reefs. Such grass flats are especially typical of Tarut Bay, and probably of other bays where strong tidal water movements provide an abundant supply of sediment. In essentially non-tidal bays, such as Dawhat Zalum or the bays of al-'Uqayr, grass flats are not well developed, though the greater part of the bay bottom is covered with grass.

Elsewhere, wherever strong water movements occur as a result of either tidal or wave action, erosional forces break up the homogenous grass surface, producing several types of topographical features. The sand belts parallel to shore, and the rip current channels more or less perpendicular to them, so typical of sublittoral grassbeds along the exposed coastal beach, have already been mentioned. These features are produced by water movements in which wave action is the primary source of energy. In bays and other sheltered shallows, by contrast, tidal streams are the main source of water movement, and the distribution of energy as a function of both depth and time is very different. The typical erosional features of bay type grassbeds are therefore different from those of grassbeds along the beach front. These features may be considered as falling into two types, "blowouts" and tidal channels, according to whether the peak current velocities are only slightly or very much greater than the equilibrium speed of water movement, at which the rates of sediment deposition and sediment removal are exactly in balance.

Blowouts and Channels

Blowouts are bare sand patches which tend to occur along the axes of tidal flow, in places where the speed of the current removes sediment faster than it can be accumulated or stabilized by the grass cover. In the most typical case they are shallow, bowl-shaped depressions, 5 to 10m in diameter and 0.5 to 1m deep, lined with bare sand and a collection of coarser debris such as large shell fragments and rocks. They tend to occur in chains along the paths of medium strength tidal currents. In other locations, where currents are stronger, the blowout area is more extensive and the grass area reduced. Such channels (for instance that just west of Za'l Island in Tarut Bay) are mostly lined with loose sand, with many exposed rocks. The remaining grass occurs in the form of large hummocks or mounds, usually 2 to 4m across and as much as 2m higher than the adjacent sand bottom. In channels with still stronger currents no grass can survive, and the sand is usually scoured away down to bare rock. These are the tidal channels proper, and their biota is that of subtidal rock bottoms, entirely different from that of the grassbeds themselves. A network of such channels drains the upper portion of Tarut Bay.

Much of the sediment removed in the formation of blowouts and tidal channels is redeposited in the grassbeds on

Fig 68. A two year old female green turtle Chelonia mydas *of about 55cm carapace length – half adult size. Juvenile individuals of this size are commonly seen around the islands, but do not go ashore. Several were captured and tagged during 1973. [Jana Island]*

either side, where current velocities are slightly lower. This favors the formation and upward growth of grass flats in the low-velocity areas. As a result tidal water movements become increasingly concentrated into the channels, accentuating the difference in velocities between the channels or blowout chains and the immediately adjacent grass flat. This in turn further emphasizes the topographic relief in a "positive feed-back cycle," eventually producing a mosaic of level grass flats, steep-banked tidal channels and blowout chains such as that found in Tarut Bay today.

As the whole system develops, the deeper portions of the large, main tidal channels frequently become areas of sediment deposition again, which means that grassbeds can form once more, usually on somewhat muddy sediments. At the seaward end of the main channels, on the other hand, current velocities remain high, and an alluvial fan or "delta" of coarse sand usually forms. Another characteristic feature of this region is the formation of giant-sized ripples of very coarse sediment. These "mega-ripples" may be 4 to 6m high, and resemble aeolian dune systems on land.

As these examples illustrate, one result of grassbed deposition and erosion patterns in Tarut Bay, and other similar bay systems along the western Gulf coast, has been the formation of a mosaic of greatly differing habitat types, often intimately interwoven with one another. Grass flat and tidal channel may be separated horizontally by only a very few meters. Although each of these habitat types has its own characteristic populations of organisms, it is not surprising that many of the more active animals move freely from one habitat to another.

INHABITANTS OF THE GRASSBED

The most spectacular inhabitants of the grassbed are probably the sawfish *Pristus zysron* and *P. cuspidatus*. The former species attains a length of at least 6m, and is probably the largest animal typical of the grassbed habitat. Sawfish are not aggressive, but are so powerful as to be extremely dangerous when molested. Several species of large sting rays[2] are also common in grassbeds. Some of these attain a length, including tail, of 4m and a width of 1.5m or more, and would be extremely dangerous if stepped on. They feed mainly on clams, which they dig out of the sediment and crush in their powerful jaws.

Another large animal typical of grassbeds is the green sea turtle *Chelonia mydas* (Fig 68), which as an adult is mainly vegetarian, and lives mostly on sea grass (Chapter 6). Yet another is the sea snake. Sea snakes (family Hydrophiidae) are

2 *Dasyatis uarnak, D. gerrardi, D. sephen* and *Taeniura* sp.

distantly related to cobras and kraits, and the most primitive of their kind (subfamily Laticaudinae) lay eggs on land like sea turtles. Evolutionarily advanced sea snakes (subfamily Hydrophiinae) give birth to live young in the water, and normally never go ashore at all. At least five species of Hydrophiinae are found in the Gulf. All but one are shallow water inhabitants and feed on the sea bottom. The common species are *Hydrophis cyanocinctus* (Fig 69) and *H. lapemoides*, two virtually indistinguishable greyish-green banded snakes growing up to 150cm long. The more vividly marked *H. ornatus* and the much larger *H. spiralis* are also encountered occasionally. Like all snakes, sea snakes are strictly carnivorous; they feed mainly on fish. Since they are slow swimmers, however, most of them, including the local species of *Hydrophis*, eat sluggish or burrowing fish species such as gobies, eels, and even the venomous catfish *Plotosus*. A hungry *Hydrophis* swims slowly along close to the bottom, poking its head into likely-looking crevices and holes. When it finds a burrow containing a fish, it crawls inside and swallows the unfortunate inhabitant. The small head and long slender neck of many sea snakes represent an adaptation to this method of feeding.

The venom of sea snakes is primarily adapted to paralyzing and predigesting the fish they eat. It is, however, extremely toxic to humans, and some of the larger sea snake species must be regarded as very dangerous. In Southeast Asia, where large sea snakes are frequently entangled in fishermen's nets and unwittingly grasped by the fishermen in the murky water, bites are frequent and many of the victims die. The local *Hydrophis* species, however, are not at all aggressive and are even quite reluctant to bite in self-defense. To date, only two cases of sea snake bite in the Arabian Gulf have been authentically documented, and neither victim suffered significant ill effects. An injured or roughly handled sea snake will, however, attempt to bite, and live sea snakes are therefore best left alone by the non-specialist.

Fig 69. Hydrophis cyanocinctus *is a common shallow-water sea snake. This snake searches for its food in holes and crevices near the sea bottom, swallowing any sluggish or unwary fish it finds. Its small head and long slender neck are an evolutionary adaptation to this method of feeding.*

Fig 70. The black sea cucumber Holothuria atra *is a common and conspicuous inhabitant of the grass flat zone. [Tarut Bay]*

Only one sea snake can be regarded as a truly pelagic, open water species. This animal, *Pelamis platurus*, is able to feed on pelagic fish and consequently has a much wider distribution than any other sea snake. Aramco biologists have so far found three specimens of *Pelamis* washed up on Saudi Arabian exposed beaches, and at least one has been recorded from Bahrain (Gallagher, 1971). Individuals are usually about 60cm long with dark blue or green coloring on top and yellow underneath; the tail has yellow and black bars. Coloration of this type (dark above and light below) is common in open water animals, helping to make the body appear less visible from above and below. A hungry *Pelamis* floats at the surface, somewhat resembling a piece of driftwood, and small pelagic fish attempt to take shelter under it, only to be seized and eaten. The jaws of this species are elongated as an adaptation to this mode of feeding, in contrast to the bottom feeding sea snakes which have shorter jaws.

Many other typical grassbed animals, though less spectacular than sawfish or sea snakes, are much more likely to be encountered by the casual snorkler or diver. The black sea cucumber *Holothuria (Halodeima) atra*, up to 5cm thick and 60cm long, lies extended on the bottom, sweeping up microscopic food particles by means of its fringed oral tentacles (Fig 70). Another particle feeder is the tunicate *Botryllus* sp., which forms bright red or orange gelatinous masses attached to the grass (Fig 64). Such a mass is actually a colony of many thousands of tiny individuals or zooids, each busily straining water through its fine-meshed pharyngeal sieve to obtain the microscopic plankton on which it feeds. Another filter feeder is the large pen shell *Pinna* sp., an elongate bivalve of which only the upper end is seen protruding from the sand (Fig 66). The shell is normally open to permit feeding, but closes rapidly at the approach of a potential predator. Each pen shell is inhabited by a pair of commensal shrimp *Anchistus* sp., which share the food collected by the mollusk, and may compensate by giving warning of the approach of an enemy.

Other common, larger animals include the bubble shell *Bulla ampulla*, which crawls in or under the detritus layer; the carnivorous snail *Murex kusterianus* (Fig 82), usually seen half buried in the sand (such individuals, when picked up, are often found to be holding a clam on which they are feeding); and several species of small, striped fish hiding or flitting about among the grass blades.[3] The large, edible swimming crab *Portunus pelagicus* commonly inhabits this region, lying buried in the sand or concealed among the grass during the daytime. The grass flat is also the principal habitat of juvenile stages of the commercial shrimp *Penaeus semisulcatus*, which like *Portunus* lies concealed during the day, and emerges at night to move about and feed.

The animals that inhabit blowouts tend to be somewhat different from those living in the grassbeds themselves, and in-

3 *Helotes sexlineatus, Therapon puta, Pomadasys stridens, Lutjanus fulviflamma,* and *Plotosus anguillaris.*

clude many which are also found on subtidal sand bottoms in other situations. Typical inhabitants include the burrowing heart urchin *Metalia townsendi* and the related, flattened sand dollars *Clypeaster humilis* (Fig 71) and *Echinodiscus auritus;* the tunnel-building pistol shrimp *Alpheus* sp., whose burrows are inhabited by numerous commensal organisms; and the large hermit crab *Dardanus* sp., usually found in a *Murex* shell covered with symbiotic sea anemones *Calliactis* sp. The same animals are also found, together with a scattering of typical mud-bottom animals such as the burrowing sea anemone *Cerianthus* sp., on the soft and somewhat muddy sand deposits which collect along the bottoms of the larger tidal channels. These animals probably benefit from the combination of a loose, sandy substrate in which they may easily burrow, and the abundance of food which may be derived from the high organic productivity of the grassbed. Many of the more active kinds[4] exploit the juxtaposition of these different habitats by lying buried in the soft sediment during the daytime, and visiting the adjacent grass flat at night in search of food.

Symbiotic Associations

Symbiotic associations are a common feature of many different biotopes, and by no means confined to the grassbeds. One particular association is an especially common feature of shallow, soft-bottom biotopes in the Gulf, and particularly of the grassbeds and their vicinity. As it is so common and conspicuous it is worthy of description in some detail.

The visible member of the association is a goby[5] – apparent even to a casual observer as a finger-thick, elongated fish sitting in a watchful attitude, propped up on its fins on the bottom (Fig 72). If approached at all closely, the fish disappears into a nearby hole in the sand, to emerge again cautiously when danger appears to be past. In a favorable area such goby holes may occur only a meter or two apart. If one has the patience to watch quietly from a slight distance until the goby has decided that the coast is clear and resumed his sentry duty, one may catch a glimpse of the goby's senior partner. This is a 5cm long snapping shrimp *Alpheus* sp., which appears briefly at the entrance, pushing a pile of sand ahead of it, afterwards returning to the burrow for another load. The shrimp is largely responsible for excavating the burrow; it digs untiringly for hours at a time, except when warned by the goby's behavior that danger is near. Each burrow houses a male and female snapping shrimp, which may be seen alternately, or even together, at the tunnel entrance. The male is recognized by his larger snapping claw. The activities of the goby serve to indicate to the shrimp, whose eyesight is poor, whether it is safe to go outside the entrance.

This is, however, by no means the end of the story. The hole is frequently, perhaps usually, inhabited by a pair of another

4 such as *Portunus pelagicus, Penaeus semisulcatus* and flounders.

5 Perhaps *Cryptocentrus* sp., though possibly more than one species is involved.

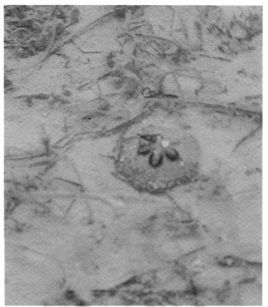

Fig 71. The sand dollar Clypeaster humilis *usually lives just beneath the surface of the sediment, but sometimes moves about in plain sight as in this picture. [Tarut Bay]*

Fig 72. Unidentified goby (possibly Cryptocentrus *sp.) and snapping shrimp* Alpheus *sp. at the entrance of their shared burrow. Length of the goby is about 12cm [Ju'aymah]*

JOHN BURCHARD

Fig 73. A pearl oyster Pinctada radiata, center, *shares a subtidal rock surface with coralline algae* Lithothamnium *sp. (bottom left), and several corals (*Montipora *just below the oyster,* Acropora *at right, and an undetermined encrusting species at the left rear). Other space competitors visible in the photograph include barnacles* Balanus tintinnabulum, *rock oysters (possibly* Spondylus *sp.) and small algae. [Jurayd Island]*

species of gobies, very long and slim and almost transparent. They are only occasionally seen outside, and dive into the hole at the slightest disturbance. Additional commensals which regularly make use of the burrow include a species of porcellanid crab and several polychaetes of the families Polynoidae and Hesionidae. These presumably benefit from the food-gathering activities of its inhabitants, though this is not yet properly understood.

SOME SEASONAL CYCLES AND LIFE HISTORIES

The grassbed is a perennial phenomenon. The rhizomes apparently persist for several years at least, and thus stabilize the sediment from one growing season to another. In the Gulf the growth of grass shows a distinct seasonal rhythm because seasonal changes in temperature are very marked. At the end of winter (mid-February) the above-sediment portion of a grassbed is at a minimum. Many or most of the previous year's leaves have died and been torn loose in winter storms. Vegetative growth begins in late February or March, and by mid-April new leaves are visible above the sand surface. The vegetative maximum is reached in June, and growth continues throughout the summer, tapering off as water temperatures begin to drop in September. By fall the blades are heavily encrusted with algae, young pearl oysters, and other growth, and photosynthesis by the grass is probably minimal.

One consequence of this seasonal pattern is that loss of sediment from the grass flat occurs mainly in winter, when emergent grass cover is sparse and wave action at its height. Sediment accumulation occurs mainly in summer, when the reverse conditions prevail. In most sites the grass flat reaches its upward limit at a level somewhat below that of low spring tides. This probably reflects the outcome of this cyclical deposition and removal of sediment.

Another consequence of the markedly seasonal growth pattern of grassbeds in the Gulf is that animals ecologically dependent on grassbeds during a particular stage of their life cycle must synchronize their cycles to match that of the grass. Two outstanding examples are the life cycles of the pearl oysters *Pinctada margaritifera* and *P. radiata* (Fig 73), and of the commercial shrimp *Penaeus semisulcatus*.

Pearl Oysters

Adult pearl oysters are benthic: they live firmly attached to some hard object, such as a rock or an oil platform, by a bundle of tough byssus threads. Unlike true oysters they can, if necessary, let go the byssus threads and move about by spinning new threads to nearby points of attachment. The active locomotory capacities of an adult pearl oyster are limited, however, to several centimeters per day. Like most other bivalves, pearl oysters feed on small plankton organisms obtained by filtering quantities of water through their fine-meshed gill filaments. Pearl oysters also resemble most other bivalves in their method of reproduction. They discharge enormous numbers of eggs and sperm into the water, where fertilization takes place. The larval stages are planktonic, but after a short time the larvae attach themselves to a solid object and begin the sedentary, filter-feeding existence of their parents.

The main "spatfall" or settling of pearl oysters takes place in late spring, and the preferred site for settlement in the Arabian Gulf is the leaves of sea grass, especially *Halodule uninervis*. Attaching at the rate of dozens to hundreds on each grass blade, the oyster spat grow during the summer from near-microscopic size to a diameter of 5mm or more. During most of this period they are grass-green and very difficult to see, even when they are so thick on the grass blades that they overlap like shingles on a roof.

By October the grass blades begin to die and come adrift. The young oysters apparently turn loose their attachment and re-attach themselves to the remaining upright blades, leading to dense concentrations which can be seen, even from the air, as blackish patches. As the grass blades continue to die off, the oysters are carried down-slope attached to drifting grass fragments, and re-attach themselves to more solid substrates as the opportunity occurs. The result is dense beds of pearl oysters wherever suitable hard substrata, such as rock or dead coral, occur seaward of a grassbed area. Survival of oyster spat may be greater on grass than on other substrata, and the grass-oyster cycle may probably play a large part in sustaining the pearl oyster beds for which the Gulf has long been famous.

Shrimp

Shrimp[6] are one of the many animals whose ecology cuts right across the conventional subdivision of marine habitats into benthos, plankton and nekton. In the daytime adults lie buried in the sand or mud, but at night they emerge to crawl and swim about. They are usually considered benthic, since they feed mainly on small animals (notably bivalves and polychaetes) caught by probing through the bottom sediment. They also swim well and migrate over considerable distances, so they might with almost equal justification be classed as nekton.

Strictly speaking, there are two types of shrimp, known to specialists as carids and penaeids. Carids are present in both temperate and tropical seas, whereas penaeids are mainly confined to warm waters and support a number of important fisheries such as those in the Gulf of Mexico, Japan, and of course in the Arabian Gulf. Penaeids, often called "prawns" to distinguish them from carid "shrimp," can be recognized easily by their first three pairs of walking legs which bear small pincers known as chelae; in carids only the first two pairs are chelate. Many kinds of carids occur in the Gulf, but none are at present exploited as human food.

JOHN BURCHARD

Fig 74. Freshly captured male and female shrimp of the three local species of Penaeus. *The female is the larger in each case. Upper pair:* P. japonicus, *a colorful, but rather uncommon shrimp in the Arabian Gulf. In other countries such as Japan this is an important commercial species, and is also reared artificially. Middle pair:* P. latisulcatus *normally makes up a few per cent of Saudi Arabian catches. Post larvae and juveniles of this species are commonly found around sandy beaches. Lower pair: the important commercial shrimp* P. semisulcatus. *This species is found among grassbeds and other soft bottom habitats. The conspicuously colored tail fan is different in each species and probably serves as a recognition signal. [photographed on the deck of a shrimp trawler off Dammam]*

6 The term "shrimp" is used throughout Saudi Arabia, and accordingly in this book, to refer to all penaeids, especially the commercially important *Penaeus semisulcatus.*

At least ten species of penaeids have been identified in hauls taken in the Gulf, but the most important by far is *Penaeus semisulcatus* (Al Attar and Ikenoue, 1974; Ellis, 1975; Enomoto, 1971), generally accounting for over 90% of the catch (Boerema, 1969, 1976; Price and Jones, 1975). *Penaeus latisulcatus* and *Penaeus japonicus* are the other species of the genus *Penaeus* found locally. The former is usually present in modest numbers, whereas *P. japonicus* is rare. These three species can be distinguished by body coloration alone (Fig 74). The only other large shrimp species is *Metapenaeus affinis*, which makes an occasional minor contribution to the commercial catch. The remaining species are small, and when caught are generally discarded along with the "trash" fish (Fig 75).

Shrimp are present in the Gulf wherever suitable habitats occur, and are exploited by most of the Gulf countries. In Saudi waters the mechanized trawlers concentrate their fishing mainly around Manifa and around Dammam, although previously Abu 'Ali was also a popular fishing ground. Local fishing boats operate in many areas along the coast, generally favoring the shallow water grassbeds which are shrimp nursery grounds.

Penaeus semisulcatus and *P. latisulcatus* are found together in the trawl catches of the commercial fishing boats, which operate over a variety of bottom types and in water of varying depth. There is reason to believe, however, that the two species have somewhat different habitat preferences; at least, this is definitely true of their juvenile stages. Adults of both species are usually captured near the bottom in water several meters deep. Since the trawl net is usually dragged for a period of three or four hours, and during this time passes over several different bottom types, this does not necessarily mean that the two actually occur in the same places. Juvenile *P. semisulcatus* have been recovered in significant numbers only from the grassbed biotope, except for the smallest stages which are found in nearby thickets of algae. *P. latisulcatus* juveniles, in contrast, have not been found at all in grassbeds, but are abundant on sandy bottoms just below the wave-wash zone, along many of the open coast beaches and especially around the coral islands. One of the smaller sized shrimp species, the very abundant *Metapenaeus stebbingi*, shows yet another type of habitat preference. Juveniles of this species are found in immense numbers in tidal creeks of the intertidal mud flats, while adults are found both in the creeks themselves and in adjacent shallow, muddy subtidal habitats.

LIFE HISTORY: Penaeid shrimp have a fascinating life history (Fig 78). Unlike other decapod Crustacea such as crabs and lobsters, which carry their eggs glued to the female's abdomen until they hatch, penaeid shrimp broadcast their eggs into the sea, where they drift with the plankton. Tiny larvae hatch within a few hours, and go through a series of stages as planktonic animals. After two or three weeks of planktonic life, they graduate to a "post-larval" stage and begin to spend more

Fig 75. A typical trawl net catch freshly landed on deck, showing a variety of organisms from soft bottom habitats. More than 25 species of fish and invertebrates can be recognized in the photograph. Among the more important or easily recognizable animals are the large starfish Luidia maculata, *the shrimp* Penaeus semisulcatus *and* P. latisulcatus, *mole lobsters* Thenus orientalis *and crabs* Portunus pelagicus; *also a nurse shark* Chiloscyllium griseum, *flatheads* Platycephalus indicus, *striped catfish* Plotosus anguillaris, *bream* Lethrinus *spp. and* Crenidens crenidens, *and several species of mackerel and flounder. A stonefish* Leptosynanceja melanostigma *is partly visible at bottom center, recognizable by its black-bordered, orange pectoral fin. [off Dammam]*

99

Fig 76. Hormophysa triquetra, *a large and highly developed brown alga which grows attached to subtidal rocky outcrops. This species is abundant and widespread along the Arabian Gulf coast of Saudi Arabia.*

and more of their time on the bottom. For a time they probably rest there during the day, and return to a planktonic existence at night. At any rate they also soon transfer their feeding activities to the bottom and, in so doing, are highly selective in their choice of habitat.

The earliest benthic, juvenile stages of *Penaeus semisulcatus* have been collected from dense thickets of large algae, mostly *Hormophysa* (Fig 76) and *Sargassum*, growing in the tidal channels and rocky areas in Tarut Bay. At a slightly larger size, however, and still only about 1cm long, juvenile *P. semisulcatus* are no longer found among the algae, but rather in the nearby grassbeds, where they remain for several months, and grow nearly to adult size. In so doing their body weight increases about 2,000 times, which graphically illustrates the high productive potential of the grassbed biotope.

Although many details remain to be worked out by future research, it is already clear that the spawning of *Penaeus semisulcatus* occurs mainly during winter and spring (Badawi, 1975; Price and Jones, 1975).[7] This means that most shrimp larvae of this species are ready to leave the plankton and begin benthic life in late winter or early spring. They thus settle in the beds of algae at a time when these are at their maximum development, and move from algae to grassbeds just as the latter begin their period of most vigorous growth. The adaptations of this particular shrimp species, which enable it to exploit the abundant and very productive grassbed biotope, are probably an important factor in making it the most abundant, and therefore the most commercially important shrimp in the Gulf.

From late April or May onwards, partly grown immature shrimp begin to leave the grassbeds and move into deeper water habitats, where they become liable to capture by the mechanized trawlers. A closed season is in force, however, from late April until late July, in an attempt to minimize mortality of the smaller sized shrimp. Growth continues throughout the summer and fall, and the first fully grown adults generally appear in November. Initially, there is little difference in size between the sexes, but as growth proceeds females become progressively larger than males (Fig 77). Breeding occurs during winter and spring, and by the following June most of the previous year's generation have died off. The average lifespan of this species thus appears to be only slightly more than one year.

SHRIMP AS A RESOURCE: There has been a longstanding limited exploitation of shrimp along the shores of the Gulf, primarily by means of reed traps and small manually operated nets. Fishing for shrimp with trawlers, however, is comparatively recent. In Saudi Arabian waters trawler fishing began in 1963, when the Gulf shrimping industry as a whole

Fig 77. Seasonal change in mean carapace length of the commercial shrimp Penaeus semisulcatus *showing larger size of the females. (Data from Dammam grounds; after Price and Jones, 1975)*

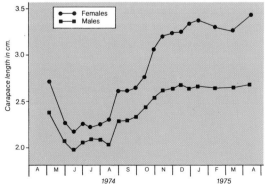

7 Populations in different areas apparently differ somewhat in the timing of their breeding cycles. Dates mentioned here apply mainly to the southern Saudi Arabian population, based on Tarut Bay.

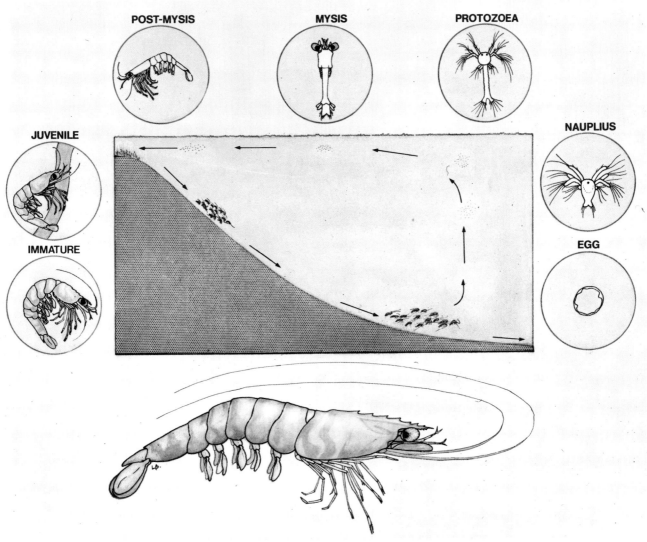

Fig 78. Life cycle of the commercial shrimp Penaeus semisulcatus. This species breeds mainly in early spring, and spawning apparently takes place at night, when each ripe female discharges thousands of eggs into the sea. The eggs, about 0.3 mm in diameter and barely visible to the naked eye, drift around in the plankton for some 18 hours before hatching. The pear-shaped first stage larvae are called nauplii; they swim actively, but do not feed. After moulting rapidly several times they change into a second, more elongate type of larva called a protozoea, and begin to feed on phytoplankton. After three protozoea stages they again change shape, transforming into mysis larvae, so called from their resemblance to the "opossum shrimps" of the Order Mysidacea. Mysis larvae are carnivorous, and feed on small zooplankton animals. After three mysis stages the larvae change shape once again, becoming "post-mysis" larvae with a structure basically similar to that of the adults. At first the post-mysis are very slender and transparent, and lead a largely planktonic existence; but after several further molts they settle to the bottom, and are thenceforth usually known as juveniles. By this time their appearance is that of a miniature adult. The time required for development from egg to post-mysis is very much dependent on water temperature. In the Gulf, the larval duration for P. semisulcatus is thought to be two or three weeks.

In March and early April large numbers of post-mysis and juveniles have been found in Tarut Bay. Initially they inhibit clumps of large algae such as Hormophysa and Sargassum, but soon move into the grassbeds. Many of the juveniles later migrate offshore to complete their growth into adults, although some probably remain in the grassbeds throughout their lives. In the Tarut Bay area, the largest adults are found from November to February. Like many other species of penaeid shrimp, P. semisulcatus has a life-span of little more than one year.

101

was undergoing rapid development. The Saudi Arabian fleet of mechanized trawlers grew to 16 vessels by 1969, and thereafter has remained fairly constant, although during the past three seasons (since 1974) many of the vessels have been laid up due to uneconomic catch rates. Maximum shrimp catches for the Saudi Arabian mechanized fleet, and for the Gulf industrialized fishery as a whole, were taken in 1967–68 and have not been matched since. Catches declined steadily thereafter until 1970–71, recovered slightly until 1973–74, and in the 1974–75 season fell off drastically to the lowest levels yet recorded. More detailed evaluation of the shrimp catch statistics has been published in a series of technical papers (Boerema, 1969, 1976; Ellis, 1975; Enomoto, 1971; Lewis, *et al.*, 1973; Price and Jones, 1975), with the suggestion that overfishing has played a major part in the decline of the industrial shrimp fishery.

Local fishing vessels, which previously used to catch fish solely by means of pots and lines, have followed the example of the mechanized vessels and have also begun shrimp trawling (Fig 81). There are approximately 300 such vessels operating along the Saudi Arabian coast, and they catch both fish and shrimp, depending on what is available. Contrary to popular belief, the landings made by the inshore fishing craft are substantial, equalling or even exceeding those achieved by mechanized vessels in some areas (Price and Jones, 1975).

The discrepancy between the declining state of the mechanized fishery and the thriving state of the inshore fishery has now been largely resolved by the realization that there are at least two distinct shrimp stocks in Saudi Arabian waters. The northern stock is found along the coast from Abu 'Ali northwards to Safaniya, and breeds in the shallows near Safaniya. Other breeding sites may also exist, since the northern bays have not yet been surveyed for shrimp larvae. The southern stock occupies the area between Dammam and the northeastern side of Bahrain. Its major breeding ground is Tarut Bay, though breeding also occurs on the eastern side of Bahrain Island.

Fig 79. Fishing gear of a Saudi Arabian mechanized shrimp trawler. Hanging down at lower left is a "try-net," which is towed for about 15 minutes in order to test the fishing ground. If the catch is favorable, the two main nets will be lowered. One of these can be seen in the center of the picture. [Dammam]

Fig 80. Two Saudi Arabian trawlers returning to Dammam after a night's fishing. The trawlers operate mostly at night, since the commercial shrimp is nocturnal.

Fig 81. Local fishing craft or dhows at anchor over a Tarut Bay grassbed. The scars on the grass "turf" are caused (at least in part) by trawling operations. [Darin]

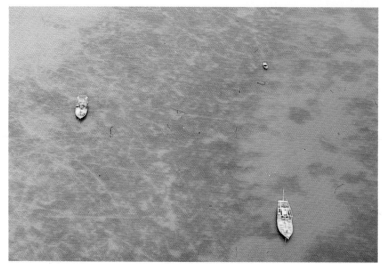

The northern stock is fished jointly by Saudi Arabian and Kuwaiti trawlers, and is at present seriously depleted, primarily as a result of overfishing. The southern stock is fished jointly by Saudi Arabian and Bahraini trawlers, and though the population fluctuates considerably from year to year, no overall downward trend has yet been observed. The Saudi Arabian mechanized fishery has devoted most of its effort to the northern stock, and so has had seriously reduced catches. The small craft and trap fisheries have been directed mainly to the southern stock, and at present continue to prosper.

ROLE OF GRASSBEDS IN THE ECOSYSTEM

In most of the world's oceans, phytoplankton provide the most important source of primary production (see Chapter 1) and form the base of the food web for most temperate region fisheries.

In tropical estuaries, lagoons, bays and shallow seas, however, where ample light energy reaches much of the bottom area — as in the Arabian Gulf — benthic plants often contribute a major portion of total photosynthetic primary production.

Grassbeds at Khawr al-'Umayrah (Khor Umaira) in South Yemen have been studied by Hirth, Klikoff, and Harper (1973), who also summarize much relevant data from studies in other parts of the world. Depending on the species composition of the stand, dry weight biomass (above-ground portion of leaves only) for 100% ground cover at Khawr al-'Umayrah was 300 to 400g per square meter. Values for leaves only, given in the literature for other parts of the world, range from 98 to 608g dry weight per square meter. Data from a limited number of samples from Tarut Bay give an estimate of 128g dry weight per square meter, or rather less than half of the values obtained at Khawr al-'Umayrah.

Several investigators have determined the energy content of sea grass leaves (data summarized by Hirth *et al.*, 1973). Corrected to a basis of ash-free dry weight, all the values are very similar and show little variation from one kind of sea grass to another. Values obtained at Khawr al-'Umayrah for five different genera varied only between 4.54 and 4.66 kcal per gram ash-free dry weight. Ash content varied between 32 and 34%. On a total dry weight basis this gives a value of 3.1 kcal per gram dry weight for both *Halodule uninervis* and *Halophila ovalis*. According to our preliminary measurements, *Halophila stipulacea* apparently has a higher ash content and probably therefore a lower energy yield per gram of total dry weight.

Grass cover was observed at 33 out of 50 randomly chosen sample points in Tarut Bay, giving an estimate of 66% grass cover for the bay as a whole (see Appendix A). The total area of Tarut Bay is 410 km², of which approximately 35% consists of intertidal habitats unsuitable for grass. 66% of the remainder gives an estimate of 175 km² of grassbed in Tarut Bay, corresponding to a total dry weight (leaves only) of 22.4 million kg or 22,400 metric tons. Since sea grass blades contain about 80% water, the fresh weight (wet weight) of this material would be about five times higher, or 114,000 metric tons. At 3.1 kcal per gram (dry weight) the energy content of the standing crop in Tarut Bay (leaves only) amounts to 69.4×10^9 kcal.

The Tarut Bay estimate of 650 g wet weight or 128 g dry weight per square meter for the standing crop of grass leaves may also be regarded as a lower-limit estimate of annual production. All the leaves are apparently renewed at least once a year. Indirect evidence from grass-harvesting schemes in various parts of the world (Hirth *et al.*, 1973) indicates that annual leaf production of grassbeds is actually between 2 and 4 times the standing crop, depending on the length of the growing season. During the growing season the entire leaf biomass is apparently replaced in approximately three months, at least under conditions of periodic harvesting. Taking the lower figure of 2 times the standing crop, applicable to a 6 month growing season, we arrive at a minimum estimate for annual leaf production of Tarut Bay grassbeds of 1.25 kg per square meter (wet weight), or 256 g per square meter (dry weight), equivalent to 794 kcal per square meter as energy input available to the ecosystem. The totals for Tarut Bay as a whole, based on the estimate of 66% grass cover for the subtidal area of the bay, then become 228×10^6 kg per year (wet weight) or 228,000 metric tons; 45×10^6 kg per year (dry weight) or 45,000 metric tons; and an energy equivalent of 1.4×10^{11} kcal per year available as input into the ecosystem. Since these figures ignore what is probably a substantial production of non-leaf materials by the grass plants, the true values are likely to be somewhat greater. It is likely, furthermore, that production by algae of the periphyton is of comparable magnitude to that by the grass itself; and also that six months represents an underestimate of the growing season. A productivity study of the entire grassbed system, therefore, would probably give total annual production values much greater than those just cited.

In terms more familiar to the non-biologist, the energy yield of the Tarut Bay grassbeds can be compared to that of another

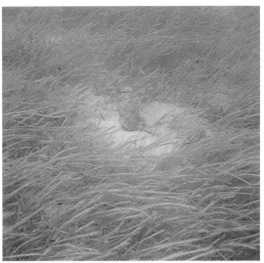

Fig 82. The average biomass of this Tarut Bay grass flat is about 650 g (wet weight) of leaves per square meter, and the annual production is at least twice this amount. The large, predatory snail Murex kusterianus *is only one of more than 500 animal species benefiting from this productivity.*

Fig 83. *Four small fish species popular in local markets.* Top: Gerres *sp. (18cm) from shallow sandy bottoms;* left:
Acanthopagrus bifasciatus *(13cm) or "Captain's daughter," a common inhabitant of rocky and reef biotopes;* right:
Lethrinus *sp. (17cm) from deeper sand bottoms and reef edges;* bottom: Therapon puta *(15cm) from grassbeds and
tidal creeks.*

familiar Gulf product – crude oil. If the energy obtained by burning crude oil is estimated at 140,000 BTU per gallon, the grassbed annual production of 1.4×10^{11} kcal is equivalent to the energy from about 95,000 barrels of oil, with a market value of slightly over one million dollars at current prices. Instead of concentrating on the energy yield, however, it might be more realistic to evaluate grass production in terms of its potential for conversion into some useful marine product, such as fish (Fig 83) or shrimp. If we assume that such conversion takes place in a two-step food chain (for example, snails eating the grass and fish eating the snails), and that the conversion efficiency of the food chain is 10% per step or 1% overall, then the annual production of 2.3×10^{8} kg (wet weight) of grass would yield 2.3×10^{6} kg of fish with a market value, at an average price of 12 Saudi Riyals per kg, of nearly 8 million dollars. If the grass were converted with the same efficiency to shrimp instead, at an average price of 18 Saudi Riyals per kg the value of the product would become nearly 12 million dollars. Very few marine animals are able to convert plant material directly into edible protein, suitable for human consumption, in a single food-chain step. One of these is the green turtle, which feeds on sea grass. If, then, the grass were intensively grazed by green turtles, as might happen on a large-scale turtle ranch, and the conversion efficiency of grass into turtle biomass were 10%, the annual production of 2.3×10^{8} kg of grass would yield 2.3×10^{7} kg of turtles. At a market price of \$2 per kg live weight, the product would then have a value of 46 million dollars.

Such numbers are, of course, largely hypothetical: they do not correspond with present exploitation patterns, nor do they take sufficient account of the ways in which the energy input is distributed throughout the ecosystem. They do, however, provide at least a crude basis for estimating the magnitude of the resource under consideration. The nearly fifty-fold discrepancy between the lowest evaluation of the annual grass product as oil combustion energy(\$1 million), and the highest evaluation as turtle protein (\$46 million) is particularly instructive. This discrepancy graphically demonstrates that different patterns of utilization of the same biological resource are, in general, not at all equivalent. It may also be viewed as a direct consequence of the operation of well-known thermodynamic laws, illustrating the relative inefficiency of combustion as compared to biological energy transformation processes.

This Tarut Bay example clearly shows the importance of grassbeds as a source of energy for the regional ecosystem. A significant fraction of the energy is undoubtedly converted into marine products useful to man. Energy is, however, only part of the story. Grassbeds also play a vital role as the nursery or critical habitat for young stages of many important animals such as shrimp, and shelter a diverse and abundant community of organisms which interact in manifold ways with the rest of the regional biota. All in all the grassbeds must be considered as one of the key biotopes in the western Arabian Gulf.

JOHN BURCHARD

Fig 84. Pencil urchin Prionocidaris baculosa *nestled between growth of* Stylophora *(left) and* Cyphastrea *(right). Broken coral fragments litter the sand in the foreground.* [Tarut Bay]

6
CORAL REEFS AND ISLANDS

CORAL REEFS

Among the most spectacular manifestations of life on this planet are coral reefs, some of which represent by far the largest structures made by living organisms, completely dwarfing the most ambitious constructions of modern man. The Great Barrier Reef off the coast of Australia, the largest coral structure of recent times, is nearly 2,000km long, and contains roughly 21,000km^3 of limestone rock, all formed by the activity of coral polyps and other reef organisms. Equally striking is the fact that coral reefs are among the most productive of all marine biotopes, whether measured in terms of energy or of the rate of production of new organic matter. For the ecologist interested in the details of relationships between organisms and their environment, coral reef communities have the greatest diversity of species found anywhere in the sea, and offer an intricacy of adaptation and degrees of ecological specialization rivalled only by tropical rain forest biotopes on land. The evolution of specialized symbiotic cleaning relationships, and of cleaner mimics which exploit these relationships for predatory purposes, is only one widely publicized example. The staggering variety of forms and colors among the corals, fish and other animals has captured the popular imagination, and made reefs the favorite resort of sport divers, underwater photographers and researchers.

The Red Sea reefs of Saudi Arabia are justly world famous, and have provided a large proportion of the material for several beautifully illustrated books in recent years. It is much less generally realized that large, flourishing coral reefs are

Fig 85. Intense competition for space is a feature of the coral reef. In this picture, which covers an area 7 x 10cm, four or five coral species compete with algae for the available surface. Top, Montipora *sp. Left,* Pavona *sp. Left front,* Porites *sp. Center,* Favia *sp. Bottom right,* Psammocora *sp. [Karan Island]*

109

Fig 86. Close-up of a cleaned skeleton of Leptastrea sp., a typical faviid coral. In life the cups, or calices, are filled by the soft tissues of the coral polyps.

Fig 87. Close-up of a cleaned skeleton of Acropora sp., showing the enlarged polyp at the end of each branch.

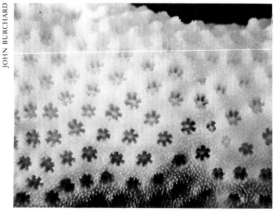

Fig 88. Close-up of a cleaned skeleton of Stylophora sp., a common shallow-water coral. The calices have a very simple structure, and the basic six-rayed pattern of the scleractinian polyp can be clearly seen.

common in the Gulf, especially off the Saudi Arabian coast.

The high salinities and wide temperature fluctuations of the Gulf, especially the low temperatures in winter, fall well outside the optimum range for reef coral development; and consequently Arabian Gulf coral reefs support far fewer species of both corals and associated fauna than, for example, the reefs of the Red Sea or of the western Indian Ocean. The limiting effects of the Gulf environment now appear, however, to be much less severe than had been previously supposed. During a relatively cursory examination of the Saudi Arabian reefs, Aramco biologists have encountered about twice as many genera of reef corals as the total recorded by previous investigators in the Gulf. Though these reefs do not rival those of the Red Sea in their variety of species, either of corals or of reef fish and other denizens, they are nevertheless spectacular. In fact, they are of particular interest to coral reef ecologists, because they offer an opportunity to study, in a simplified and therefore perhaps more comprehensible form, the processes which determine why reefs form in a particular location.

Biology of Reef Corals

One of the most amazing things about the vast limestone masses making up coral reefs is that they are produced by such small organisms. The most important reef-builders are the stony corals or scleractinians, and certain calcareous red algae. Scleractinians are sedentary, plant-like coelenterate animals belonging to the group Anthozoa, or flower animals, which also includes sea anemones. For the specialist, scleractinians are distinguished from other Anthozoa by certain details of their interior anatomy, but the most obvious difference is that all of them secrete a massive skeleton of calcium carbonate, from which they derive their popular name of stony corals. The skeleton provides a measure of protection to the coral animals or polyps, which are usually small and rather fragile.

Many stony corals are solitary, but almost all of the reef-building kinds grow in colonies composed of enormous numbers of individual polyps, joined together into a continuous sheet of living tissue and supported by a stony skeleton of complex architecture, which has a characteristic structure for each particular species of coral (Figs 86, 87 & 88). Such colonies may be several meters across and weigh many tons, but each colony arose originally by budding from one ancestral polyp, which managed to settle as a larva on a suitable, solid substrate. The basic feature which distinguishes reef builders from other corals, however, is that their tissues contain microscopic, photosynthetic algae, known as zooxanthellae. It is the symbiotic zooxanthellae which endow reef-forming corals with the ability to deposit their limestone skeleton at a vastly accelerated rate, enabling them literally to out-grow potential competitors, and produce the mighty geological structures we call coral reefs.

Coral polyps, like sea anemones, are basically carnivorous, and capture passing animals by means of stinging cells on their tentacles, or in some cases on "gastric filaments" which can be extended through the mouth. Because of the small size of most coral polyps, the animals captured are small planktonic forms. Zooplankton animals are often more abundant in surface waters at night than in the daytime, and this has been advanced to explain why most corals extend their tentacles only at night. Another reason for this behavior might be that many kinds of day-active reef animals, especially butterflyfish, feed either on the polyps themselves or on small animals they have captured. Only one local coral, *Goniopora* sp., keeps its polyps expanded during the daytime (Fig 89). It may be significant that these polyps are very large and tough compared with those of the vast majority of coral species, and they are rapidly withdrawn if the colony is disturbed.

In spite of several studies of the physiology of corals, there is still some controversy as to whether the zooxanthellae make a significant contribution to the energy budget of the coral in which they live. It has been established beyond doubt, however, that they make a decisive contribution to their hosts' capacity for rapid deposition of calcium carbonate, the feature which sets off the true reef-forming or hermatypic corals from close relatives that lack zooxanthellae. Given sufficient light, the zooxanthellae carry out vigorous photosynthesis, consuming carbon dioxide from their hosts' metabolic processes, and liberating oxygen. Although the details are fairly complicated, the rapid removal of carbon dioxide makes it possible for the reef coral to deposit carbonates at a high rate. This means, of course, that reef formation can occur only where sufficient light is available. Different species of hermatypic corals have different light requirements, a trait which leads to well-marked depth zonation on most coral reefs, but none can live (or at least compete successfully) beyond a certain depth.

Fig 89. Daisy coral Goniopora *sp. is one of the few corals whose polyps can be seen expanded during the daytime. The large polyps of this species extend 2 or 3 cm beyond the skeleton and resemble a patch of small daisies waving in the breeze. This species is a characteristic inhabitant of the middle reef slope, where it forms rounded heads up to a meter in diameter. [Jana Island]*

Fig 90. At the lower limit of active reef growth, coral development is restricted by the lack of light. Here Turbinaria, *a shade-tolerant* Acropora *species and gorgonians occur together at 15m depth. [Jana Island]*

This depth, the lower limit of active reef growth, obviously depends on whether the water is clear or turbid, but even in the central Pacific continuous coral growth scarcely extends beyond 50m though many specialized, shade-tolerant and slower-growing corals occur as isolated colonies below this depth. In the Arabian Gulf the lower depth limit for continuous coral cover in most offshore locations is about 15m. In coastal areas, where the water is usually more turbid, the lower limit may be 10m or less.

While the vertical distribution of reef corals is controlled primarily by the availability of light, temperature is normally the most important variable controlling the geographical distribution of coral reefs. The exceptional metabolic activity of the hermatypic corals requires warm and equable temperatures, so that coral reefs reach their maximum development in the tropics; in most parts of the world they are impoverished or absent where winter temperatures fall below 18°C. Salinities appreciably above or below the normal oceanic values also limit the growth of reef corals, and this variable assumes particular importance in controlling the occurrence of reefs in the Gulf. Another important factor is the presence of sediment. Coral polyps are able to clean themselves of sediment, but except for certain specialized sand-dwelling species, this ability is rather limited. Any sediment deposit exceeding the cleaning capacity of the polyps will coat the coral, interfering both with photosynthetic activity and with the coral's ability to feed. As a result, coral reefs are generally absent in high-sediment areas, such as the vicinity of river deltas.

Types of Coral Reefs

Four different types of coral reef structures are commonly recognized, based on their size, topography and relationships to nearby land masses. **Patch** or **platform reefs** are, as their names suggest, relatively small, flat-topped reef structures, usually arising in rather shallow water. This is the predominant type of reef structure in the Gulf (Fig 91). **Fringing reefs** form a more or less continuous border close to the shore of either island or continental land masses. Familiar examples are the Red Sea reefs near Jiddah. Offshore islands in the western Arabian Gulf are usually surrounded by fringing reefs. **Atolls** are large, ring-shaped reef structures, in which shallow reefs, often topped by sand islands, surround a central lagoon which may, in turn, contain patch reefs. The most widely accepted theory of atoll formation is that of Darwin, who considered them to have developed from fringing reefs surrounding an island: gradual sinking of the island would be compensated by upward growth of the coral, leaving a ring-shaped reef after the eventual disappearance of the island. No true atolls occur in the Gulf, but familiar examples are found in the Pacific and Indian Oceans. **Barrier reefs** resemble fringing reefs in that they border a land mass, but they are much larger structures and are separated from the land by a broad, deep lagoon in which conditions are usually unfavorable for coral growth.

Fig 91. Aerial view of an offshore platform reef. This is the most common type of reef in the Arabian Gulf especially in the northern section, where there are hundreds. This reef is about 100m across. [offshore from Manifa]

These different topographic forms are not immutable, but undergo constant change and development. They are the combined product of geological events, such as changes in sea level, and biological events resulting from the coral growth itself. Once established, a reef tends to grow both upwards and sideways. Upward growth is stopped, however, near the low-tide level by the inability of corals to survive exposure to air. This results in a flat-topped, steep-sided reef form. Subsequent growth occurs mainly around the periphery, since conditions on top of the reef become more and more unfavorable for living corals as the structure increases in size. This tendency of coral growth to proceed in ring-like fashion is most obvious in the case of coral atolls, but manifests itself in coral structures of all sizes. Even a single coral head, contacting the surface in a calm lagoon environment, will form a "micro-atoll" a few meters in diameter; and such micro-atolls are a prominent feature of the reef flats surrounding the Gulf coral islands.

In the Gulf there is no clear-cut distinction between platform and fringing reefs. Many of the larger platform reefs have accumulated sand banks on their flattened tops, which are uncovered at low tide. On a few of the reefs this has gone a step further, and a permanent island has been formed. A further development found on some of these islands is the cementation of the sand, forming beachrock. In the Gulf as elsewhere, these features have all taken their existing form since the sea attained its present level – during the last 5,000 years or so.

Local Distribution of Coral Reefs

Coral reefs of widely differing size and development are a very common feature of the shallower portions of the Arabian sublittoral, wherever the bottom lies within the depth of effective light penetration. Several hundred small platform reefs, from a few dozen to a few hundred meters across, occur between Ras Abu 'Ali and Safaniya. South of Abu 'Ali there are fewer reefs, but several large reef structures, kilometers long, do occur. Notable examples are the an-Najwah reef, located about 7km northeast of the port of Dammam, the Abu Sa'fah reefs, and the reef system of Umm al-Jamal between Ju'aymah and Jubail.

113

Temperature fluctuations, high salinities and sedimentation are all more frequent and more pronounced close to the shore than in the more central regions of the Gulf. In the various bay systems, these conditions are still more pronounced. In addition, salinities increase gradually from Abu'Ali southward to Ras Tanura, and very rapidly from Ras Tanura southward. From al-Khobar southward, the Saudi Arabian coast lies within the Gulf of Salwah. Salinities here are $55^0/_{00}$ or more, and reef corals probably do not occur.

These gradients in physical conditions are reflected in the occurrence and composition of coral reefs. On the open coast, reef corals are found right up to the low tide mark, but reefs inshore are made up of few coral species compared to those offshore. This reduction of species diversity is even more noticeable in the reefs that occur in bays. One extreme example is a small reef in Tarut Bay,[1] which consists of a pure stand of *Stylophora* sp., with large patches of *Acropora* sp. and occasional heads of *Platygyra* sp. A curious feature of this particular assemblage is that perhaps a dozen other species of reef corals grow, as isolated colonies, on the rocky bottom in the immediate vicinity, without entering into the formation of the reef.

CORAL ISLANDS

A considerable proportion of the skeletal material of coral reefs is broken down by the action of the waves, by the boring action of certain sponges which attack coral, and by the grazing activities of animals such as parrot fish and sea urchins, which feed directly on the living coral or algae. The coral sand resulting from these breakdown processes settles on any horizontal surface. This sand is shifted about by waves and currents, and accumulates in sheltered locations, especially on the leeward portions of the flat reef top or platform.

On many of the larger platform reefs, extensive sand bars have formed in this way, and uncover at low tide. At the an-Najwah reef near Dammam, a sand bank hundreds of meters long is exposed at low tide, but resubmerged completely at high tide. On a few Saudi Arabian reefs, however, topographic and oceanographic conditions have combined to allow the process to go one step further, and permanent sand islands have formed. Once formed, the islands have grown by accretion of sand in successive layers, plainly visible from the air (Fig 92). This is the same process that produces the low islands or "motus" so characteristic of South Pacific coral atolls.

All the islands are low and flat, with an elevation of only 2 or 3 m above spring high tide levels. The larger islands are covered by a dense growth of low bushes, belonging to the salt tolerant genera *Suaeda* and *Salsola* which are also common on salt flats along the mainland coast. The vegetated central area is surrounded at the same level by a narrow "beach platform," practically bare of vegetation, from which a moderately steep sand beach descends to the water's edge. The smallest island, Har-

1 At approximately 26°36'30"N, 50°08'30"E.

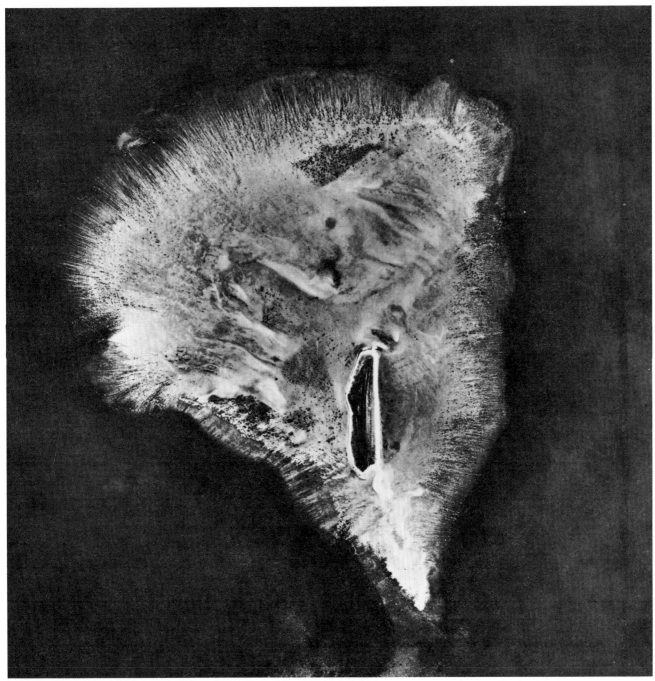

Fig 92. Aerial view of Jana Island, showing various features of the island and its surrounding reef. The various zones of the reef flat (p. 119) are clearly visible, along with the spur and groove pattern near the reef edge. Portions of the reef deeper than about 3 m do not, however, show up in the picture.

Fig 93. Coral islands in the Gulf provide a safe breeding ground for large populations of sea birds, especially terns. [Karan Island]

qus, is very low and lacks terrestrial vegetation, probably because it is situated on a very small reef platform, so that sand is lost over the edge of the platform almost as fast as it is piled up on the island. Around much of the perimeter of the islands there is a "storm berm" at the top of the beach slope, slightly higher than the general level of the platform.

On Karan, Jana and al-'Arabiyah islands, extensive areas of exposed rock occur along the lower portion of the beaches. This material appears to be beach rock formed by cementation of sand grains, a process in which the biological activity of microscopic algae inhabiting the beach sand probably plays a prominent role.

The main features of the six Saudi Arabian coral islands may be seen in the following table:

Name	Position	Size (meters)	Biological features
Karan	27° 42' 45" N 49° 49' 30" E	2,024 × 632	Vegetated; major turtle and bird breeding site
Jana	27° 21' 50" N 49° 54' 0" E	1,105 × 300	Vegetated; major turtle and bird breeding site
Jurayd	27° 11' 30" N 49° 59' 25" E	732 × 282	Vegetated; turtle and major bird breeding site
al-'Arabiyah	27° 46' 30" N 50° 10' 15" E	488 × 267	Low scrub only; minor turtle breeding site; various military and technical installations
Kurayn	27° 38' 45" N 49° 49' 15" E	312 × 251	Scattered bushes; turtle and bird breeding site
Harqus	27° 56' 15" N 49° 41' 0" E	259 × 76	No vegetation; minor turtle breeding site

The coral islands occupy a unique and irreplaceable position in the Gulf ecosystem, primarily because they provide a safe breeding site for important animals, especially two species of sea turtles and three species of terns. The presence of an island on top of a reef also increases the number of different types of habitat associated with the reef, providing ecological niches for a greater number of species. Thus, the reefs of Jana, Kurayn, and especially Karan Island, are richer in diversity of species than any others so far examined. Indeed, there is every reason to believe that Karan Island represents the maximum development of coral reef communities in the Arabian Gulf.

GROWTH FORMS OF ARABIAN GULF CORALS

Most Gulf coral species are either **branching, massive, foliose** or **encrusting** in their growth (Fig 94).

Branching or bush-like coral colonies, of the growth form known to specialists as ramose, are particularly characteristic of

Fig 94. Some growth forms of Arabian Gulf corals. In center and at right, two ramose colonies of Acropora. *In center background, massive colonies of* Platygyra. *At right, foliose and encrusting* Montipora *sp. In center foreground, encrusting growth of* Echinophyllia *sp. [Karan Island]*

Fig 95. Acropora.

Fig 96. Stylophora.

Fig 97. Platygyra.

species of *Acropora*. In this genus the calices, or cups containing the coral polyps, project above the surface of the branches, giving them a spiny or bumpy appearance (Fig 95). In *Acropora*, the tip of each branch is formed by a single enlarged polyp. This is the largest of all coral genera, with over two hundred species, of which several occur on local reefs. Smooth, finger-like branches, with a delicate greenish shimmer when alive, probably belong to *Stylophora* (Fig 96), a genus which often grows in shallow water where conditions are unfavorable to most other corals. Delicate, angular branches resembling *Acropora*, but without the raised calices or enlarged terminal polyps, are likely to belong to a species of *Pocillopora*.

Massive coral growth is most familiar in the form of "brain coral," large rounded heads covered with convoluted furrows somewhat resembling the surface of the human brain. Those on local reefs are either *Platygyra* (Fig 97) or the similar *Leptoria*. The closely related "honeycomb corals"(also of the family Faviidae) also form rounded heads. Instead of convolutions, however, their surface forms a honeycomb of closely fitting cups or calices in which the polyps are lodged. A large number of species of this type occurs on local reefs, mostly belonging to the genera *Favia*, *Favites*, and *Goniastrea*. Yet another type of massive coral appears almost smooth, since the polyps are very small and the calices shallow. By far the commonest corals of this type are species of *Porites*, one of the most important reef builders in the Gulf. Two distinct types of *Porites* (subgenera *Porites* and *Synaraea)* occur locally. *Goniopora*, with larger polyps, is also a member of this group, and in the living state can be recognized immediately since its polyps are usually fully expanded during the daytime, hiding the coral mass under what looks like a field of small flowers (Figs 89 and 98). *Psammocora* is a small greyish "knobbly" coral, with an irregular shape and surface texture. Another small massive form, with raised star-like calices, is *Cyphastrea*.

Foliose or leaf-like coral growths are most likely to be found in shady nooks, or fairly deep on the reef. *Pavona* is rather reminiscent of a head of crinkly lettuce, brown with whitish edges. Two types of *Pavona* occur locally, one very delicate and lettuce-like (subgenus *Pavona*, Fig 99) and the other considerably more compact (subgenus *Polyastra*, Fig 85). Another distinctive foliose coral is the dark red *Turbinaria*, one species of which forms large cornucopia or "elephant-ear" growths (Fig 106), while another bears a remarkable resemblance to a toadstool (Fig 107). Both these are found only where there is little light, usually at the base of the reef. Probably the commonest foliose corals likely to be encountered on the reef itself are species of *Montipora*, some of which resemble a gigantic form of lichen, encrusting the underlying surface and projecting above it in overlapping, semi-circular sheets.

Encrusting corals, as their name suggests, form a crust or coating over the surface on which they grow. This is a less distinctive growth form than the others, since colonies of branching, massive or foliose corals usually begin as an en-

118

crusting growth before developing their characteristic form. In very dim light, furthermore, many massive corals adopt a more or less encrusting type of growth. Besides these, however, there are also corals for which the encrusting growth form is typical in all situations. These include some species of *Montipora* and several members of the faviid group such as *Echinophyllia* (Fig 100). Another distinctive encrusting faviid is *Hydnophora*, covered all over with raised tooth-like projections.

CORAL REEF ZONATION

Zonation on coral reefs has been studied by Aramco biologists at Jana and Karan Islands. Except for minor topographical details, the two reefs are very similar. From casual observations, it appears that similar zonation patterns occur on the other islands and on the larger platform reefs at some distance from shore. In relatively shallow areas near shore, the sequence of zones is modified by vertical compression due to reduced light penetration, and by the absence of many coral species unable to tolerate conditions in these areas.

The reef structure underlying each island is composed of three major regions: the **reef platform, reef slope** and **reef base.** Each of these spans a range of environmental conditions, and includes several different biological communities, which it is convenient to describe in terms of subdivisions or zones. In some cases zone boundaries are clear-cut, while in others they represent a gradual transition from the predominance of one type of community to that of another (Fig 101).

Reef Platform

Reef platforms surrounding Jana and Karan Islands are extensive, almost perfectly horizontal, and covered by a meter or less of water at low tide. Their limit on the landward side is the base of the island beach. The reef platform is widest on the windward side of the island, where it extends 2 to 3km from the beach. On the leeward side it is about half that width. At low tide the thin sheet of water covering the platform undergoes intense solar heating, which increases the temperature and salinity. The platform is therefore an unfavorable area for coral growth, except near its edges. Much of its surface is covered by sheets of loose sand, which are shifted about by the strong tidal currents. Other areas consist of exposed rock, formed from old coral growth and cemented coral fragments, or of beach rock. On these foundations scattered colonies of the most resistant coral species grow, becoming increasingly abundant toward the periphery of the platform. Upward growth of these colonies is limited by the level of spring low tides, resulting in characteristic flat-topped microatolls. The seaward edge of the platform is formed by a reef crest of actively growing corals, forming a slightly raised rim at the top of the reef slope. Just behind the crest, especially on the windward side of the reef, is a rubble zone of broken coral blocks and fragments, thrown there by wave action during storms.

Fig 98. Goniopora.

Fig 99. Pavona.

Fig 100. Echinophyllia.

119

CORAL REEF ZONATION (SCHEMATIC)

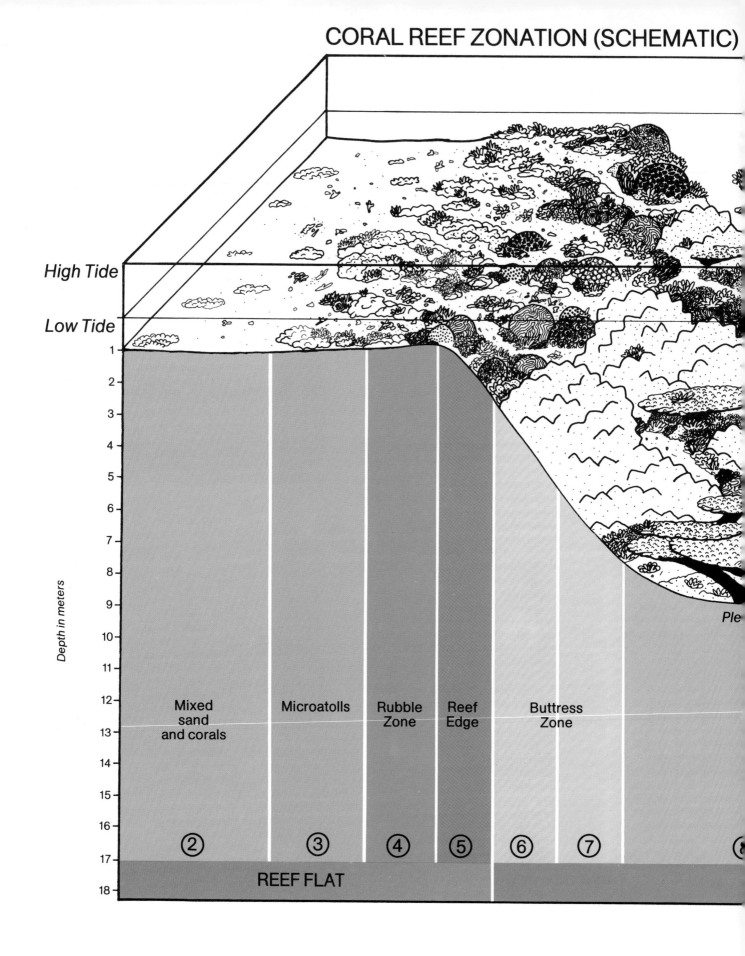

High Tide

Low Tide

Depth in meters

1
2
3
4
5
6
7
8
9
10
11
12
13
14
15
16
17
18

Mixed
sand
and corals

Microatolls

Rubble
Zone

Reef
Edge

Buttress
Zone

Ple

② ③ ④ ⑤ ⑥ ⑦ ⑧

REEF FLAT

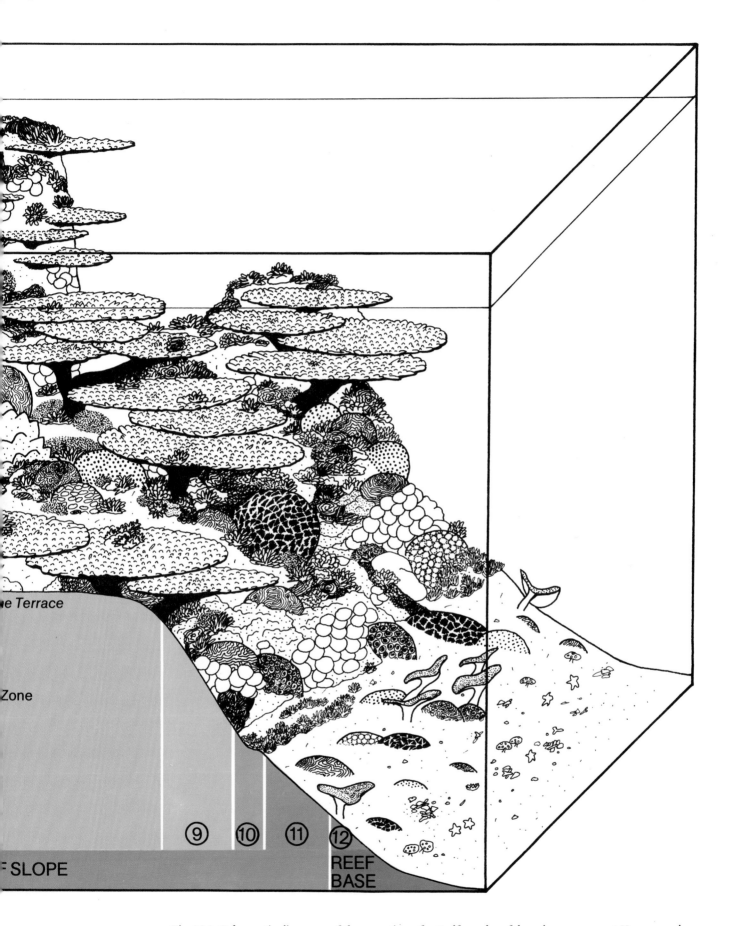

Fig 101. Schematic diagram of the zonation of a Gulf coral reef, based on surveys at Karan and Jana Islands. The shore and inner part of the reef flat region are not shown.

Fig 102. In the back reef zone, coral growth is limited by adverse conditions. Upward growth is prevented by exposure at low tide, and the surviving colonies are usually flat-topped. [Karan Island]

ZONE 1, the innermost reef flat, is the most extensive, with a measured width of 1,390m on the windward side of Karan Island. This might also be called the sand flat zone, since a flat expanse of sand overlying the rocky reef platform is the most prevalent feature here. In places, more or less extensive sheets of rock are exposed. Close to the beach the sand is rather fine-grained, and colored greenish by the growth of microscopic algae. During summer, countless numbers of the small conch *Strombus decorus persicus* gather on this part of the reef flat to mate and lay their eggs. Farther seaward the sand is coarser, and extensively burrowed by a variety of invertebrates. Near the seaward edge of this zone, small colonies of several resistant coral species begin to make their appearance. These are, in general, the same species found just below low tide mark on exposed beaches, e.g. *Stylophora* and *Cyphastrea*.

ZONE 2 might be called the back reef zone, and on the windward side of Karan Island extends 450m seaward from the outer edge of Zone 1. The low-tide water depth in this zone is about the same as in Zone 1. Sand is still predominant, covering about 60% of the bottom area, and is inhabited by a great variety of burrowing organisms, especially alpheid pistol shrimps with their attendant gobies. Dead coral and coral fragments make up the remainder of the bottom, and there are small living colonies of many kinds of corals. Aramco biologists identified at least 7 coral genera in this zone on the Karan Island reef (Fig 103).

ZONE 3 is characterized by a much more vigorous growth of living coral, which covers a considerable proportion (about 40%) of the bottom. This growth is largely dominated by "micro-atoll" forms of *Stylophora* and *Porites,* which rise above the general level of the reef flat to near the level of low spring tide. These growths are most abundant toward the outer edge of the zone, raising the general level of the flat toward that of the reef crest (Zone 4). This and the two following zones occupy a total width of 530m on the windward Karan Island reef. Sand still covers much of the bottom in Zone 3, and is shifted about by the strong tidal streams that pass over the reef, in a radial direction, as the tide rises and falls. Because of this, coral growth in Zones 3, 4 and 5 tends to occur in the form of long ridges or spurs, perpendicular to the reef edge, and separated by sand-filled, shallow tidal channels. This "spur-and-groove" pattern is clearly shown in the aerial photograph of the Jana Island reef (Fig 92).

ZONE 4 is composed largely of living and dead fragments of broken coral, torn from the reef by storm waves and deposited just behind the reef edge. The mass of coral rubble supports small, young colonies of a great variety of coral species, as conditions here are favorable, apart from the sporadic occurrence of high levels of wave energy. All the colonies are small, however, since the whole region is probably smashed into

Fig 103. Section of a sampling transect on the coral reef flat at Karan Island. The transect line runs across the center of the picture, with a knot indicating the boundary between two adjacent 1m transect subdivisions. Six species of common reef corals are visible in the photograph. 1a, Acropora sp., staghorn coral; 1b, A dead portion of the same coral colony; 1c, Acropora sp., another colony of the same species; 1d, Acropora sp., a second species of staghorn coral; 2, Platygyra sp., several colonies of brain coral; 3, Porites (Porites) sp., the most important knoll-former; 4, Goniastrea sp., one of several common honeycomb corals; 5, Lithothamnium sp., a growth of coralline algae; 6, Stylophora sp., a common shallow-water finger coral.

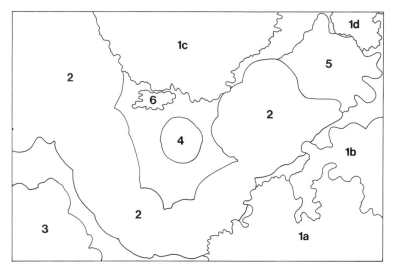

123

Fig 104. The upper part of the reef slope (Zone 5) is buttressed by massive growths of Porites *several meters high. On the sides and in the shadow of the* Porites *buttresses are found many other species of corals. Shown are* Porites *buttresses (left), with encrusting growth of* Hydnophora *and* Echinophyllia, *and in the foreground two heads of* Platygyra. *On the base of the upper* Platygyra *is a large sea cucumber* Stichopus *sp. about 40cm long. [Jana Island]*

fragments every couple of years or so. No particular type of coral is dominant, probably because none of them live long enough for competition to become a factor; those which do become established are usually the beneficiaries of chance. This rubble heap is covered by only about 0.5m of water at low tide, and so forms the top or crest of the reef.

ZONE 5 is the reef edge, forming the transition between the virtually flat reef platform and the incline of the reef slope. The depth of this zone ranges from 0.5 to 2.5m, and it is here that most waves break, except during severe storms. Only the most compact growth forms of coral can survive these conditions, and the living coral is composed almost entirely of moderate-sized, rounded heads of massive species, especially *Porites*, the brain coral *Platygyra* and various other faviids or honeycomb corals. On the windward side most of the reef in this zone is not composed of coral at all, but of the coralline alga *Lithothamnium*, which forms rounded compact masses, well suited to withstand the impact of breaking waves.

Reef Slope

The **reef slope** is the region of maximum coral development and almost continuous coral cover. It extends from the reef crest near the surface, down to a depth of about 15m where it ends in a gradual or abrupt transition to the reef base region. The steady incline of the reef slope region may be interrupted in places by relatively extensive flat terraces. These terraces, especially one at 9m depth which is found in many places, apparently represent previous sea levels of the fairly recent geological past, the Pleistocene age. Others may represent older topographic features, pre-dating the present day development of the reef. Sand tends to accumulate on the terraces, creating conditions especially unfavorable for the slower-growing reef coral species. The terraces are therefore dominated by massive heads and knolls of *Porites*, or the large fans of a species of *Acropora*. Both of these are among the fastest-growing reef corals. Aside from the terraces, which are in a sense interruptions of the slope, several distinct zones can be recognized in this region, characterized by the preponderance of different coral species.

ZONES 6 and 7 together may be called the buttress zone, since their most prominent feature is pillar or buttress-like growths of massive coral species, especially *Porites* (Fig 104). Zone 6 occupies the depth range of 2.5 to 4m, and receives most of the impact of breaking waves under storm conditions. Coral growth in this zone consists largely of big heads of *Porites*, with small specimens of *Acropora*, *Montipora* and a variety of other species growing in the sheltered niches in between. Zone 7 extends from 4 to 6m depth (Fig 105), and is characterized by somewhat smaller *Porites* heads, the lettuce-like *Pavona*, encrusting or massive growth forms of *Montipora*, and others. A typical species in this zone is *Goniopora,* which forms rounded

Fig 105. View of the reef face at about 5m depth, showing at least ten different species of hermatypic corals. [Karan Island]

Fig 106. Turbinaria.

and often quite massive heads somewhat like those of *Porites*, but covered with inch-long fleshy polyps which remain fully expanded during the daytime unless they are disturbed. Large coral pillars, built mainly by *Porites* but encrusted on their sides with growths of many other species, arise in this zone and commonly reach to just below the surface. These free-standing coral knolls, which can reach really impressive dimensions, are best developed on the leeward side of the reef. Fish of many kinds are especially abundant in these two zones (Fig 163).

ZONE 8 extends from about 6 to about 10m and may be called the coral table zone after its most characteristic feature, the horizontal fan or table-shaped growths of species of *Acropora*. These consist of a level fan or table, sometimes several meters in diameter, composed of an intricate network of delicate coral branches, and supported underneath by a tree-like system of trunk and branches. A great variety of other coral species is also found here, and this zone probably contains the most diverse coral assemblage of any level of the reef. Many of these are encrusting forms, such as *Montipora*, *Echinophyllia*, *Hydnophora* and others. There is also a great diversity of faviid species. The widely occurring Pleistocene sea-level terrace at about 9m depth falls in this zone, and because of its flat topography collects quantities of sand. The patches of sand are surmounted by a forest of large *Acropora* tables, and by small coral knolls on which are found most or all of the species otherwise characteristic of the zone.

ZONE 9 extends from about 10 to about 12m, and might be called the lichen zone, since it is largely dominated by foliose and encrusting growths of *Montipora*, which resemble oversized, brownish lichens. Species of *Montipora* are found at many levels of the reef, but predominate here.

ZONE 10 occurs at about 12m depth. Where it occurs, which is not everywhere around the reef periphery, it consists of a dense growth of delicate coral "bushes" about 20cm tall, covering virtually all the available surface and consisting usually of *Acropora* sp., or sometimes of *Pocillopora* sp. Any given patch of this growth appears to consist entirely of one species. This zone occurs in many places, but does not form a continuous belt around the reef, as do most of the others. The reasons for this patchy occurrence are still not known.

ZONE 11 is the foot of the reef, the lowest zone in which living corals form a more or less continuous bottom cover, and ranges from depths of about 12 to 15 or sometimes 18m. Because of the low light intensity, low growing corals predominate, especially various faviids forming low knolls, and encrusting forms such as *Echinophyllia*, *Acanthastrea* and others. The large, trumpet or vase-shaped growths of *Turbinaria* (Fig 106) are a conspicuous and characteristic feature of the lower part of this zone.

Reef Base

The **reef base,** beginning usually at a depth of about 15m, is generally noticeably flatter than the reef slope region. At this depth, the dim light does not permit the more rapid and luxuriant forms of coral growth, and much of the bottom is covered with coral fragments and other non-living debris from the reef above. A considerable variety of hermatypic corals occurs here nevertheless, including both specialized types such as *Turbinaria* which are restricted to this level, and low-growing species of genera commonly found higher up the reef. Since the limited light intensity cannot sustain high rates of carbonate deposition, coral colonies in this region are flat, encrusting, or, like *Turbinaria*, take the form of thin plates raised above the bottom. With increasing depth the proportion of living coral colonies becomes progressively smaller, and the proportion of sand to larger coral fragments greater, forming a gradual transition to the deeper-water sedimentary bottom found around the coral structure.

ZONE 12 lies just below the level at which corals dominate the bottom cover, and forms a transition between the reef proper and the sediment bottom found at greater depths all around the reef. It is essentially a talus slope, composed largely of coarse sand and coral debris, with scattered small colonies of a variety of corals. Some of these are also found on the reef slope, while others are peculiar to this zone. One of the latter is a species of *Turbinaria*, shaped like a mushroom (Fig 107). Another particularly characteristic animal is the large gaudy starfish *Pentaceraster mammillatus* (Figs 1 & 61), which is common on sand bottoms at the foot of coral reefs. This zone is also subject to frequent visits by large predatory pelagic fishes, including barracuda, king mackerel and sharks.

Fig 107. These spectacular deep red starfish, Euretaster cribrosus, *not previously recorded from the Gulf, were found just below the reef base at 20m depth, along with small corals* Turbinaria *sp. and coral rubble. [Jana Island]*

JOHN BURCHARD

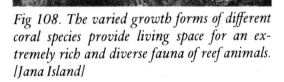

Fig 108. The varied growth forms of different coral species provide living space for an extremely rich and diverse fauna of reef animals. [Jana Island]

Environmental Factors

This apparently complex zonation is primarily the result of two main gradients in environmental conditions, one horizontal and the other vertical, though accidents of the pre-existing topography have caused some local modifications. The horizontal gradient extends from the upper reef edge inward across the reef flat to the beach. Along this gradient fluctuations in temperature and salinity, and the burden of sediment, increase shoreward. Wave energy is greatest at the reef edge, and decreases rapidly shoreward. Tidal streams are also strongest at the reef edge, but decrease more gradually toward the shore. The vertical gradient, on the other hand, extends from the reef edge downward across the reef slope, and continues in the same direction across the reef base as well. This is primarily a gradient of light and wave energy, both of which are greatest at the reef edge and decrease downwards. Below a certain depth, generally known as the wave base, wave energy even during storms is insignificant. In the Arabian Gulf at least, the wave base seems to coincide fairly closely with the bottom of the reef slope. The range of daily and seasonal temperature variation is greatest at the top of the slope, and decreases gradually downwards. It is unlikely, however, that significant differences in the availability of plankton or oxygen occur over the limited vertical range of the reef slope (Stoddart, 1969).

In the Gulf, winds do not blow with equal frequency or force from all points of the compass; and on the average, the northern and northwestern faces of each reef receive much more wave energy than the portions facing in other directions. The southern and eastern faces are largely sheltered, except for occasional violent storms. The unequal distribution of wind and wave action around the reefs results in characteristic differences between "windward" and "leeward" reef formations (Fig 109), as well as the displacement of islands or sandbars toward the leeward side of the reef top.

Fig 109. Karan Island reef profiles. A — sand flat; B — back reef; C — outer flat and reef edge; D — reef slope; E — reef base. The windward sand flat is actually 1,390m wide.

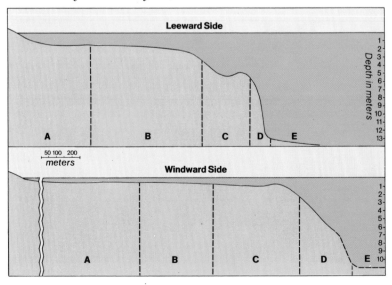

128

CORAL REEF AS HABITAT

In areas of maximum coral diversity, such as the central Pacific and the western Indian Ocean, up to 3,000 species of animals are estimated to inhabit a coral reef, exploiting in various ways the great variety of available ecological niches. While the diversity of reef animals in the Gulf, like that of the corals themselves, is restricted by adverse environmental conditions, especially high salinities and temperature fluctuations, coral reefs still probably represent the most diverse ecological communities found in the Gulf. Coral reef fauna is notoriously difficult to sample adequately, and only about 540 species of reef animals have so far been identified by Aramco biologists. This small number, however, also reflects the very limited effort so far expended on studying reef animals as compared to those of the grass beds, for instance; and the final count of Gulf coral reef fauna will certainly exceed 1,000 species.

The extreme diversity of reef communities, as compared to those of other biotopes, results directly from the unusual variety of both physical and ecological features found on the reef. Each species of coral has its own characteristic growth pattern, different from that of any other species, and many reef animals exploit, in one unique way or another, these structural peculiarities.

The massive, smooth-surfaced heads of *Porites*, for example, are inhabited by several species of rock-boring bivalves, which live in chambers inside the coral skeleton and extend their siphons to the outside through specially constructed openings in the living "skin" of coral tissue that covers the outside of the head (Fig 110). Several species of polychaetes, of the feather-duster or fan-worm type, also inhabit *Porites* in a similar way. Brain and honeycomb corals are colonized by other polychaete species, and especially by barnacles of the suborder Acrothoracica, which allow themselves to be overgrown and enclosed by the living coral, but maintain an opening to the surface through which they obtain their food and oxygen.

Branching corals such as *Acropora* and *Pocillopora*, on the other hand, offer few inducements to boring animals, but in-

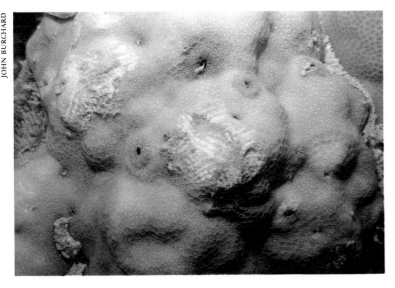

JOHN BURCHARD

Fig 110. Porites sp. is the commonest Arabian Gulf coral of massive growth form. It provides a home for several kinds of rock-boring animals, especially bivalves which live embedded inside the coral skeleton and protrude their siphons, through holes in the living coral surface, to obtain food and oxygen. The gouge marks visible in the photograph were made by the teeth of parrot fish, which bite off chunks of the living coral and digest the organic part, voiding the remainder in the form of coral sand. [Karan Island]

129

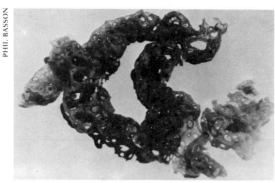

Fig 111. The brown alga Hydroclathrus clathratus *forms extensive growths of a characteristic meshwork pattern on subtidal rocks of the reef flat, and great masses of it sometimes collect in the sand-filled hollows of the reef flat. [Karan Island]*

stead are inhabited by a variety of animals which hide among and clamber about the branches. These are usually specific to each particular coral species, and include representatives of many animal types, especially carid shrimp, xanthid crabs and fish. Common local examples include the xanthid crabs *Trapezia cymodoce* and *Tetralia glaberrima*, the fish *Gobiodon citrinus*, and as yet unidentified shrimp-like species of Galatheidae, Alpheidae and Palaemonidae. There is also the peculiar crab *Hapalocarcinus* sp., the female of which allows itself to be overgrown and imprisoned within a branch of *Acropora*, maintaining only tiny openings to the outside, through which it obtains a circulation of water containing plankton and oxygen. At mating time the tiny males gain access to the female's chamber through these openings.

Another result of the intermingling of corals of many different structural types is the formation of an almost infinite variety of surfaces, projections, nooks, crannies and holes of every conceivable shape and size. These provide attachment surfaces for a large variety of sessile animals and algae. If the surface is exposed to light, the sessile animals most likely to colonize it are other species of reef corals. Shaded surfaces, and the interior of the numerous coral caves, are colonized by sponges, hydroids and alcyonarians, of which sea fans are probably the most familiar. Alcyonarians appear to be rather sensitive to high salinities and are therefore less conspicuous on Arabian Gulf reefs than, for example, in the Red Sea. Many species of bivalves, bryozoans, tunicates, and others also colonize these habitats. The most conspicuous algae are *Hydroclathrus clathratus* (Fig 111), which forms great net-like masses on dead corals and coral rock, especially in the back-reef zone; *Pocockiella variegata* (Fig 112), whose lichen-like growth sometimes covers even living coral colonies; and the abundant

Fig 112. Pocockiella variegata *is a conspicuous alga common on the coral reefs. It sometimes completely covers living coral, or living* Lithothamnium *as in this photograph, with its lichen-like growth. [Jana Island]*

Fig 113. The brightly-colored spiny lobster Panulirus versicolor *hides out during the day in the nooks and crannies of the coral reef, with only its conspicuous white antennae showing. At night it emerges from its hiding place to wander about. This striking crustacean is one of the best-known edible marine animals, but is only rarely encountered on Gulf reefs. [Jana Island]*

Lithothamnium, which is actually a major structural component of the reef, rather than a colonist.

The nooks and crannies of the reef structure are inhabited by an incredible variety of large and small crabs, mostly of the family Xanthidae. The most striking of these is the large, red coral-crab *Carpilius convexus,* the male of which carries garish eye-like spots on its back, while the female is more or less plain red. *Carpilius* is usually found clambering about in the complex cavern systems at the base of large coral knolls. Another even more striking crustacean found in the same habitat is the gaudily colored spiny lobster *Panulirus versicolor,* which wanders about the reef during the night, but in daytime is usually found resting in a crevice, with only its conspicuous white antennae showing outside (Fig 113). *Panulirus,* also known as crayfish or langouste, one of the best-known edible marine animals, is only occasionally encountered on reefs in the western Gulf.

Gastropods are also particularly well represented on the reef. Many of the large spectacular types of shells, familiar from coral reefs in the tropical Pacific, have not yet been found in the Gulf; but a fair number of interesting species occur. The textile cone *Conus textile* (Fig 114) is infamous for its ability to deliver a dangerously venomous sting to anyone handling it carelessly. Actually, the stinging ability of cone shells is not primarily a self-defense mechanism; rather it is an adaptation to unique feeding habits. Cones prey on large active animals, such as polychaetes, other snails, octopus or even fish, which are able to move much faster than themselves. Their mouth structures are accordingly modified into a sort of harpoon gun, by means

131

Fig 114. A textile cone shell Conus textile *creeping over the coralline alga* Lithothamnium. *The textile cone, which derives its name from its intricate shell pattern, is a venomous marine snail commonly found on coral reefs. Snails of this genus feed on various active marine animals, which they capture by "harpooning" with a specially modified, venom-injecting tooth. A few species feed on fish and have especially powerful venom, sufficient to paralyze fish as large as the snail itself. Cone shells readily use their "harpoon" in self-defense and some species, among them* Conus textile, *can cause serious or even fatal poisoning in humans. If it is necessary to handle them at all, this should be done with great care, holding them by the large end only, and avoiding all contact with the soft parts of the snail. The bright red, 1cm long coral crab* Tetralia glaberrima *lives only among the branches of living coral, and is here pictured hiding in the branches of a bush of* Acropora. *The small red fish* Gobiodon citrinus *also makes its home here.*

of which they impale their prey and inject it with the paralyzing secretion of modified salivary glands. The paralyzed prey is
then swallowed whole. Those species feeding on fish have, as
one might expect, especially powerful venom, since they must
be able to paralyze a medium-sized fish within a few seconds to
prevent its escape; and some of these, including *C. textile*, have
caused human fatalities. Several other cones, including the
large *C. sumatrensis*, are found on coral reefs in the Gulf, but are
considered much less dangerous than *C. textile*. The other
widely distributed, dangerous cone, the map cone *C.
geographus*, has so far not been reported from the Gulf.

Fish of the Coral Reef

The best-known coral reef animals are undoubtedly the fish,
which populate the reef in a bewildering variety of color and
form, and which have long fascinated amateur aquarists, underwater photographers and scientists alike. The Gulf reef-fish,
like most other groups of organisms, are limited in variety as
compared to the reef fishes of the Red Sea or Indian Ocean, but
are nevertheless much more diverse than is generally supposed,
and include several species not found elsewhere.

Reef fishes use the myriad holes and crannies of the reef as
hiding places, living quarters and sometimes nesting sites. They
also enter into many specialized relationships with the corals
themselves, as well as with other reef animals, in order to gain
nourishment. A good example of this type of trophic
relationship is provided by the colorful butterflyfish
(Chaetodontidae). Most of them feed either on the living coral
polyps themselves, or on small plankton animals snatched
away from the coral polyps. Three species are common in the
Gulf. Of these, the brilliant orange *Chaetodon melapterus* (Fig
117), and the russet brown *Chaetodon nigropunctatus*, are found
only in association with living coral communities, whereas the
flagfish *Heniochus acuminatus* is less specialized in its choice of
habitat, and is regularly found around artificial structures as
well as on coral reefs.

*Fig 115. Callyodon guttatus is one of several
species of parrot fish found in the Gulf. The color
patterns of these beautiful fish vary so much according to the age and sex of the fish that males,
females and young have often been thought to
belong to different species. [The specimen
illustrated was 21cm long.*

Closely related to butterflyfish are the angelfish, of which the blue *Pomacanthus maculosus,* with its conspicuous orange blaze mark, is one of the most ubiquitous of all Gulf fish (Fig 185). This species is even abundant around rocky outcrops in hypersaline bays at over $60^0/_{00}$ salinity. The imperial angelfish *Pomacanthus imperator,* and the blue-and-orange banded *Pygoplites diacanthus,* are much less abundant and usually confine themselves to the vicinity of coral reefs.

Another typical group of reef-fish, the surgeonfish, possess one or more pairs of folding, razor-sharp bony "knives" at the base of their tail. These weapons are used in self-defense, as well as in fighting between members of the same species. Surgeonfish are vegetarian, grazing on soft algae, and are most commonly seen on the outer reef flat and reef edge where such algae abound. *Acanthurus sohal,* the larger of the two local species, can be recognized by its pattern of lengthwise pinstripes on a blue-black background, highlighted by markings of electric blue, beige and bright yellow. *Zebrasoma xanthurus* (Fig 116) is even more strikingly colored, being deep indigo with bright yellow tail and pectoral fins. Distantly related to surgeonfish are the triggerfish, so named for the locking arrangement of their dorsal fin spines, by means of which they can wedge themselves into coral crevices and resist the efforts of the strongest predator to pull them out. *Sufflamen albicaudatum* is a warm brown color, with conspicuous white markings in its tail fin. Another common local triggerfish is *Rhinecanthus aculeatus,* whose bizarre color pattern has given it the popular name of "Picasso fish."

Another major group of reef fish is the wrasses and their relatives, which are usually brilliantly colored in shades of blue and green. These fish glide rapidly among the corals propelled by rowing motions of their pectoral fins, rather than by the more usual body undulations. This method of locomotion is also characteristic of many other reef fishes, notably the surgeonfish. Extremely widespread and abundant locally is the green wrasse *Thalassoma lunare,* which like many others of this group wears several different color patterns at different stages in its life history. Another strikingly colored wrasse is the cleaner fish *Labroides dimidiatus,* black with a broad stripe of iridescent blue running the length of its body. *Labroides* spends most of its time picking off tiny parasites from the body surface of other fish, which actively seek out the stations occupied by the cleaner, and adopt various peculiar postures as a signal that they are ready to be cleaned.

Parrot fish are large wrasse relatives that have become specialized feeders on dead or living coral, and have evolved extremely powerful jaws and a parrot-like beak. This enables them to bite off chunks of solid coral (Fig 110), with a crunching sound that can be heard a long way underwater. The organic parts of the coral are digested and the remainder is voided in the form of sand, which makes a substantial contribution to the sand supply on the reef. The common local parrotfish are species of *Callyodon,* which in the adult stage are

Fig 116. Zebrasoma xanthurus *is a local species of surgeonfish commonly seen grazing on the reef flat and reef edge. Like other surgeonfish it feeds mainly on algae. [Jana Island]*

Fig 117. *The orange butterflyfish* Chaetodon melapterus, *which always swims in pairs, is a common sight on the reef. In this picture two species of staghorn coral* Acropora *can also be seen. [reef slope, Jana Island]*

Fig 118. A small nesting colony of Lesser Crested Terns Sterna bengalensis, *showing close spacing of the eggs. [Karan Island]*

beautifully colored in pastel shades of blue, green and orange (Fig 115). Like the wrasses, parrotfish go through striking changes of color and pattern during their life history, and males, females and young look so different from one another that they are frequently thought to belong to different species.

Among the hundreds of other fish species found on local coral reefs are the damselfish group, which includes the sergeant major *Abudefduf saxatilis* with its vertical black stripes on a bronzy background, as well as the anemone-fish *Amphiprion* living in giant sea anemones. *Pseudochromis persicus* is an elongate small fish colored fluorescent blue on the upper and front parts of its body, and fiery orange on the lower and rear parts. Of the various groupers or sea-bass, *Cephalopholis miniatus* (Fig 119) is a small crimson-red or brownish species covered all over with iridescent blue polka-dots. *Cephalopholis rogaa* is another small species, dark blackish-brown with a conspicuous reddish or orange mouth. Larger, blackish groupers with indistinct light spots are either *Epinephelus coeruleopunctatus* (Fig 163), locally known as sub-aitee or burtam, with a high forehead, square-cut tail fin and generally bluish color tones, or *E. summana* locally known as summan, with a low forehead, large golden eye, rounded tail fin and predominantly warm brownish coloration.

CORAL ISLANDS AS SANCTUARIES

The unique significance of coral islands, as protected breeding places for birds (Fig 118) and marine turtles, has already been mentioned. These animals are extremely vulnerable to a variety of terrestrial predators, as well as to human interference, and the Gulf populations are entirely dependent on the sanctuary of a small number of offshore islands for their continued existence. The nature of this dependence is well illustrated by the life history of the green turtle.

Fig 119. Cephalopholis miniatus *is a small, brilliantly colored grouper and one of the most characteristic fish of the coral reef. [The illustrated specimen was 27cm.]*

Turtles

There are seven living species of sea turtles, of which two are common in the Gulf. The green turtle *Chelonia mydas* is the commonest species locally; the hawksbill turtle *Eretmochelys imbricata* is a smaller species and less abundant in local waters. The leatherback or leathery turtle *Dermochelys coriacea*, the largest of all sea turtles, sometimes over 200cm in length and weighing more than 540kg, is at best an occasional visitor. The loggerhead *Caretta caretta* has been recorded from Bahrain (Gallagher, 1971).

Sea turtles are widely distributed in the Gulf. From May through September, gatherings of several hundred individuals are found in the vicinity of certain offshore islands where the females deposit their eggs. Individual green turtles may be sighted at any time of the year in the vicinity of the sea grass pastures on which they feed. They are commonly seen in Tarut Bay, and occasionally get caught in shrimp trawls.

The remarkable breeding biology of sea turtles is well studied, and several popular accounts are available (e.g. Carr, 1967). After attaining sexual maturity, at an age of about six years, a female green turtle visits the nesting grounds on a regular cycle, usually every third year though individuals with two- and four-year cycles also occur. This involves a migration of at least several hundred kilometers from the feeding grounds. During an approximately two-month stay near the nesting beach, each female goes ashore four or five times, at intervals of about thirteen days, and each time lays a clutch of about 100 eggs. During the early part of the nesting season males also frequent the vicinity of the nesting beaches, and mating takes place in the water at this time. The males, however, do not go ashore.

Egg laying always occurs at night. Nesting (Figs 121–125) involves an elaborate, largely stereotyped instinctive sequence of actions, one result of which is to conceal the actual nest site very effectively beneath quantities of loose sand.

Green turtle nests are readily recognized by the deep body pits left behind by each nesting female (Fig 120), as well as by tracks going up the beach and back down again. The eggs,

JOHN HARDY

Fig 120. Body pits excavated by nesting turtles are a common sight on the beaches of the offshore islands. [Karan Island]

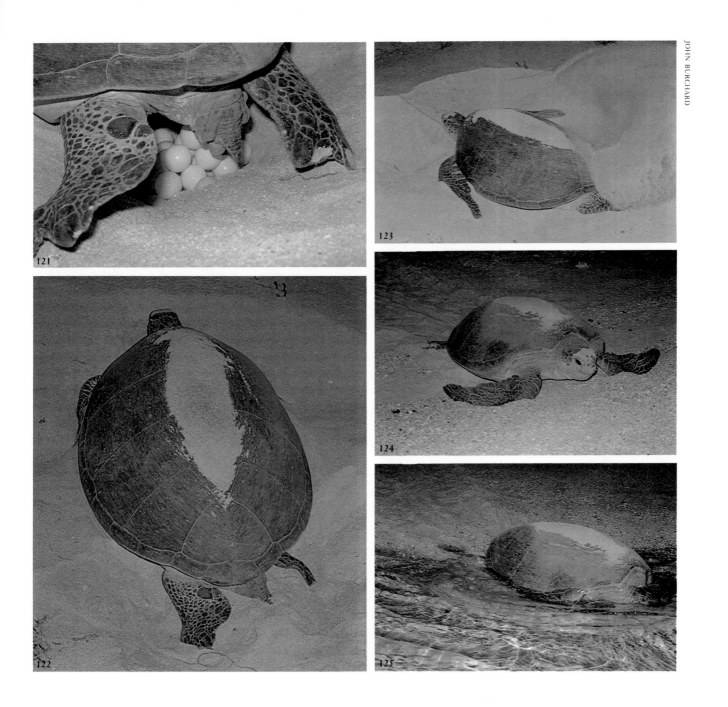

Figs 121–125. The female turtle prepares a "body pit" with great sweeps of her front flippers and after excavating a flask-shaped nest with her hind flippers, proceeds to fill it with eggs (121). After covering over the nest and carefully patting down the sand over the eggs (122) she conceals the nest site by throwing sand behind her until she has moved the body pit several meters from its original location (123). She then heads down to the shore (124) and into the water (125). [Karan Island]

139

Fig 126. Ghost crabs Ocypode saratan *also prey heavily on baby turtles. [Karan Island]*

Fig 127. House mice Mus musculus *are now very abundant on the offshore islands. They are important predators of baby turtles and turtle eggs; here, one is seen carrying off a newly-hatched green turtle which it has just captured and killed. [Karan Island]*

however, are buried some distance away from the final location of the visible pit, and so are well concealed from most potential predators. A clutch of eggs takes roughly 50 days to hatch. Heat of incubation is provided both by the sun and by the metabolic activity of the growing embryos, which results in the nest being measurably hotter than its immediate surroundings.

After hatching, the baby turtles rest for a while, and then make their way, over a period of several days, to the surface of the sand. Digging to the surface is a group activity, requiring the co-operative efforts of a certain minimum number of baby turtles. If too few hatch in a given clutch, none of them will be able to reach the surface. Under normal conditions at least 50% of the eggs hatch, and most of these young reach the surface. The babies emerge from the sand, rapidly proceed straight to the water, and then swim at top speed directly out to sea.

On emerging from the nest, baby turtles must run a formidable gantlet of predators. Mass predation by sea birds has been well publicized in various documentary films; but on the Gulf islands, at least, most babies emerge at night and so largely escape the attentions of the birds. Numbers of baby turtles, are however, captured and eaten on the island beaches by ghost crabs *Ocypode saratan*, hermit crabs *Coenobita* sp. and feral house-mice *Mus musculus*, all of which are very abundant (Figs 126 & 127). In the sea predation is even more intense, and on calm summer nights an observer on shore can hear the splash and gulp of groupers and other fish snapping up the baby turtles as they swim full-tilt for the open sea. Mass nesting is practiced by all species of marine turtles, and produces so many young in such a short time that they swamp the eating capacity of the local predators, even when these gather in swarms around the nesting beaches. In this case putting all the eggs in one basket is only apparently wasteful, since it actually increases the chances of survival of any individual baby turtle. From an evolutionary point of view, mass nesting is a successful system; sea turtles are (or rather, were until very recently) abundant and widespread animals. The nesting aggregations are, however, extremely vulnerable to various kinds of interference by man.

The whereabouts and activities of young turtles during their first year of life are a mystery, since no one has ever seen or captured one at this stage of development. On the basis of rather indirect and circumstantial evidence, however, it is thought that they inhabit the surface of the open sea, perhaps frequenting masses of floating gulfweed *Sargassum*, and feed on animal matter. At a shell-length of about 30cm – presumed from the growth rates of turtles in captivity to represent an age of about one year – they appear on the feeding pastures, and live thereafter on a diet consisting mainly of sea grasses. Their largely vegetarian habits contrast with those of most other species of sea turtles, which remain carnivorous throughout life.

Size relationships are noteworthy. An adult female green turtle averages about 100cm in shell-length, and weighs 125kg or more. A newly hatched baby is about 5cm long and weighs only about 23g. If mature size is really attained at six years, this means that the green turtle has a yearly rate of weight increase of roughly 419%.

The Gulf turtle population breeds mainly on Karan, Jana, Kurayn and Jurayd islands, in descending order of importance. A little breeding occurs on other islands, and also on certain mainland beaches. Breeding success on the mainland is low, however, due largely to human interference. Both adult and half-grown turtles are often seen on local sea grass pastures from Safaniya to al'Uqayr, but the bulk of the population probably migrates to more distant feeding grounds.

Feeding turtles are seen in grassbed areas off the coast of the southern Arabian Gulf, and especially in the large grass beds along the west coast of Pakistan and India, where they are harvested commercially. Breeding of green turtles does not occur in those areas, and it is possible that the commercially important turtle population of India and Pakistan may in fact be based on the Arabian Gulf breeding sites. This hypothesis would be confirmed by recovery on the southern Gulf coast or Indian Ocean feeding pastures of turtles tagged on the Saudi Arabian nesting beaches. Accordingly, Aramco biologists have initiated a program of tagging nesting female turtles, and it is hoped to expand the tagging operations in the future (Fig 128).

Besides green turtles *Chelonia mydas*, hawksbill turtles *Eretmochelys imbricata* also use the islands as breeding sites. This is the species from which true tortoise-shell is obtained and its populations, like those of the green turtle, have been critically depleted by over-exploitation in many parts of the world. It is fairly common in the Gulf, but much less abundant than the green turtle. Hawksbills are considerably smaller than their near relatives the green turtles, and feed on various kinds of marine animal life. On the island beaches their nests can usually be recognized by being much shallower than the deep, conical pits excavated by green turtles. Scattered observations indicate that nesting of the hawksbill turtle takes place slightly earlier in the year than that of the green turtle. Hawksbills in the Gulf appear to nest from April to July, while the green turtle nesting season runs from May or June through most of September. Apart from this, little information is available on the biology of this species in the Gulf.

Status of Turtle Populations

In spite of their high egg production, which in the case of the green turtle amounts to about 500 eggs per female per three-year breeding cycle, turtle populations are easily depleted by over-exploitation or by disturbance of their habitat. This sensitivity to disturbance is partly due to the tremendous natural mortality of the young turtles, and partly to the very specific requirements of the adults, especially their complete dependence on a few specific sites for breeding. According to present estimates, for example, about 80% of the entire Saudi Arabian population of green turtles uses Karan Island for

Fig 128. This female green turtle has just had a numbered, stainless steel tag attached at the base of her fore flipper. The subsequent finding and returning of such tags is the only way in which scientists have been able to trace the long-distance migratory movements of these animals. [Karan Island]

Fig 129. Lesser Crested Terns nest in dense colonies on the beach flat, where each pair incubates a single egg. Soon after hatching, the young congregate in a flock or "creche" near the water's edge, where they are fed by their parents until fledging. [Karan Island]

Fig 130. Nests of the White-Cheeked Tern are well spaced out on the beach flat, and are often neatly built of twigs. Two eggs is the usual complement, and the young remain near the nest during the fledging period. [Karan Island]

Fig 131. Bridled Terns conceal their nests at the base of shrubs, on the vegetated parts of the island. The single young remains hidden in the nest until fledged. [Karan Island]

breeding. Since turtle eggs, baby turtles and even the adult females on the beach have no real protection against many kinds of predators common on mainland beaches, turtle nesting grounds are often located on small islands. The accidental introduction by man of dogs, rats, or other animals has decimated turtle populations on many of these island refuges. On the Gulf islands, house-mice *Mus musculus* are extremely abundant, probably introduced from local fishing boats, and cause significant losses of eggs and baby turtles.

Female turtles are easily captured while nesting, and commercial exploitation of turtle populations in various parts of the world has usually centered around the nesting beaches. Since every butchered female is permanently prevented from reproducing, this represents a most inefficient and destructive way of utilizing turtles as a resource. The uncontrolled slaughter of nesting females, has, in fact, already reduced populations of the commercially valuable turtle species, and especially of the green and hawksbill turtles, to near extinction in most parts of the world. Only further study can clarify the status of the Gulf populations, and determine whether or not they are holding their own. On the basis of rather limited observations, it appears that only small numbers of nesting female green turtles are caught on the beaches by local fishermen to obtain turtle steak and/or the unlaid eggs. Substantial losses of incubating eggs are, however, probably caused by the practice of some fishermen of searching for buried eggs by poking a long stick into the sand. Puncturing one or more eggs is likely to cause loss of the entire clutch due to fungus growth. Probably many nests are so destroyed for each one found and excavated by the fishermen.

Whether or not the present level of such interference is adversely affecting the turtle population, it is clear that any large increase in this kind of human activity on the nesting beaches would result in the rapid disappearance of sea turtles from the Gulf. Although not the world's largest, the green turtle population using the Saudi Arabian nesting sites does represent a significant resource of extremely high quality animal protein. The rational and efficient utilization of such a resource involves strict protection of the nesting females, and the carefully controlled harvest of a very limited proportion of the eggs or hatchling turtles. They are then reared to market size in captivity, on so-called turtle ranches, using a combination of natural and artificial foods (FAO, 1973). Pending the development of such a program, however, the main consideration in a Saudi Arabian turtle conservation scheme must be the control of human interference at the nesting sites.

Birds and Other Animals

Terns form another animal group heavily dependent on the coral islands for their continued existence. There are many species of these seabirds in the Gulf, but three in particular nest in vast numbers on the islands. These are the Lesser Crested Tern *Sterna bengalensis* (Fig 132), the White-Cheeked Tern

Fig 132. Lesser Crested Terns Sterna bengalensis *over their nesting site. [Karan Island]*

Fig 133. Sunset on Jana Island.

Sterna repressa and the Bridled Tern *Sterna anaethetus*.[2] All three species occur together on most of the islands, but each has distinctive nesting habits (Figs 129, 130 & 131).

Besides terns, which breed in summer, several other species of birds use the islands for breeding, notably various species of plover *Charadrius* spp., and land birds such as larks. These birds also breed on the mainland, however, and unlike the terns are not strictly dependent upon the islands. At migration time in spring and in fall the islands are visited by a great number and variety of shore and land birds, including herons, a variety of waders, several species of hawks and falcons, and indeed most of the birds familiar as winter visitors to Arabia. Most of these birds migrate across the Gulf, and the islands serve as stop-over points.

Some terrestrial animals also inhabit the islands. These include a considerable variety of insects and spiders, which have not been studied in any detail, a couple of species of lizards, and innumerable mice.

The sandy and rocky beaches of the islands support the same types of organisms as these biotopes elsewhere. Conspicuous among beach animals are the tower-building ghost crab *Ocypode saratan* on sand beaches, and turban snails *Turbo* sp. on the algae-covered rocks. Several species of intertidal animals which are either uncommon or absent on the mainland beaches are abundant on the islands. These include the large rock-dwelling crabs *Eriphia sebana smithii* and *Grapsus tenuicrustatus*, frequently seen running about the exposed rocks at night. Another beach animal common on the islands, but not so far found on the Gulf coast of the mainland, is a large, terrestrial hermit crab *Coenobita* sp. which clambers about the rocks at night in large groups, apparently feeding on algae. During the daytime it buries itself in the damp sand near high tide mark. Like *Ocypode*, *Coenobita* captures and eats baby turtles when it encounters them.

At present the offshore islands of the Gulf, with their coral reefs, present a picture of unspoiled beauty (Fig 133). Their plant and animal populations are rich and unique, and are exceptionally beautiful and instructive as well as being of great scientific interest. Much of the beauty and uniqueness of these sites, however, results from the fact that they have so far remained relatively free from human interference. They represent a valuable, fragile and irreplaceable resource, whose preservation for the benefit, enjoyment and instruction of future generations will demand increasingly careful attention in the face of the rapid development of industry, population and recreational activity now taking place in the Gulf.

2 The Lesser Crested Tern is mostly white, with a pale grey "mantle," a black cap, and a conspicuous large yellow bill. The White-Cheeked Tern is smaller, leaden grey both above and below, with a white cheek, a black cap and dark orange-red bill. The Bridled Tern is of medium size, noticeably slender and long winged, with the upper side dark chocolate-brown, a black cap separated from the brown back by a white ring or "bridle," white underparts, and a blackish bill.

Fig 134. Platform 25 in the Berri Field. Such structures support a rich growth of "fouling" organisms, and form an important habitat for marine life in the Gulf.

7
ARTIFICIAL STRUCTURES

Almost any man-made object placed in the sea is soon colonized by marine organisms. Ships, buoys, piers, pipelines and oil production platforms, to name only a few, all become covered with marine growth within a short time. On ships, especially, such growth is unwelcome, since it causes greatly increased friction with the surrounding water; and the regular removal of "marine fouling" is a key item of ship maintenance. The manufacture of paints and coatings, designed to repel or prevent fouling, has become a major industry. Another economically important aspect of marine fouling is the destruction of wooden ships, pilings, bulkheads, etc, by the boring activities of certain marine animals, especially the shipworms *Teredo* and *Bankia* and the gribble *Limnoria*.

There is, however, a positive side to fouling growth. Stationary, man-made structures such as oil production platforms, which are initially barren of life, soon become coated by a dense and complex community of fouling organisms, which furnishes food and shelter to a variety of invertebrates and fish. Within a few years such a structure assumes the status of an "artificial reef" and becomes the focal point for a marine life community especially rich in desirable game-fish and food-fish. Sport fishermen and skin divers in various parts of the world have not been slow to take advantage of this.

Artificial structures are made of hard materials such as steel, concrete or sometimes wood. As might be expected, the organisms colonizing them generally belong to species typical of hard-bottom biotopes. As a rule, however, the fouling community constitutes a distinctive entity or species mixture, and is not simply a variant of one of the hard-bottom communities. This is because artificial structures, especially the larger ones

Fig 135. Gorgonian corals at about 20m depth on an oil platform leg. This species has the largest biomass of any fouling organism on the platform, and completely dominates the community below 12m depth. [Berri Well 25]

*Fig 136. The climax community on oil plat-
forms in the Gulf is dominated by filter feeding
animals such as oysters, gorgonians and
sponges, of which several species are seen here at
about 15m depth. [Berri Well 25]*

such as oil production platforms, offer a combination of environmental conditions different from that of any naturally occurring biotope. Oil production platforms in the Gulf, for example, are populated by a mixture of species from several different types of intertidal and subtidal rock biotopes, and from coral reefs. Some of these organisms are much more abundant on the platform legs than in their original habitat. This is due not only to the differing physical environmental conditions on the platform, but probably also to reduced competition there, since not all species of the natural biotopes succeed in establishing themselves on platforms. For example, rock-boring animals are unable to colonize steel or concrete, though some of them may eventually invade the shells of oysters or barnacles growing on a platform leg. Scleractinian corals, which are certainly one of the most important groups of animals inhabiting shallow hard-bottom biotopes in the Gulf, also appear to have little success in colonizing the steel pilings of oil platforms. The reasons for this are not yet known.

Fouling communities show a well-defined "ecological succession"; i.e., the composition of the community changes in an orderly way with time. Some fouling organisms, known as pioneers, can attach themselves directly to a clean, bare surface. Most species, however, can establish themselves only after the surface has been modified by the growth of pioneer organisms. As a result, when a new artificial structure is installed in the sea, its surface is occupied by a succession of different communities, in a definite and predictable sequence. In general, each consecutive community in the succession will have a greater diversity of species and a larger biomass than the communities it replaces. The size of the largest individual organisms also tends to increase. Eventually a more or less stable "climax" or mature community composition is reached, which tends to persist thereafter without major changes.[1] Similar patterns of succession also occur on natural substrates if the established climax community is destroyed or removed.

The early stages of such a succession can be illustrated by an experiment which was carried out by Aramco biologists in Tarut Bay. Small glass plates were exposed below the surface and at the end of two weeks were coated by a fouling community consisting almost entirely of diatoms and other very small algae, with a few small barnacles *Balanus amphitrite*. By the end of three weeks' exposure, about 50% of the surface was occupied by barnacles; also present were numerous hydroid colonies up to 5cm long, tube-dwelling polychaete worms, and a few amphipods and other small Crustacea. After six weeks' exposure, barnacles covered nearly 100% of the surface of the plates and most of the hydroids had disappeared. Amphipods were extremely numerous, occurring at the rate of several individuals per square centimeter of surface, and other animals included pearl oysters up to about 15mm diameter, small swimming crabs, etc.

1 In some cases the "climax" may consist of a cyclic alternation of communities, rather than a steady state condition.

Another feature of marine growth on artificial structures is a well-defined vertical zonation, since the composition of the fouling community is profoundly affected by light, water movement and other factors which change systematically with the depth. In fact, artificial structures offer a particularly good opportunity for studying the depth zonation of Gulf marine life (Fig 145). The vertical or near-vertical pilings of oil production platforms provide, at one location, a uniform surface over a range of depths from the surface to the sea bed, in a way not matched by any of the natural habitats of the gently sloping Saudi Arabian shore.

Artificial structures are numerous and ecologically important in the Gulf. Aramco, alone, has over 350 offshore producing platforms and other oil-well structures, as well as various port installations and navigational aids. During the preparation of this book, two representative structures were examined in some detail. These were the floating pier at the Sandy Hook Yacht Association in Tarut Bay, and an offshore oil-well platform about 24km NNE of Jubail.

FLOATING PIER IN TARUT BAY

The pier at the Sandy Hook Yacht Association at Ras Tanura is a wooden structure supported by sealed, air-filled sections of steel pipe. It rises and falls with the tide, and consequently the water level on the pontoons themselves is always about the same. The pier is located in the lee of the Ras Tanura spit, where wave action is minimal. Fouling communities, especially algae, on the curving sides of the pontoons were studied throughout the year.

A greater number of species of algae was obtained from the Yacht Club pier than from any other biotope studied by Aramco biologists so far. One factor in producing this somewhat surprising result was probably especially favorable chemical and physical conditions in the water. Tarut Bay waters are relatively rich in nutrients and a considerable range of temperatures is available during the course of the year. Another contributing factor may be that the pontoons are always at the same depth in the water, so that the algae are never subject to desiccation as a result of tidal action.

The tubular pontoons are 60cm in diameter and float with slightly more than half their diameter below water. A marked vertical zonation of organisms is evident along the curve of the immersed portion. Algae dominate the fouling community within 15 to 20cm of the water surface, on the more or less vertical, well-illuminated sides of the pontoons. On the undersides, which receive very little light, the community is dominated by animal forms including brightly colored sponges, tunicates, bryozoans and hydroids. A gradual transition connects these two types of communities, and in the intermediate region algae and sessile animals occur intermixed. Abundant small animal life, especially amphipod Crustacea and blenniid fish, is found among the algae.

Fig 137. Ceramium luetzelburgii is a filamentous red alga common in the Arabian Gulf. The filaments of this species have characteristic pincer-shaped tips. [Sandy Hook Yacht Club]

Fig 138. Centroceras clavulatum, is a beautifully tiered red alga in which one or more branches arise at the distal end of each segment. This alga, like many others, provides a support for the attachment of other organisms. [Sandy Hook Yacht Club]

Fig 139. Hypnea cornuta is a much-branched red alga common in the Arabian Gulf. The star-shaped asexual reproductive bodies, called stichidia, are characteristic of this species. [Sandy Hook Yacht Club]

149

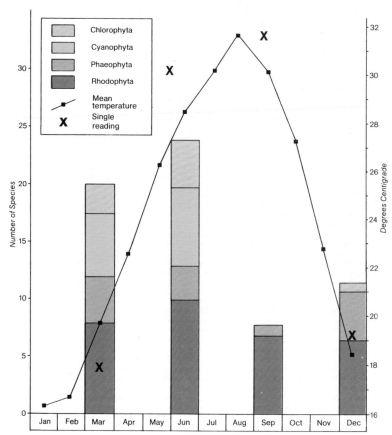

Fig 140. Number of species of macroalgae on the Ras Tanura Yacht Association pier and seasonal surface sea water temperature means. (Ras Tanura mean surface sea water temperatures outside bay taken daily at 0800, 1950 through 1974; single surface temperature readings taken in bay about 500 meters out from pier, 1975.)

The various groups of algae show an interesting seasonal cycle in the numbers of species present on the pier (Fig 140). Red algae are the dominant members of the algal community throughout the year, as may be expected in tropical or subtropical waters; but all types of algae show a dramatic decline in numbers in September, following peak water temperatures which are reached in August. The green and blue-green algae are apparently eliminated from the pier at this time, and do not begin to re-establish themselves until the cooler winter months.

OFFSHORE OIL PLATFORMS

The offshore platform selected for study is at Well 25 in the Berri oil field northeast of Jubail.[2] This platform stands in 31m of water and consists of a tripod structure with one vertical and two inclined legs, supporting a vertical conductor pipe. The tripod legs and conductor are all made of steel pipe about 75cm in diameter, tied together by cross members at several levels (Figs 134, 141 & 145).

2 At 27°12′23″N, 49°46′47″E.

Fig 141. The platform legs of Berri Well 25 at about 3m depth. Every available surface is encrusted with a dense growth of fouling organisms.

150

This structure was installed on the sea bed in January 1970, and the fouling communities were sampled and photographed a little more than five years later, in March and September 1975. Although little is yet known of the successional stages involved, it seems likely that these communities had reached a climax or near-climax state of development.

The first impression from a dive among the underwater parts of the platform structure is one of rich and varied marine life. The surface of the pilings is completely covered with sea growth, which on the deeper parts of the structure reaches a thickness of 30 to 50cm. Innumerable small fish, crabs, etc frequent this growth. Near the surface, shoals of small and medium-sized fish hover near and among the platform legs, while many large hamour lurk about the deeper parts of the structure, and schools of barracuda and other predators patrol the waters just outside. Schools of tuna, jacks, king mackerel and other pelagic species are frequent visitors, and some will be seen during almost any dive at the platform.

Closer examination shows that marine growth on the platform legs is arranged in a series of concentric layers around the steel piling itself. The structural base or inner supporting framework of the fouling community is made up of permanently sessile, hard-shelled organisms, especially barnacles and several kinds of oysters. The outer layers consist largely of softer organisms, especially sponges, various algae and gorgonians. Each of the dominant species, furthermore, has its own characteristic pattern of vertical distribution, so that the fouling community shows a vertical series of distinctly different-looking zones.

Vertical Distribution of Fouling Organisms

BARNACLES are among the first organisms to settle on a newly erected structure, and they provide an important part of the hard calcareous base on which the remainder of the fouling community grows. Two species are very abundant on the platform at Berri Well 25. A small species, tentatively identified as *Balanus amphitrite*, occurs in vast numbers throughout the intertidal zone, and less abundantly in the first 2 or 3m below low tide level. In the lower intertidal zone this species covers 50 to 95% of the available piling surface. The largest individuals are about 1cm in diameter at the base. The other, much larger species has been tentatively identified as *Balanus tintinnabulum* (Fig 142). Average individuals are about 4cm across the base and 5 to 8cm high, and occasional specimens grow considerably larger. This species is found attached to the platform legs at all depths from about 2m to the bottom. Living specimens are abundant, however, only in the depth range between 3 and about 8m. At greater depths almost all the barnacles are dead, and overgrown by other organisms. The maximum numbers occur between 3 and 6m, and in this region barnacles may cover up to 40% of the available piling surface.

The restricted depth range of living *B. tintinnabulum*, as compared with dead specimens, results from their role as

Fig 142. Barnacles Balanus tintinnabulum *encrusting an oil platform piling at about 4m depth. Small bivalves can be seen near the left side of the piling just below the middle, as well as sponges in shades of orange, lavender and white.* [Berri Well 25]

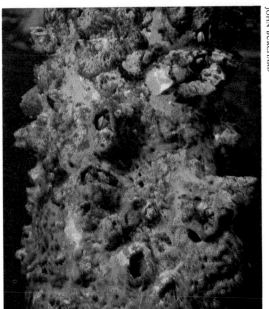

151

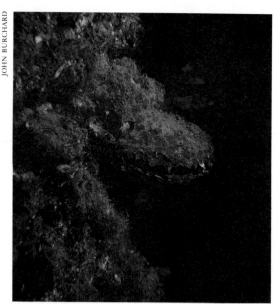

Fig 143. Pearl oyster Pinctada margaritifera *about 20cm across, attached to a piling of an oil platform. Note barnacles attached at the base of the oyster valve, and other encrusting organisms. [Berri Well 25 at 6m depth]*

Fig 144. Oysters Lopha cristagalli *(left, with zig-zag aperture) and* Crassostraea *sp. (right, with sinuous aperture), with sponges and sparse growth of gorgonians, at 10m depth. [Berri Well 25]*

pioneers of the fouling community. On a very similar platform at Berri Well 70/75, examined 20 months after installation on the sea bed, this species was almost equally abundant at all depths from 2m to the bottom at 33m; at that time other dominant members of the fouling community, particularly oysters and gorgonians, had not yet become established in significant numbers on the platform.

OYSTERS of several kinds are the other main constituent of the fouling community "skeleton." Both numerically and structurally, the most important of these are species which live with one valve permanently cemented to the supporting substrate. This group includes several different types, with differing depth preferences. The most abundant, and at the same time the most distinctive in appearance, is a cocks-comb oyster[3] with its shell aperture folded into a remarkable zig-zag shape (Fig 144). This species occurs from a depth of 10m to the bottom, with a maximum abundance at about 15m. *Spondylus exilis* is a large, thick-shelled, dome-shaped oyster with a straight aperture. It is found from about 6m to the bottom, but is less abundant than *Lopha*. Large species of *Crassostraea* and *Saxostraea* also occur on the pilings. A smaller oyster, particularly firmly cemented to the substrate, is *Chama* sp.

Another type of oyster, instead of being cemented to the substrate, is attached by a bundle of tough threads called "byssus." The best-known members of this group are the pearl oysters *Pinctada radiata* and *P. margaritifera*, both of which occur on the platform legs between 3 and 10m depth. Neither species is particularly abundant on the platform, but some individuals, especially of the black-lip *P. margaritifera*, reach exceptionally large size in this biotope. A black-lip oyster 22cm in diameter was found at 6m depth on the structure at Berri Well 25 (Fig 143). Very large individuals of the black bird oyster *Pteria* sp. also occur in this depth range.

GORGONIANS probably have the largest biomass of any fouling organism at Berri Well 25. A single, as yet unidentified species dominates the community throughout some 60% of the total depth range occupied by the structure. This organism takes the form of a branching bush, which in life is bright red and covered with white, star-like expanded polyps (Figs 135, 136, 138 & 144). These capture plankton by means of their eight feathery tentacles. The "bush" is supported by an internal skeleton of horny material, which remains after the death of the gorgonian and can serve as a substrate for the attachment of other fouling organisms.

Gorgonians are confined to the deeper parts of the platform structure. The main species forms a dense growth, completely dominating the fouling community, from 12m depth nearly to the bottom. This growth is most luxuriant at about 20m depth. Small, scattered colonies occur between 10 and 12m depth,

3 Tentatively identified as *Lopha cristagalli.* Other authorities have identified this species as *Hyotissa hyotis*, or as *Dendrostraea* sp.

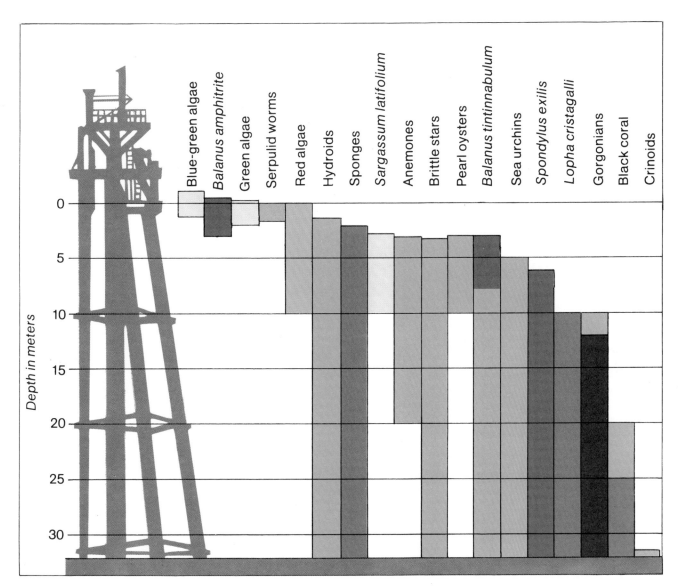

Fig 145. Vertical distribution of plants (green) and animals (ochre, brown and maroon) on Berri Well 25, an offshore oil platform. The dominance of different organisms at different depths is indicated by lighter and darker colors, with the darkest color indicating the greatest dominance. Thus, gorgonians dominate the community from 12m depth to the bottom.

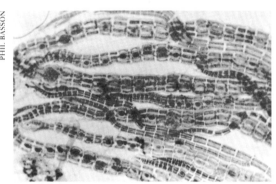

Fig 146. Black coral at 25 m depth. [Berri Well 25]

Fig 147. Polysiphonia variegata *belongs to a common and widely occurring genus of red algae. Here the tetraspores, visible as rounded dark bodies, are developed within the axis of the plant, rather than in specialized reproductive structures as in* Dasya. *[Berri Well 25]*

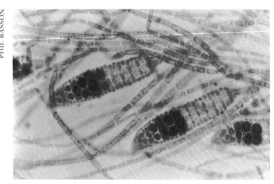

Fig 148. Reproductive structures of the highly-developed red alga Dasya ocellata, *showing several elongate sporangia containing dark, rounded clusters of tetraspores. The cleavage lines separating individual spores can be seen clearly in some of the clusters. [Berri Well 25]*

and the species is absent at depths less than 10m. Gorgonians of several other species occur, but only in the form of scattered individual colonies, and at depths greater than about 15m.

BLACK CORAL (Fig 146) is another type of colonial coelenterate found on the platform legs, with an even more restricted depth distribution than gorgonians. Several colonies of this distinctive, but rather rare animal were found on the structure between 25m and the bottom. One small, stunted colony was found at about 20m depth.

ALGAE are another group showing a well-defined depth zonation. In the intertidal region of the platform legs, three species of blue-green algae[4] characteristically occur. Between the intertidal and a depth of about 3m, red algae[5] predominate, but one species of green alga[6] also occurs, as well as the brown alga *Ectocarpus irregularis.* The relatively conspicuous brown alga *Sargassum latifolium* is limited to the depth range between 3 and 10m. Other species found in this interval include *Ectocarpus* and the cosmopolitan red alga *Polysiphonia* (Fig 147). Below 10m, where reduced light intensity is unfavorable for plant growth, only the red *Dasya ocellata* (Fig 137) and one as yet unidentified green alga have been found.

SPONGES are actually one of the most important animal groups found on the artificial structure, and occur throughout the subtidal region, forming a thin coating – often brilliant red, orange or white (Fig 149) – over any available substrate. Sponges are most abundant between the surface and a depth of about 8m, and at 3m depth probably cover 80% of the entire available surface, including the shells of oysters and barnacles. At greater depths they are less abundant, or at any rate less conspicuous, since they are screened from view by the dense growth of gorgonians. Although many different species are certainly involved, and probably have distinctive depth preferences, the collected material has not yet been identified. A study of sponge zonation on Gulf artificial structures remains a challenge for future workers.

CRINOIDS or sea lilies (Fig 150) are picturesque relatives of the starfish and sea urchins. Two different, as yet unidentified species of the type known as comatulids or feather stars were found at the very bottom of the Berri Well 25 structure, clinging to various solid objects with their feathery "arms" spread out to catch plankton and detritus. At this depth they were active and feeding during the daytime, but animals of this type are normally nocturnal, and spend the day in places of concealment. It is possible, therefore, that at night crinoids would be found at higher levels on the platform.

4 *Oscillatoria limosa, O.* sp., *Spirulina subsalsa.*
5 *Ceramium transversale, Polysiphonia crassicolis* and the calcareous *Amphiroa fragilissima.*
6 *Cladophora* sp.

154

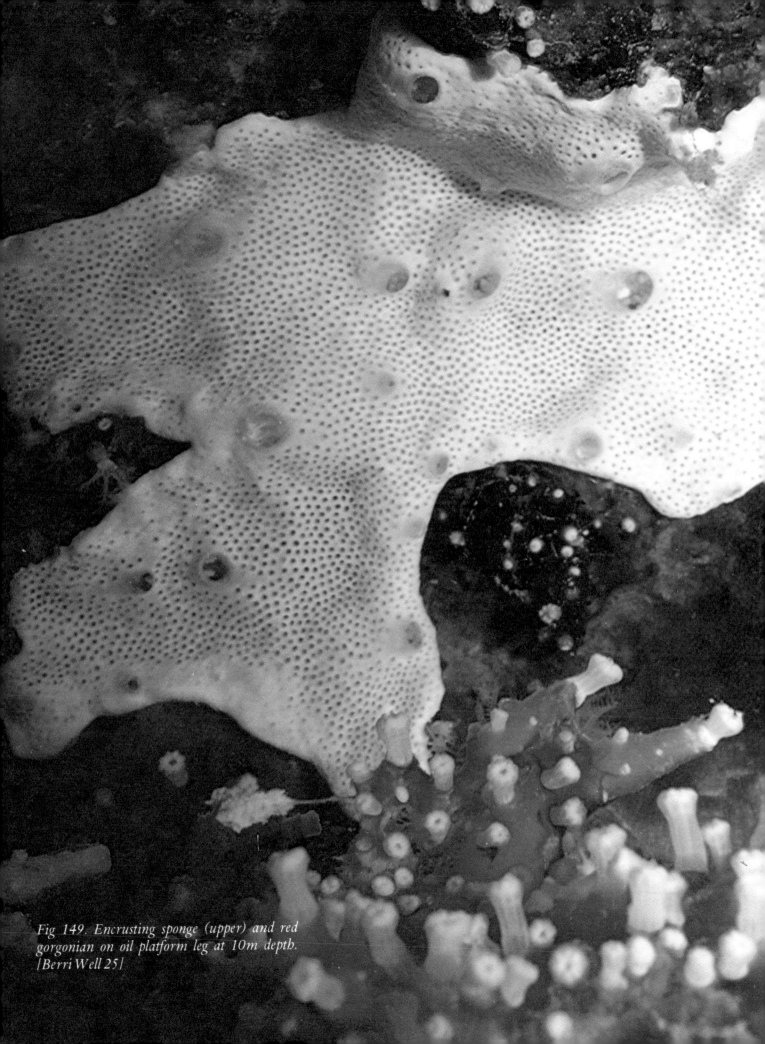

Fig 149. Encrusting sponge (upper) and red
gorgonian on oil platform leg at 10m depth.
[Berri Well 25]

Fig 150. Comatulid crinoid at 32m depth. [Berri Well 25]

HYDROIDS (Fig 151), tunicates and many other forms of sessile animal life were also observed or collected on the platform legs. Until the collected material has been more fully analyzed, however, it would be premature to make detailed statements about the identity or distribution of these organisms.

FISH are abundant and conspicuous around the platform, though many of them are not, strictly speaking, members of the fouling community. Some of the smaller kinds in particular, however, are dependent in highly specific ways on the marine growth around the pilings. Examples are certain blennies[7] which seem to live only in the empty shells of large barnacles, and at least one cardinal fish[8] which appears to occur only among the growths of gorgonians. Many other small and medium-sized fish probably have equally specific ecological ties to the platform fouling growth, though nothing is known of the details. Most of these are members of the coral reef fauna, such as the angelfish *Pomacanthus maculosus*, the flagfish *Heniochus acuminatus*, the butterflyfish *Chaetodon nigropunctatus*, the damselfish *Abudefduf saxatilis*, the batfish *Platax pinnatus*, the grouper *Cephalopholis miniatus*, and many others. Other inhabitants of the platform, especially larger ones, may have much less specific ecological affinities. An outstanding example is the hamour, which is found in almost all of the Gulf biotopes, though it is especially large and numerous around platforms.

The fish community associated with an artificial structure is not as diverse as that on a coral reef, but fish are numerous and often large. Predators such as hamour, barracuda, king mackerel, etc are obviously attracted to these structures and remain in their vicinity over long periods of time. Judging by the well-fed condition of such fish obtained around oil platforms in the Gulf, the main basis of this attraction is that the platforms provide a particularly favorable food supply.

The surface area of an oil platform fouling community is very limited, and much of it is not exposed to sunlight of sufficient intensity to support photosynthesis. Even on the upper and better-illuminated parts of the platform legs, furthermore, the fouling community is largely dominated by filter-feeding organisms such as sponges, oysters and barnacles, rather than by a luxuriant growth of algae. It is thus very unlikely that primary production of the fouling community is responsible for the undoubted effectiveness of a platform in enhancing the local fish population. Because of its massive populations of filter-feeding animals, however, a platform does provide a center where the plankton production of a considerable area of ocean can be transformed into small fish and invertebrates, which form an abundant and concentrated food supply for large predatory fish. These, in turn, provide sport and food for anglers and spearfishermen.

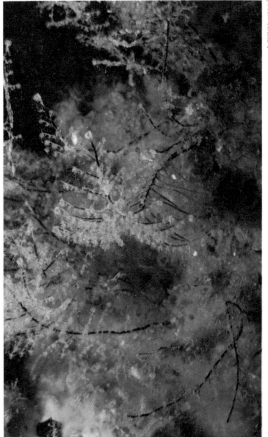

Fig 151. Colonial hydroid showing tentacles extended to catch small plankton organisms. [Berri Well 25]

7 As yet unidentified.
8 *Apogon* sp.

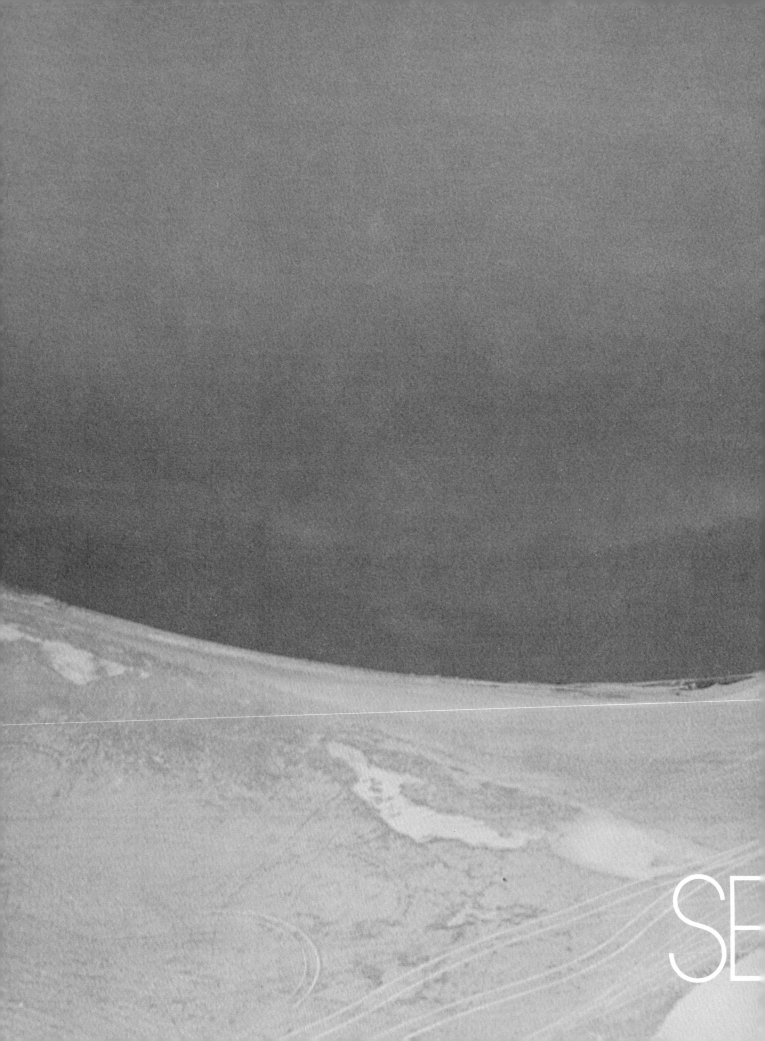

CTION THREE

In addition to the organisms which inhabit the shore (intertidal organisms) and those which inhabit the sea bottom at various depths (benthic organisms), there are organisms which carry on most or all of their life activities in the water column itself. The water column, or open sea, is able to support a more or less abundant plant life, which in turn provides sustenance for a variety of animals.

The main requirements for plant growth are adequate light and the availability of certain nutrient substances. Nutrients are generally available in sea water in quantities sufficient to support plant life, though concentrations vary and often limit the rate of growth. Light, however, is strictly limited to the uppermost layers of the sea: light intensities sufficient for photosynthesis penetrate to a maximum depth which varies from less than 20 to about 100m, depending on the clarity of the water. To take full advantage of the biological potential of the water column, therefore, organisms must be capable of remaining at a suitable depth without sinking into regions where no light penetrates. They accomplish this in one of two ways. Microscopic and near-microscopic organisms have a large surface area compared to their weight, and so sink very slowly, if at all. Plants and animals of this size drift about more or less passively with the movements of the water mass, and are known collectively as **plankton.** Large organisms, on the other hand, must literally sink or swim, and because vigorous locomotion requires an output of energy beyond the capacities of any large photosynthetic organism, plant life in the open water is mostly microscopic.

On the other hand, many kinds of animals have developed powerful locomotory abilities, and have taken to life in the open sea. The largest group of such pelagic animals are fish: tuna, mackerel, marlin and oceanic sharks, to name but a few. Other important open sea animals include whales and sea turtles, squids, jellyfish and deep-sea shrimps. Animals of this type are called **nekton,** or active swimmers, to distinguish them from the passively floating plankton. The distinction between the two categories is not clear-cut, since large plankton animals have appreciable swimming abilities, and some of the nekton, such as jellyfish, are relatively weak swimmers. Many nektonic animals are more or less dependent upon particular benthic biotopes, as for example the green turtle, a powerful swimmer capable of remarkable long-distance migrations, which requires sea-grass beds as a source of food. "Pelagic," however, is a somewhat narrower concept, implying that the animal so described spends most of its life actually in the open sea.

Finally, the term **neuston** is used to distinguish those organisms whose ecological relationships are primarily with the water surface film rather than with the water mass. Oceanic water-striders *Halobates* sp., and many microscopic algae are examples of this group.

Because the Arabian Gulf lies entirely within the continental shelf, deep-water animals and specialized open-ocean forms are at best accidental visitors to the Gulf.

Fig 152 (preceding page). A bloom of Dunaliella salina *colors the water blood red in the salt lake near Dawhat Zalum. In late summer numbers of this unicellular plant exceed 19 million per liter of water. Salinity exceeds 300⁰/₀₀. (Aerial photo by John Hardy)*

Even so, it is useful to distinguish three main sub-divisions or "provinces" of open-water biotopes within the Gulf, which have slight but significant physical and chemical differences and noticeably different plant and animal communities. These are the offshore province, including most of the waters of the Gulf deeper than about 15m, except where these lie close to shore; the nearshore or coastal province, including coastal waters out to about the 15m contour; and the bay province, including the waters of the numerous embayments and lagoon systems that occur along the Saudi Arabian coastline. Certain bay and lagoon waters, especially those partly or entirely cut off from the Gulf, have very high salinities, even when compared with the already high salinities of the Arabian Gulf in general. These are truly extreme environments, whose biological peculiarities merit their consideration as a distinct sub-province, the hypersaline biotope.

Both the relationships of organisms to their environment and the methods of studying these relationships are different for tiny, passively drifting planktonic plants and animals, as compared to the more strongly swimming nekton. For this reason the two categories of organisms have been dealt with separately, though they both may be said to belong to the same biotope.

The subject of Chapter 8 is **planktonic communities** of the offshore, nearshore and bay provinces, with special emphasis on the phytoplankton or plant members of these communities. Chapter 9 deals with a selection of typical **nekton organisms,** especially pelagic and semi-pelagic fish and dolphins. Chapter 10 is devoted to the peculiar biological communities found in **hypersaline environments,** which are probably better developed around the Arabian Gulf than anywhere else in the world.

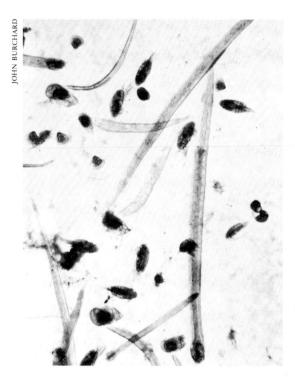

Fig 153. Part of a mixed sample of zooplankton showing both holoplankton and meroplankton of various sizes. Holoplanktic animals shown include elongate chaetognaths (arrow worms) about 1cm long, larvacean tunicates Oikopleura sp. with a 5mm long "tail" set at right angles to a pear-shaped body, and small copepods of several species. Meroplanktic forms include the larvae of gastropods, pelecypods and crabs.

Fig 154. This "pluteus" is the planktonic larval stage of an echinoderm (ophiuroid).

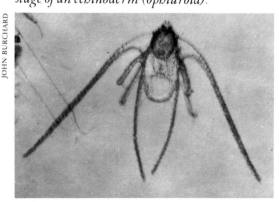

8
PLANKTON

Plankton is a term used to describe collectively small, mostly microscopic organisms which drift about passively in the water. Although tiny, most of the thousands of described species differ from one another in size, shape, color, mode of movement, method of reproduction, or life history. Their importance in marine ecology cannot be overemphasized, since they form the base of the food web upon which larger organisms, including fish, ultimately depend. Because they are small and can reproduce rapidly, the population abundance can change drastically over a period of only a few days in response to changing environmental conditions. Therefore, the physical properties of local water masses are discussed below in some detail. Plant and animal members are considered separately under the terms **phytoplankton** and **zooplankton,** respectively.

PHYTOPLANKTON, or photosynthetic micro-algae, are made up of representatives of at least five very diverse taxonomic groups within the plant kingdom. Like all plants, the photosynthetic phytoplankton convert light energy and carbon dioxide into organic material, and so represent the primary producers or "grass of the sea," forming the base of the food web upon which almost all marine animal life depends.

In marine waters the phytoplankton community is often dominated by diatoms – microscopic representatives of the plant phylum Chrysophyta which possess characteristic silica-impregnated cell walls (Fig 155). Some species are unicellular, while others have groups of cells in colonies. In some waters, especially in the tropics, the dinoflagellates, another group of microscopic plants, dominate. They belong to the plant phylum Pyrrophyta, contain a different set of pigments, and swim about by means of two flagella. In other areas, especially

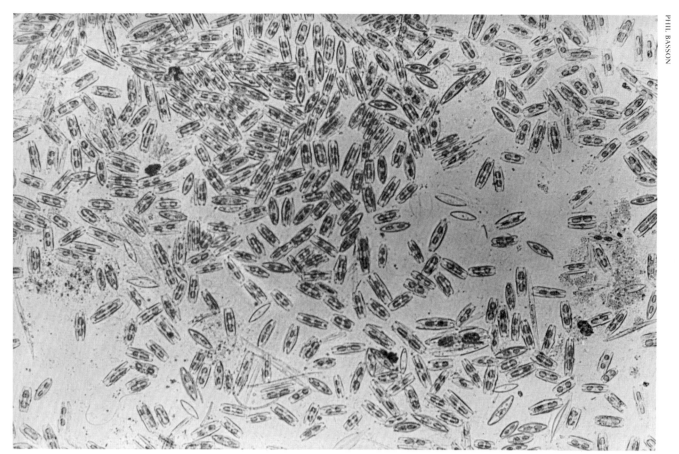

PHIL BASSON

Fig 155. Pennate diatoms of the genus Navicula *are found world-wide. Because of their mode of reproduction, these diatoms often form extensive "picket fence"-like colonies. Diatoms are often among the most important members of the phytoplankton community.*

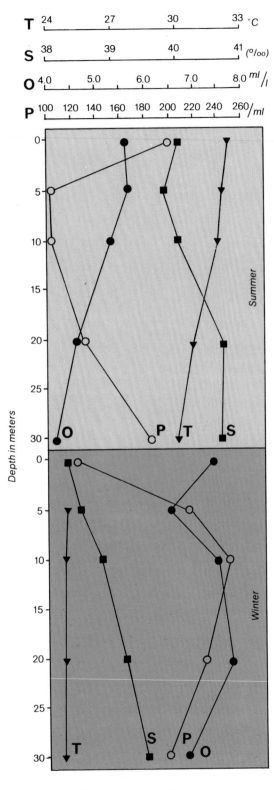

T 24   27   30   33 °C
S 38   39   40   41 (°/oo)
O 4.0   5.0   6.0   7.0   8.0 ml/l
P 100 120 140 160 180 200 220 240 260 /ml

Summer

Winter

Depth in meters

Fig 156. Offshore depth profiles of temperature (T), salinity (S), dissolved oxygen (O), and phytoplankton density (P). Points represent mean values of several locations between Karan Island and the Berri Field.

in nutrient rich enclosed waters, the microplankton flagellates, phylum Euglenophyta, and blue-green algae, phylum Cyanophyta, grow rapidly and become dominant. Each species of these tiny plants has its own environmental requirements for optimum photosynthesis and growth. The relative success of one species with respect to another depends upon such factors as salinity, temperature, light intensity, pH and the concentration of dissolved nutrients such as nitrate, phosphate, ammonia and silicate.

ZOOPLANKTON (animal plankton), on the other hand, are consumer organisms and depend upon the phytoplankton, and to some extent on dead organic matter, for their source of food and energy. The larger species are clearly visible to the naked eye. Many zooplankton organisms are planktonic during their entire life cycle, and are known as holoplankton or permanent plankton. In the marine environment crustaceans of the order Copepoda are particularly important, while other permanent plankton organisms include foraminiferans, radiolarians, tintinnid ciliates, tiny mollusks, jellyfish, ctenophores (comb jellies), certain tunicates (sea squirts) and a few free-floating polychaete worms. Much of the nearshore and bay plankton is made up of meroplankton organisms, which are larval stages of bottom living animals and fish. These live only temporarily or seasonally in the plankton community, settling later to the bottom or developing into adult free-swimming organisms of the nekton (Fig 153).

The western part of the Gulf contains an extremely diverse set of planktonic habitats, including the open waters of the Gulf itself, shallow nearshore exposed coastlines, large areas of sheltered bays, and extremely saline lagoons and ponds, each with different seasonal patterns of water temperature and salinity (Fig 157). All these habitats will be discussed in this chapter except for the last (Chapter 10).

THE PHYSICAL ENVIRONMENT

OFFSHORE in the Gulf itself, the high net evaporation of surface waters and the very limited inflow of fresh water leads to a circulation pattern whereby surface water from the Gulf of Oman flows in through the Strait of Hormuz, moving slowly over the surface of the Gulf towards the margin. As a result of evaporation, it becomes more saline, sinks at the margin, and flows back out towards the Strait of Hormuz along the bottom. In summer especially, this leads to a somewhat stratified situation with the more saline, denser water occurring at the bottom.

Surface water temperature, measured offshore during sampling trips in 1975, ranged from 18.5°C in February to 33.2°C in September; salinities ranged from 38°/oo in December to 40°/oo in June. Water samples collected offshore at several locations between Karan Island and a point 14 miles east of Jubail, indicate that in summer salinity increases with depth, while dissolved oxygen and temperature decrease (Fig

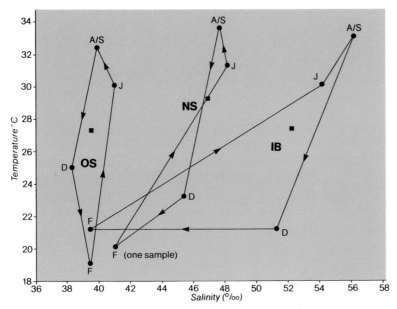

Fig 157. Seasonal changes in temperature and salinity in 3 locations: offshore (OS), nearshore (NS), and interior bays (IB). F – February, J – July, A/S – August/September, D – December.

156). The water is thus stratified, with a lighter layer above 20m and more saline, colder and denser water below that depth. These depth differences are less pronounced in winter, and salinity and temperature are more evenly distributed from top to bottom. Dissolved oxygen is considerably greater offshore in winter than in summer, primarily because its solubility is less in warmer water (Fig 156).

Concentrations of the dissolved nutrients nitrate + nitrite, phosphate and ammonia are generally low offshore as compared to the nearshore waters or to bay areas. Concentration differences within one area, however, are not great enough to show clear-cut trends according to season or depth, at least not on a limited sampling basis.

NEARSHORE shallow waters along the coastline offer a somewhat different habitat for plankton. Compared to offshore areas, the average annual surface salinity and the concentration of dissolved nutrients are somewhat higher, and the temperature warmer (Figs 157 & 160).

INTERIOR BAYS along the coast offer a third and extensive type of habitat for plankton communities. Sheltered bays such as Tarut, al-'Uqayr, al-Musallamiyah and al-Musharrihah enclose hundreds of square kilometers of shallow waters. In midwinter the salinity of these bays is higher (mean 52.4⁰/₀₀) than in offshore waters (39.7⁰/₀₀, Fig 157). In the shallow margins of these bays summer water temperatures are rarely higher than nearshore or offshore. This may result from the cooling effects of the high surface evaporation rate during the day, and from cooling at night. Mean dissolved phosphate values are not greater than they are offshore, but the nutrients nitrate + nitrite and ammonia are generally higher in interior bays (Fig 160).

Fig 158. Copepods (here a member of the family Pontellidae) are among the most important holoplanktic animals, which spend all stages of their life cycle in the plankton.

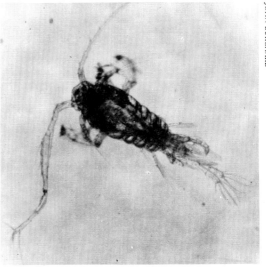

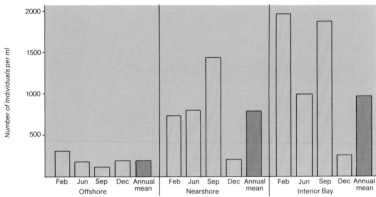

Fig 159. Mean phytoplankton density in surface waters at different seasons in three locations.

PLANKTON

OFFSHORE the phytoplankton is a highly diverse mixture of diatoms, dinoflagellates, and other taxa. The average density of individuals is always lower offshore than either nearshore or in bays (Fig 159), probably due to the lower level of growth-promoting nutrients. In summer, the population density is low and dominated by diatoms. The population at that time has its minimum density at depths between 5 and 10m. Numbers increase below this depth, but because of the low light levels photosynthetic production is probably minimal (Fig 156). Others (Enomoto, 1971) have also found phytoplankton populations in the Gulf to be lowest in summer.

Higher phytoplankton population densities, often dominated by dinoflagellates, occur in winter. Maximum densities between 185 and 352 individuals per milliliter are found at about 10m depth.

The offshore zooplankton community is very diverse, containing representatives of seven major animal phyla. For example, samples taken near Karan Island in June, 1975, contained 45 species totaling 1,990 individuals per cubic meter of seawater; the most abundant forms were the copepod *Paracalanus parvus*, and tiny snails *Limacina inflata*. In a sample taken off Jana Island in July 1973, 2,849 zooplankton individuals, distributed among 33 species, were found per cubic meter of seawater. Large comb jellies[1] and pelagic tunicates[2] are also sometimes found in bloom proportions, especially during the summer months.

NEARSHORE, as in the offshore water region, phytoplankton communities contain a large number of species of diatoms, dinoflagellates, and other microalgae. Samples collected along most of the Saudi Arabian coastline indicate major differences in species and abundance of phytoplankton between the northern and southern sections of exposed coastline. In the extreme north, salinity is low, and the community is dominated

Fig 160. Seasonal differences in the mean concentrations of dissolved nutrients, in microgram atoms per liter of seawater.

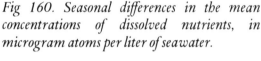
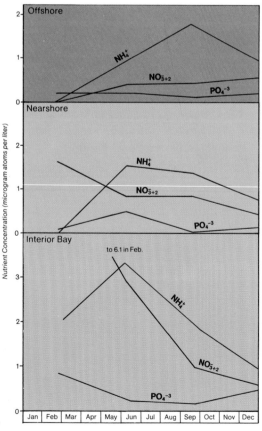

1 *Beroe* sp. and *Mnemiopsis* sp.
2 *Doliolum* sp.

166

by a single species, *Leptocylindrus danicus*, which is rarely found further south. On the other hand, several species are common at all southern nearshore sites, but absent in the extreme north, as for example *Amphora laevis, A. macilenta, Synochococcus custos* and *Phormidium* sp. The mean density of phytoplankton individuals is generally higher in nearshore surface waters than offshore, the greatest abundance appearing in summer and the minimum in winter (Fig 159).

Judging by the few samples of nearshore zooplankton analysed, it appears that the community is less rich in terms of both numbers of species and individuals per cubic meter than that of offshore waters. The communities off Juaymah and Abu 'Ali Island were dominated by calanoid and cyclopoid copepods.

IN THE INTERIOR BAYS abundant phytoplankton serves as food for a rich zooplankton population. A higher concentration of growth-promoting nitrogen compounds may be responsible for the greater abundance of phytoplankton populations in the bays than in other nearshore or offshore waters (Fig 160). These populations are usually composed mainly of diatoms, but dinoflagellates are common in some of the areas from time to time.

In general, zooplankton is more abundant in the interior bays than in nearshore waters. Unfortunately, little winter data are available, but during spring and summer at least, zooplankton has a greater number of species in this area than nearshore, but still less than offshore communities. The summer populations of Tarut Bay are dominated by calanoid copepods and gastropod larvae.

Community Organization

Populations of phytoplankton are denser in nearshore and interior bay waters, as compared to those of the offshore areas. This is undoubtedly related to the higher nutrient concentrations of nitrate and ammonia found in coastal and bay areas (Figs 159 & 160).

The diversity of species in a community is important in so far as it indicates the state of the community in relation to the environment (Chapter 1). The average diversity of the offshore phytoplankton community is high, 0.895, which is above average for many similar communities elsewhere.

The mean diversity of nearshore phytoplankton is, however, even greater, 0.930, perhaps because in addition to the plankton this area often contains benthic species broken loose from the bottom by surf waves. Other species found nearshore may have been carried out on tidal cycles from interior bays. All of these separate populations are mixed with the endemic nearshore population. The average annual diversity was lowest in interior bays, 0.869. There, the larger seasonal changes in temperature and salinity (Fig 157) constitute a less stable environment and, as expected, this reduces the taxonomic diversity.

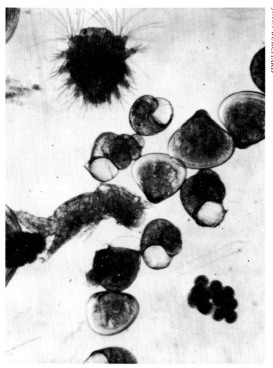

Fig 161. An assortment of zooplankton animals including larvae of clams and snails, and the larva of a polychaete worm provided with extra-long anterior bristles to keep it from sinking. A copepod Clytemnestra sp. also appears with an attached egg-mass. Another detached egg-mass of the same species is visible at lower right.

167

Fig 162. Two batfish *Platax* pinnatus *with their distinctive yellow pelvic fins swim together over the coral reef. [Jana Island]*

9
OPEN WATER ANIMALS

Many species of animals move about freely in the open water, and are properly classed as **nekton.** Some of them, however, are closely associated ecologically with one or another of the benthic biotopes. This type of relationship is illustrated, for instance, by the many kinds of "coral reef fish," which are hardly ever found far away from living coral (Fig 163). Other kinds of "nekton" have close temporary relationships to several benthic biotopes at different seasons, or at different stages in their life cycle. Examples include the green turtle, which feeds in sea-grass beds but breeds on coral islands, and the commercial shrimp which begins life as a member of the zooplankton, but at later stages of development inhabits grassbeds or subtidal muddy bottoms.

Truly pelagic animals, in contrast, have their main ecological affiliations with the open water as such, and cannot be said to be associated primarily or exclusively with any particular benthic biotope. Tuna, with their far-flung migration routes, are a well-known example.

A great many kinds of animals, however, fill the middle ground between pelagic forms like tuna, and ones bound to a particular benthic biotope like reef fish. All sorts of intermediate degrees of dependence on (or independence from) the benthos occur. Such animals could be called semi-pelagic, since they are at least loosely associated with particular benthic biotopes or groups of biotopes. Examples of this type are provided by the numerous fish species which, though moving and feeding in open water, are consistently found in the immediate vicinity of some particular type of bottom feature or biotope, rather than in the open sea. One local example is the barracuda *Sphyraena* spp. (Fig 172), characteristically found in numbers in the vicinity of coral reefs or of oil-producing platforms. Another, with different ecological preferences, is the well-known subaitee *Acanthopagrus cuvieri*, a fast-moving and wide-ranging predator which typically frequents the shallow subtidal in the vicinity of sandy beaches.

The wide ranging pelagic and semi-pelagic marine animals are much more difficult to assign to any particular biological

JOHN HARDY

Fig 163. *Fish of many kinds abound on an unspoiled coral reef. Most reef fish have close ecological ties with the benthic community. Seen here at about 6m depth are two black groupers or burtam* Epinephelus coeruleopunctatus, *the right-hand one displaying characteristic white spots; a small grouper or reef perch* Cephalopholis rogaa, *above and behind the right-hand burtam; a large hamour* Epinephelus tauvina, *well camouflaged just to the left of the reef perch; and more than 20 individuals of the common angelfish* Pomacanthus maculosus, *which is primarily a reef inhabitant but also occurs in many other hard bottom biotopes. [Karan Island]*

Fig 164. Reef sharks of several species regularly frequent the coral reefs. Here a large black-tipped shark Carcharhinus sp. *is accompanied by a remora (behind the dorsal fin) and by a young jack* Gnathanodon speciosus *playing the role of "pilot fish." [Jana Island]*

community than the more or less sedentary benthic forms. Each species tends to have its own particular network of ecological relationships. Thus it is difficult to draw distinct boundary lines except between very general groupings, such as those typical of bays, nearshore areas, or offshore waters. Because the entire Gulf, in a wider sense, belongs to the continental shelf province, even those differences are less marked here than in other parts of the world where truly oceanic conditions are encountered closer to the shore.

The most conspicuous forms of pelagic marine life in the Gulf, as elsewhere, are fish, squids, whales (especially dolphins) and birds. Of these, by far the greatest number of different kinds are fish. More than 300 species of fish have already been identified in the Gulf, several of them for the first time during the Aramco study. Even this number, however, probably represents at most about a quarter of the species actually present.

CARTILAGINOUS FISH

The vast majority of living fish belong to the group of "modern bony fish," technically known as teleosts. We will turn our attention first, however, to a more archaic and much less numerous group, which has always attracted special attention because of the large size of most of its members and the fact that some of them occasionally attack human beings. These are the "cartilage fish," or sharks and rays, which are well represented in the Gulf.

Sharks

Sharks are too well known to require lengthy description in these pages. Those occurring in the Gulf can be grouped into three broad ecological types: **bottom-dwelling, coastal** and **offshore.**

A single **bottom-dwelling** species, the cat or nurse shark *Chiloscyllium griseum*, is common almost everywhere. By day this innocuous little shark is usually found hiding under a coral head, rock fragment or piece of debris on the bottom. By night it swims around close to the bottom, feeding on small invertebrates. These sharks are sometimes caught by dozens in shrimp trawls. The maximum length is a little over 1m.

Several species of **coastal** sharks are found along the Saudi Arabian shores of the Gulf. These sharks are most commonly encountered in 10 to 20m of water, around the edges of coral reefs or along the open coastline. The group includes several species potentially dangerous to man. The commonest large species locally is the bull or cub shark *Carcharhinus leucas*, a heavy-bodied shark averaging about 2.5m long. It can be distinguished from other, similar "reef shark" types by its broad, blunt head, pale greyish coloration and the lack of distinct black tips on any fins. It occurs world-wide in warm coastal waters, estuaries, rivers,[1] and even inland lakes. The sharks of Lake Nicaragua, the Zambezi River and the Ganges are all

1 Including the Euphrates at least as far up river as Baghdad!

170

closely related to this species. The bull shark is a voracious predator with a large mouth and broad, triangular teeth. Its natural food seems to consist mostly of other sharks and rays. Specimens captured by the Aramco team have all had numerous sting-ray spines embedded in their jaws. Probably most cases of shark attack on humans in Gulf waters can be attributed to this species.

Another common coastal species is a black-tipped reef shark *Carcharhinus* sp. (Fig 164). This is also a fairly heavily built shark, though more slender and slightly smaller than the bull shark. Actually, many species of sharks have black tips on different fins, and accurate identification depends on recording the exact shape and location of the black marks, as well as other characteristics such as the proportions of the head and the number of rows of teeth. The reef black-tip is the only black-tipped shark in this area having a narrow white tip or border on its first dorsal fin. The second dorsal, pectorals, and caudal are black-tipped.

The lemon shark *Negaprion brevirostris* (Fig 165) is another large heavy shark, found especially on the reef flats and shallows adjacent to the coral islands. It is readily recognized by its distinctly brownish or yellowish coloration, and by the second dorsal fin which is about the same size as the first. This or similar species occur world-wide in suitable habitats.

Probably the commonest of all sharks in the Gulf is a sort of miniature reef shark, with the typical streamlined body form but a maximum length of less than 125 cm. This is listed in most books on fishes of the region as *Carcharhinus menisorrah*, though there is some doubt as to the correctness of the name. It is a sleek, tapering shark with a sharply pointed head and a distinctive, round black spot on the second dorsal fin. The first dorsal is unmarked. This shark is very abundant in coastal waters and is frequently caught by hundreds in the shrimp trawls. Unlike some other sharks, this species is an excellent eating fish.

Another, superficially similar small shark is the smooth dogfish *Mustelus manazo,* which greatly resembles smooth dogfish found elsewhere in the world. It is distinguished from the reef sharks by several features of body proportions, etc, but most characteristic are the teeth which are flat and pavement-like, suitable for crushing small mollusks and crustaceans and quite unlike the sharply pointed teeth of the reef-shark group. This species, too, is commonly caught by the shrimp trawls.

Sharks typical of the **offshore** province include several species of black-tips rather difficult to distinguish without close examination.[2] As compared with coastal members of the reef-shark group, they are more streamlined, with sharply pointed

Fig 165. The lemon shark Negaprion brevirostris *is a large species found especially on reef flats and shallows near coral islands. A distinctive feature of this species is its large second dorsal fin, nearly equal in size to the first. [Jana Island]*

2 The shape and arrangement of the fin markings is different and distinctive for each species of black-tipped shark. These markings are probably visual signals by which these sharks recognize members of their own species. Natural selection will have tended to produce, during the evolution of each species, a unique signal pattern different from that of any other species inhabiting the same geographical area. The gaudy colors of many coral-reef fish are a better-known example of the same process.

Fig 166. Dissection of the female tiger shark (Fig 167) revealed a number of fully-developed young of strikingly beautiful coloration.

heads rather than blunt rounded ones. Their teeth are narrow and pointed, and they appear to feed primarily on fish. Most of them are about 2m long. A typical representative of this group is the spinner shark *Carcharhinus maculipinnis*. This species closely resembles the reef black-tip but is smaller and more slender with a long, pointed snout. Another similar species is the silky shark *Carcharhinus sorrah*. This differs from all the species so far mentioned in having a distinct, sharp ridge along the back between the first and second dorsal fins.

The tiger shark *Galeocerdo cuvieri* (Fig 167) is probably best considered with the offshore province, though it also frequents the reefs around coral islands. This is a much-feared and much-publicized species, but little is actually known of its natural history. The average size of specimens from the Gulf seems to be about 4m; the large mouth, formidable serrated teeth and indiscriminate appetite make it undoubtedly one of the most dangerous sharks. Tiger sharks have been known to eat almost anything; one is even reported to have consumed an entire side of beef. Under more natural circumstances, tiger sharks are known to prey on dolphins, large sea turtles, and especially on other sharks. Two encountered by the Aramco team were in the process of devouring large bull sharks which had been caught on a hook and line.

The mako and great white sharks, which are oceanic species, do not appear to have been recorded from the Gulf, though there seems no particular reason why they should not enter it from time to time. At least one truly oceanic shark species has, however, been seen in the Gulf on several occasions. This is the whale shark *Rhincodon typus*, the largest fish in the world. In spite of its huge size (12m or more in length) this is a harmless plankton-eater, distantly related to the nurse sharks. Apart from its large size, it is readily distinguished from any other shark by its pattern of whitish or yellow spots on a darker background, and by the longitudinal ridges along its back and sides.

Rays

Rays are closely related to sharks and share with them many anatomical features, including a skeleton made of cartilage rather than bone. During the course of their evolution rays have become greatly flattened dorsoventrally, originally as an adaptation to life on the bottom. Most of them are bottom-dwellers (Fig 169), but one group, including eagle rays, devil rays and manta rays, has become secondarily re-adapted to life in the open water. All the members of this group can be recognized by having "wings" – actually the enlarged pectoral fins – with pointed tips, in contrast to the rounded "wings" of bottom-living species.

Eagle rays (family Myliobatidae) are well adapted to swimming in the open water, but retain the ancestral habit of finding their food on the bottom. Like many other rays they dig into soft sediment in search of clams and other hard-shelled mollusks, which they crush in their powerful jaws. The

172

Fig 167. This 4m long, female tiger shark Galeocerdo cuvieri *was captured on a hook and line using a 2m reef shark as bait. The size of this voracious animal can be appreciated beside the Yemeni and American members of the study team on Jana Island.*

Fig 168. Rhynchobatus djiddensis *is a common local species of guitar fish, related to skates and rays, which may reach a length of 3m. This juvenile specimen was removed from the water and photographed on the beach. [Tarut Bay]*

flattened, pavement-like teeth are well adapted to this mode of feeding. Two species[3] are common locally, especially around the offshore coral reefs. They visit the reef flat to feed, but otherwise are usually seen in small groups swimming gracefully about in deeper water.

Devil rays (family Mobulidae) have carried the evolutionary trend toward emancipation from the bottom one step further, and feed in the open water on plankton or small fish. A pair of projecting "horns," actually highly mobile skin flaps on either side of the mouth, helps to funnel plankton into the mouth. The devil ray *Mobula diabolus* is common in the Gulf and is often seen around the coral islands. Like the smaller eagle rays, this species has a habit of leaping two or three meters out of the water, performing several back flips, and then falling back with a resounding splash. Since devil rays are heavily built and have a "wingspan" of up to 2m, the sound of such a belly landing sometimes carries for miles on a calm summer evening. Rays usually jump around sunset, and sometimes dozens may be seen leaping within a relatively small area. No satisfactory explanation has yet been given to account for this behavior.

The manta ray *Manta birostris* resembles a much larger version of the devil ray. Mantas are about 6m across the "wings" and weigh a ton or more. In spite of their huge size and fearsome appearance they are harmless mild-mannered plankton eaters, resembling in this respect the gigantic whale-shark. Mantas have the same jumping habits as their smaller relatives, and because of their immense size and weight the effect is truly breathtaking. Mantas have been spotted just outside the entrance to the Arabian Gulf and probably occur in offshore areas of the Gulf itself. There seems, however, to be no properly authenticated record to date of a manta being seen in Saudi Arabian waters.

TELEOST FISH

Teleost fishes in the Gulf range in size from anchovies 2cm long to sailfish with a maximum length of about 4m, and in shape from flounders to seahorses. Most of the smaller open-water kinds feed on animal plankton, while the larger species feed mainly on small fish or on other pelagic animals such as squids or jellyfish. The small plankton-eating fish are also the main food of many kinds of sea birds, squids and dolphins.

One of the most common of the small "bait fish" is the silverside *Allanetta forsskali*, which usually occurs in dense shoals in shallow coastal waters and in bays. Shoaling or schooling is one way in which small open-water fish, and many larger species as well, act to reduce their chances of being eaten by predators. Most predators have to take aim at a particular fish before catching it. This process takes a certain minimum amount of time, and becomes much more difficult for the predator when confronted with a shifting mass of more or less identical target objects. The aim slips from one to another, and a miss frequently results. The predators consequently become

3 *Myliobatis nichofii* and *Aetobatis narinari.*

174

Fig 169. The large sting-ray Dasyatis sephen *is primarily a bottom-living species. [Jana Island]*

extremely quick at picking off any individual which strays from the swarm. This sort of prey-predator interaction can easily be observed with *Allanetta*, since shoals of this species commonly take up position in the shade of piers or jetties, and often remain there for days on end. They are harried incessantly by a variety of predators, especially chana'ad *Scomberomorus commersoni* (Fig 172), subaitee *Acanthopagrus cuvieri* and hamour *Epinephelus tauvina* (Fig 183). Silversides feed mainly on large zooplankton organisms swept past by the tide.

Another major group of bait fish includes various species of small herring-like fish, generally known as sardines. Sardines are the object of important commercial fisheries in many parts of the world, and in some parts of the Gulf they are netted in quantities, dried and used for animal feed. In the western part of the Gulf, however, their greatest importance is probably as a staple food for sea birds, dolphins and many commercially valuable larger fish.

Numerically the most important of the Gulf bait fish are the several species of anchovies *Stolephorus* spp. They are less conspicuous than the silversides, because their shoals move about rather than remaining stationary near man-made structures. Anchovies are small, silvery sardine-like fish; but whereas sardines have an upturned mouth suitable for catching plankton near the surface, most anchovies have an underslung mouth and often feed near the bottom. Anchovies are most abundant in relatively shallow waters, and in some parts of the Gulf are the most important fish caught commercially. Along the Saudi Arabian coast their main importance, like that of the sardines, is as a food source for large valuable fish such as tuna.

Plankton is also the dietary mainstay of many small fish whose habits associate them closely with some particular benthic biotope. A good example is the sergeant major *Abudefduf saxatilis* (Fig 170), which lives in loose schools around large coral heads (or artificial structures), taking shelter in the coral when disturbed. These fish feed on the larger zooplankton organisms, catching them individually as they drift past. While feeding, the entire school rises 2 or 3m above the coral head, and often to the surface where they produce a characteristic dimpling visible from above.

Fig 170. Fusiliers Paracaesio *sp. travel in schools along the face of the reef. Below, several* Abudefduf saxatilis *and one* Gaterin gaterinus. *[Jana Island]*

Fig 171. Amberjack or yellowtails Seriola *sp. are among the more pelagic members of the jack family, and travel around in large schools preying on sardines and other bait fish. [off Ras al-Qurayyah]*

A number of somewhat larger, medium-sized fish also feed primarily on plankton. An interesting local example is the so-called chub mackerel *Rastrelliger kanagurta*, typically found in schools of a few dozen or more individuals in fairly deep water adjacent to coral reefs. In appearance this is a typical member of the mackerel family Scombridae, and like the others it is constantly on the move, travelling at high speed in a tightly knit school. Unlike many scombrids, however, it is not a predator but a plankton feeder, straining small animals *en masse* out of the water by means of its highly developed gill rakers. To do this the large mouth is opened very wide, and the gill arches lowered to make a sort of strainer basket, two or three times the normal size of the animal's head. All the members of a school open and close their strainers together with military precision, while the school as a whole performs remarkable high-speed maneuvers, which are probably designed to ensure filtration of the largest possible volume of water. The effect is rendered even more striking since the school, swimming with open gill-rakers, makes a loud roaring noise underwater. The fish themselves are rather shy, and only occasionally come within sight of a diver, but the noise betrays their presence at a considerable distance. Judging by this evidence they are fairly common around the offshore reefs.

Taken as a whole, the mackerel family and its relatives are among the most specialized pelagic fish. While many of the smaller members, such as *Rastrelliger*, feed on plankton, the most typical representatives are powerful predators such as tuna. Schools of small and medium-sized tuna are a common sight during summer and autumn throughout the offshore province and the deeper waters of the coastal region. It is not yet entirely clear which of the numerous tuna species occur in the Gulf, but the plain-colored *Thunnus obesus*, and the striped *Euthynnus affinis*, are particularly common in local fish markets. These are both medium-sized tuna ranging up to about 1m in length. Several other species undoubtedly occur.

Fig 172 (opposite). Large, predatory semi-pelagic fish are among the most highly prized and commercially valuable species in the Gulf. Top: the barracuda Sphyraena ?japonica *is one of three species very abundant around artificial structures and the edges of coral reefs. This species and* S. jello *both reach a length of 150cm or more, while* S. obtusata *is smaller. Middle: the king mackerel or* chana'ad Scomberomorus commersoni *grows to at least 180cm. Although generally considered pelagic, this species is very fond of visiting oil platforms, coral reefs and other coastal biotopes in search of food. During the winter months this fish is one of the most important species caught commercially in the western Gulf, but in summer it retreats to deeper water and so is caught less often. Bottom: the subaitee* Acanthopagrus cuvieri *is a swift, predatory member of the bream family. Its preferred habitat is the coastal shallows near sandy beaches, though it ranges widely in search of food. Shrimp, pearl oysters and even orange peel (!) have been found in the stomach of this fish.*

178

179

Fig 173. Caranx fulvoguttatus, *a common jack of the upper reef slope, is bold and curious in its approach to the photographer. This individual has a typical body coloration and pattern; but occasional specimens are bright yellow or dark slate grey all over. Both these two different color phases, seen only in fairly large, solitary individuals, may have something to do with breeding or territorial behaviour. [Jana Island]*

A particularly striking member of the tuna family, and one which plays an important role in local fisheries, is the king mackerel or chana'ad *Scomberomorus commersoni* (Fig 172). This fish, also known by various other names such as cero or spanish mackerel, is slender and streamlined, with a very large crescent-shaped caudal fin. The large mouth is filled with razor-sharp teeth. This species grows to a length of approximately 180cm and travels about individually or in small groups feeding on small or medium-sized fish. In attacking schools of bait fish, it often leaps 3 or 4m into the air, and such leaping chana'ad are a common sight on summer evenings wherever bait fish congregate. Large chana'ad can probably swim at more than 65km per hour and such fast-moving animals may not remain long in any one biotope or province. More than most pelagic fish, however, they show a tendency to visit reef edges, the vicinity of oil-producing platforms, and even the coastal bays in search of food. Chana'ad are generally considered to be among the finest eating fish in the Gulf.

A slightly smaller species *Scomberomorus guttatus* also occurs in western Gulf waters. It is easily distinguished by its spotted sides, whereas those of the chana'ad are covered with a pattern of narrow, wavy cross-bars (Fig 172).

A still more spectacular tuna relative is the sailfish *Istiophorus gladius*, which reaches a length of over 4m (although 2 to 2.5m is more usual). This is a tropical oceanic species eagerly sought by deep-sea anglers. At certain times and places in the Gulf (mainly in shoreward extensions of the offshore province) it occurs in fairly large numbers. These are the same conditions which bring other large pelagic predators close to shore. Unfortunately, details of the natural history of sailfish, and in particular whether they are residents or migrants in the Gulf, are as yet unknown.

The horse mackerel or jacks superficially resemble the mackerel family, but actually they are only distantly related. Like tuna and mackerel, jacks are mostly streamlined, fast-moving, schooling predators. They are much less specialized

Fig 174. *Schools of large, semi-pelagic predatory fish, such as these jacks* Caranx *sp., often visit the reef. [Karan Island]*

for pelagic life, however, and most of them belong to the coastal province. Jacks tend to be deep-bodied and flattened from side to side rather than cylindrical like tuna, and their fin arrangement is different. Many jacks have a distinctive sharp ridge, formed by enlarged scales called scutes, along the side of the body near the tail. The function of this ridge is unknown, but is perhaps related to swimming stability. The more cylindrical species, such as amberjacks *Seriola* spp., generally lack scutes (Fig 171).

A striking local species is the hamam *Gnathanodon speciosus*. This is a deep-bodied, streamlined fish with a high forehead, and a large thick-lipped mouth completely lacking teeth. This latter feature distinguishes it from most other local jacks. Small individuals of up to 30cm are bright yellow with black vertical bars; larger ones, which grow up to 60cm or more, are yellowish to silvery, with faint bars and irregular black spots. In spite of its streamlined shape *Gnathanodon* is largely a bottom feeder, frequently seen rooting through soft sediment in search of worms or mollusks. This fish makes very tasty eating, and it is much in demand locally.

Hamam frequent a variety of coastal biotopes but are most likely to be found around artificial structures and coral reefs. The Arabic term hamam actually includes several species of reef-frequenting jacks of somewhat similar appearance. Of these the one most likely to be encountered by anyone diving or snorkeling on the reefs is *Caranx fulvoguttatus*, which might be called the gold-spotted jack (Fig 173). This species is very inquisitive and will swim directly up to any unfamiliar object, such as a diver, to examine it at close range. *C. fulvoguttatus* frequents the reef slope at moderate depths, moving about singly or in small groups.

Several large jack species are more pelagic, and frequent waters near or around the reefs rather than directly over them. One example of this type is the amberjack *Seriola* sp., recognized by its lack of scutes and by its cylindrical, almost tuna-like shape. Another is the large, streamlined *Caranx sexfasciatus*, which is actually only one of a group of very similar, easily confused species (Fig 174). The deep-bodied, heavy-

Fig 175. *Open mouth of the jack* Ulua mentalis, *showing its remarkable gill rakers. [Karan Island]*

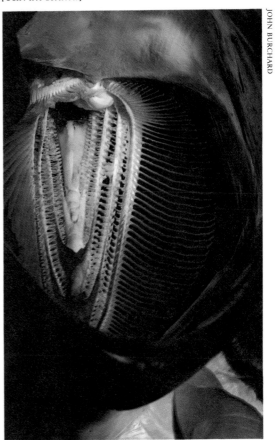

headed *Ulua mentalis* is less often seen, and in fact was first recorded from the Gulf by the Aramco team. The most distinctive feature of this species is its remarkable gill-rakers (Fig 175), longer and more numerous than those of any other jack. These gill-rakers form a large, fine-meshed strainer, presumably used in catching plankton. *Ulua* is wary and fast-moving, however, and its feeding behavior has not yet been observed.

Another ecological category of open-water fish are the inhabitants of the extreme upper storey — the layer of water immediately below the surface. A characteristic member of this group is the garfish or needle-fish (family Belonidae), of which several similar species are common locally. These fish are extremely long and slender, with a needle-like "beak" consisting of the elongated upper and lower jaws, which are studded with tiny sharp teeth. They swim slowly right at the surface of the water, almost invisible from below because of their semi-transparent greenish coloration, and feed on small fish snatched in a sudden, lightning dash. At 60cm to more than 1m long, they are too big to interest most sea birds; for a needlefish danger usually comes from below. When startled or frightened, they leap out of the water and skitter away at high speed across the surface, literally balanced on their tail which remains in the water to provide propulsion. The lower lobe of the tail fin is bigger than the upper one, which helps them maintain their balance. Because air offers much less resistance than water, they are able to travel much faster than most pursuers can follow. They can skate over the surface for 50m or more before dropping back into the water.

Rather similar to needlefish, and fairly closely related, are the halfbeaks (family Hemirhamphidae). The local species *Hemirhamphus far* is one of the most beautifully colored fish. It resembles the needlefish in having a lopsided caudal fin and a long slender snout, but is a smaller and much shorter-bodied fish of more conventional proportions. Actually the long snout consists of the elongated lower jaw only, while the upper jaw is much shorter. This arrangement, which gives the fish its name halfbeak, is an adaptation to feeding right at the water surface. Halfbeaks are common in the coastal province and sometimes in bays, generally moving about in large schools. Like needlefish, they take to the air when frightened, but unlike them they do this in a long series of jumps. The effect is the same — they travel through the air much faster than they, or most predators, could travel under water.

The culmination of this evolutionary trend — taking to the air to escape from sub-surface predators — is reached by the flying fish (family Exocoetidae). These are closely related to garfish and halfbeaks, and resemble the latter in size and shape, except that they lack an elongated lower jaw. The pectoral fins, and in some species the pelvics as well, are greatly enlarged and serve as gliding planes. In escaping from a predator, a flying fish first leaps nearly out of the water, spreads its "wings," and begins to "taxi" or skate along the surface in exactly the same

DICK MAISE

Fig 176. Cuttlefish Sepia *sp. over mixed sand and coral bottom. Cuttlefish spend much of their time partly buried in the sand, lying in wait for unsuspecting shrimp or fish on which they feed. [Jurayd Island]*

way as a needlefish, with the enlarged, lower tail fin lobe in the water. It accelerates rapidly, and within less than a second has sufficient speed to become fully airborne, gliding low over the water surface for up to 100m. If danger still threatens, it can lower its tail, taxi to build up speed, and take off again for another glide without having to drop back into the water. The limit is reached after two or three glides, when drying membranes force the fish to return to its native element. Only a few predators, however, particularly the dorado or dolphin *Coryphaena*, have the speed and stamina to follow their flight, and even then the flying fish frequently escapes.

Flying fish are primarily oceanic, but two species are fairly common in the western part of the Gulf. *Cypselurus oligolepis* is a "four-winged" species; that is, its pelvic fins are enlarged and used to increase the gliding surface during "flight." *Parexocoetus mento*, by contrast, has small pelvic fins and so appears "two-winged."

INVERTEBRATES

Only a few types of pelagic invertebrates are large and active enough to be considered as nekton rather than as plankton. Foremost among them are representatives of the cephalopod mollusks — the group that includes octopus and squid. Some cephalopods, such as the common octopus, are benthic, swimming only to escape immediate danger. Others, such as the cuttlefish *Sepia* sp. (Fig 176) are capable of rapid and extensive swimming, but remain closely bound to a particular benthic community. Many members of the group, however, are truly pelagic and show a variety of remarkable adaptations to life in open water. A majority of pelagic cephalopods are deep-sea forms, unlikely to be found in the shallow waters of the Gulf. Squids, however, have successfully invaded shallow coastal waters all over the world, and at least one species is fairly common in the Gulf.

Squids rival or surpass most fish in the quality of their sense organs, the elaboration of their nervous system and behavior, and especially in their speed and precision of movement. They are generally gregarious, and like active pelagic fishes, are capable of great speed and maneuverability. They capture small fish by shooting out one pair of tentacles to a distance at least equal to their own length.

The same features that make squids successful — their high intelligence and tremendous mobility — make them extremely difficult to capture, except under special circumstances. A few specimens have been taken from the Gulf in shrimp trawl catches, but all have been in a damaged condition. So far it has been impossible to obtain undamaged specimens, or to make any observations on their natural history except that they are often attracted to lights at night. All that can be said at this point is that they appear to be abundant, are rather small (about 20cm long), and probably belong to the world-wide coastal genus *Loligo*.

BIRDS

The plankton pastures of the open sea support, directly or indirectly, a considerable variety of birds so specialized to this environment that they are usually called pelagic, even though every species must necessarily visit some sort of land in order to breed. Familiar examples are petrels, shearwaters, albatrosses and penguins. Truly pelagic birds are conspicuously absent from the Gulf, and the abundant bird life is composed largely of **shore** and **coastal** birds. Included in the first category are all the many species of waders which visit the Saudi Arabian coast in winter: herons, flamingoes, plover, snipe, curlew, etc. Several of these remain in small numbers throughout the year, and some actually breed here. Coastal birds include ducks, grebes, etc as winter visitors, and cormorants, gulls and terns as permanent residents and/or breeders. The gulls feed mainly along the shore, and are attracted in great numbers by refuse and offal at dump sites. Ducks, grebes, cormorants and some of the terns feed in the shallow water of bays, or in some cases over shoal areas offshore. Several of the terns, especially those which nest on the coral islands, obtain their food by diving for fish in the surface layers of deeper water offshore, especially when the bait fish are driven to the surface by the attacks of tuna from beneath (Fig 177). Two kinds of sea birds among the winter visitors, however, do not fit into any of these categories, and merit more detailed mention.

The Arctic Skua *Stercorarius parasiticus* is a bird which, generally speaking, breeds in the high arctic in summer, and winters at sea in the North Atlantic and in the Mediterranean. It is a predator, feeding in summer largely on the young of other birds, and in winter on food wrested by force from gulls or terns. Skuas resemble gulls, but have a more powerful flight, and a somewhat hawk-like air. They remain offshore, and do not sit around on beaches and piers as gulls do. The Arctic Skua is fairly common in winter in the Gulf wherever gulls gather, and can often be observed stealing food from the flocks of gulls that follow shrimp trawlers. Normally, each flock of gulls is accompanied by only one Skua.

Even more clear-cut pelagic affinities are displayed by the phalaropes, which visit the Gulf in large numbers on spring migration. Phalaropes, of which there are two very similar species, are small waders of sandpiper size, with a rather peculiar breeding biology. The female is dominant and brightly colored, and the male incubates the eggs and rears the young. This is by no means a meaningless biological anomaly, but represents an adaptation to maximize breeding success under unusual ecological conditions. Phalaropes nest in swampy Arctic lowlands liable to unpredictable flooding. These floods, when they occur, destroy all the eggs being incubated at the time. The females' optimum reproductive strategy, in the face of such uncertainty, is to withdraw from parental concerns and ripen a second set of eggs.

The second peculiarity of phalaropes, as compared to the rest of the sandpipers, is that instead of running about on

JOHN BURCHARD

Fig 177. A shoal of small bait fish is herded to the surface and preyed on by tuna from below, and attacked by terns Sterna spp. *from above. [Karan Island]*

185

Fig 178. Bottlenosed dolphin Tursiops truncatus. *The very similar* Tursiops aduncus *is common in the Arabian Gulf [specimen originally from Florida, USA]*

beaches or mud flats to find their food, they spend all their non-breeding time far out at sea paddling on the surface and picking up plankton animals. As a rule they are truly oceanic, and it seems a little surprising to find them in the Gulf. Apparently, the Gulf is an important flyway for phalaropes and thousands can be found in March and April throughout the offshore province.

DOLPHINS AND WHALES

The Cetacea, or dolphins and whales, are a group of originally terrestrial mammals which during the course of evolution have taken to a marine existence. They are marvelously adapted to life in the sea, and are also noted for being among the most intelligent of all animals. All living Cetacea fall into one of two quite different groups, according to their mode of feeding. Baleen whales (suborder Mysticeti) feed on plankton; their teeth have entirely disappeared and in their place the mouth contains an elaborate filtering apparatus made of baleen or "whalebone," a horny outgrowth from the roof of the mouth. This group includes the blue whale *Balaenoptera musculus*, the largest animal that ever lived, which reaches a length of 30m and a weight of about 130 tons. Several similar species occur, ranging in size down to the pigmy right whale *Caperea marginata*, only about 6m long. This species is, however, confined to the Southern Hemisphere.

Baleen whales are occasionally found in the Gulf and sometimes become stranded on the beach or trapped in shallow bays. None of the specimens have been positively identified but they are probably either the fin whale *Balaenoptera physalus*, a widely distributed species, or Brydes whale *Balaenoptera brydei*. The latter, in spite of having baleen, feeds mainly on fish.

The other and much more varied group of Cetacea are the toothed whales (suborder Odontoceti). These range from sperm whales *Physeter catodon*, more than 20m long, to dolphins some of which (genus *Sotalia*) are only a little over 1m long when adult. In general, species more than about 3 or 4m long are called whales, while the smaller ones are called dolphins if their jaws protrude to form a "beak," and porpoises if they lack a beak and have spoon-shaped rather than cylindrical teeth. These are not scientific designations, however, and their use frequently leads to confusion, as there are several kinds of beakless "dolphins."

Well-known examples of toothed whales include the sperm whale, the killer whale *Orcinus orca* and especially the bottle-nosed dolphin *Tursiops truncatus* (Fig 178), undoubtedly the most publicized of all marine animals. This species is easily tamed and trained and is widely exhibited in oceanaria and dolphinaria. The very similar species *Tursiops aduncus* is common in the Gulf (al-Robaae, 1974). Several other species of "dolphins" also occur in the Gulf, some of them in large schools containing hundreds of individuals.

187

PHIL BASSON

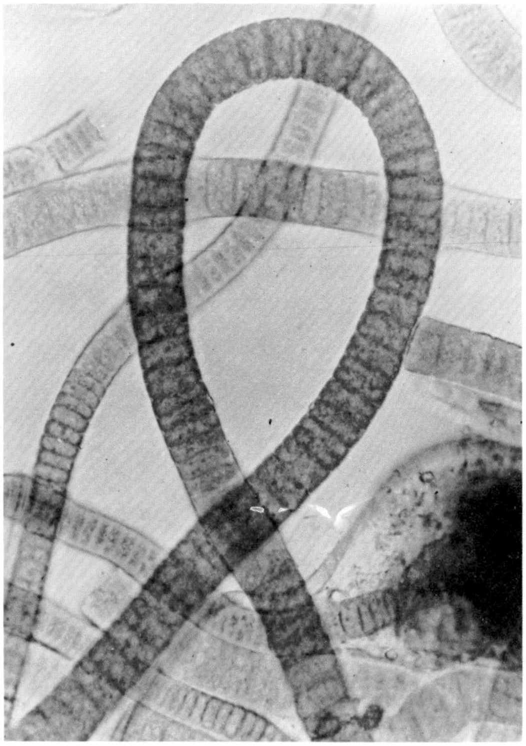

10
HYPERSALINE
BIOTOPES

Fig 179. The filamentous blue-green alga Oscillatoria limosa *is a species of world-wide occurrence found in a variety of habitats. Blue-green algae are among the simplest living plants.*

In coastal marine lagoons, especially in tropical and subtropical areas where evaporation exceeds precipitation and land drainage, the environment becomes hypersaline. Salinities of 60 to more than $200^0/_{00}$ commonly occur in shallow bays, lagoons and salt lakes along the Saudi Arabian coast. Because the solubility of oxygen in seawater decreases with increasing salinity, hypersaline environments are frequently very low in available oxygen.

The high salinity of such waters represents a type of environmental stress that few animals or plants can tolerate, though certain species, perhaps with specialized metabolic adaptations, thrive and often reach high numbers of individuals in hypersaline waters. Communities in this environment usually have a low diversity, however, and in this respect resemble those of a polluted environment. This drastically reduces the available possibilities of species interaction.

The base of the food web is often composed of photosynthetic sulfur bacteria[1] which instead of water use hydrogen sulfide anaerobically as a hydrogen donor in photosynthesis, thus liberating sulfur instead of oxygen. Brisou *et al.* (1974) found abundant populations of halophilic bacteria thriving in a lake with a salinity of $400^0/_{00}$, but no other animals or plants occurred. In waters of lower salinity (around $200^0/_{00}$), however, the tiny photosynthetic flagellate alga *Dunaliella* sp. commonly occurs, along with the brine shrimp *Artemia salina* and isopod crustaceans (Williams, 1970). Por (1972), working in the Sinai Peninsula, described hypersaline pool communities of 80 to $100^0/_{00}$ which included three species of copepods.

Hypersaline environments play an important role in

1 Purple Thiorhodaceae or green Chlorobacteriaceae.

Fig 180. Aerial view of a lagoon at the south end of al-'Uqayr Bay. Salinities in the bay (foreground) exceed 70⁰/₀₀ and in the lagoon (background) reach 110⁰/₀₀ in summer. Healthy young fish were abundant in the lagoon.

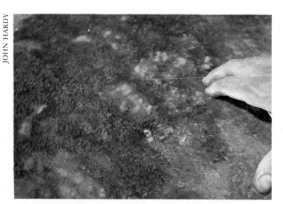

Fig 181. Blue-green algae and diatoms cover large parts of the intertidal area of hypersaline bays. The bubbles are oxygen, produced as a result of phytosynthesis. [Dohat Zalum salt lake]

sedimentary processes. At high salinities carbon dioxide, liberated by bacteria during the oxidation of the large amounts of accumulated organic matter, precipitates as carbonate even at low pH values. In addition, mats of blue-green algae commonly form along the margins or beaches of such lagoons or salt ponds, and precipitation of magnesium carbonate by these algal communities plays an important part in the production of laminated limestones, calcite and dolomite. A microenvironment is created in which high magnesium calcite, with up to 40% magnesium carbonate, is precipitated. Such a process has been shown to occur in small hypersaline pools along the Red Sea coast, where salinities reach 69 to 130°/oo (Friedman *et al.* 1973), and similar evaporite processes occur in many bays and lagoons along the Arabian Gulf coast (Purser, 1973).

A SALT LAKE COMMUNITY

Hypersaline environments of varying degree are found all along the Gulf coast of Saudi Arabia. The salt lake at the head of Dawhat Zalum is a good example of one of the extreme cases. The lake bottom slopes gently to a maximum depth of 4m. Exchange of water with the bay occurs by slow seepage underneath the supralittoral bar. The summer salinity in adjacent Dawhat Zalum waters is about 60°/oo, but the high rate of evaporation concentrates the lake water to about 288°/oo in winter and 330°/oo in summer. Temperatures in the lake range from 24.5°C in December to 32.8°C in September. Dissolved oxygen is very low – less than one fourth that of offshore Gulf waters – because the high salt content lowers the oxygen solubility. The pH and dissolved phosphate are low, but nitrate and ammonia concentrations are about nine to ten times greater than in offshore Gulf waters. Bottom samples taken from the lake by Aramco biologists were full of salt crystals. Analysis indicates that these are almost wholly sodium chloride, with small quantities of calcium and magnesium sulfates.

Within this extreme environment one finds a plankton community poor in species, but high in numbers of individuals. The base of the food web consists of great numbers of the photosynthetic microflagellate *Dunaliella salina*, numbers of this alga ranging from 420,000 per liter in June to more than 19 million in September. In late summer a *Dunaliella* population explosion or "bloom" colors the water blood red (Fig 152). Sixteen to twenty-four other species of phytoplankton, primarily diatoms, are present in much smaller numbers. This photosynthetic community supports a variety of zooplankton including five species of copepods, a turbellarian (flatworm), and various nematode worms. Aramco biologists have found no previous records of animal life from waters of such high salinity.

In addition, the lake beach is covered by a mat of blue-green algae and diatoms[2] (Fig 181), which, as previously noted, play an important part in sedimentary processes. Nematode worms

2 *Oscillatoria limosa, O. nigro-viridis, Spirulina labyrinthiformis, S. major, Amphora* sp., *Nitzschia* sp., *Pleurosigma* sp.

were abundant in core samples taken from the beach, and were also found alive among the salt crystals from the bottom of the lake! The water was not examined for the presence of halophilic bacteria, but such bacteria may be present along with the algae, and may be partly responsible for the red color of the pond in summer.

Aramco biologists also sampled four other hypersaline environments, with salinities of 60 to 73$^0/_{00}$, along the Saudi Arabian coast. The samples contained between 18 and 36 species of phytoplankton. In general, these populations are extremely dense in summer, but the species diversity is low. For example, the small lagoon at the south end of al-'Uqayr Bay (Fig 180) contained 2.6 and 3.5 million cells per liter in June and September respectively. In December, however, populations are relatively low.

SALINITY AS AN ECOLOGICAL FACTOR
Several previous investigators, working primarily in the Abu Dhabi lagoon system, have obtained data on the salinity tolerances of different groups of Arabian Gulf organisms. At

Fig 182. Grassbeds, and much of the associated biota, continue to flourish under hypersaline conditions. The salinity at this site is 56–58$^0/_{00}$, and at 8m depth a mixed stand of Halodule uninervis and Halophila stipulacea occurs, along with the fan-shaped alga Avrainvillea amadelpha. One peculiarity of these hypersaline grassbeds is a striking variety and abundance of sponges (left of center). [near Ras al-Qurayyah]

JOHN BURCHARD

Fig 183. A young hamour Epinephelus tauvina, *Hamour are one of the most ubiquitous and adaptable of all Gulf fish, and are found in virtually all benthic habitats, from coral reefs to mud bottoms. They are particularly large and numerous around oil platforms and other artificial structures. Local specimens commonly reach a length up to 1m and a weight up to 20kg, but much larger individuals may occasionally be encountered. The species is known to reach a length over 2m and a weight over 200kg, though it is not certain whether individuals of this size occur in the Gulf.*

The hamour is a powerful predator with a diet as varied as its habitat preferences. It is known to eat fish, crustaceans, cephalopods, young sea turtles and probably also the occasional sea bird. The large mouth enables a hamour to swallow another fish more than half its own size. In the Gulf its favorite food items include octopus, large shrimp Penaeus spp. *and especially the swimming crab* Portunus pelagicus.

Hamour are fished intensively by lines and traps, as well as being a favorite spearfishing quarry. Their flesh is excellent eating, and because of their size and abundance they are one of the most highly valued and commercially important food fish in the Gulf.

salinities above 48⁰/₀₀ these scientists found a marked change in community composition, due to the complete disappearance of scleractinian corals, alcyonarians, echinoderms and calcareous algae, together with most of the calcareous foraminifera. Filamentous red and green algae, however, were found to tolerate salinities up to about 50⁰/₀₀, and at salinities between 50 and 70⁰/₀₀ the animal populations were usually dominated by gastropods and imperforate foraminifera. A few brown algae survived at such salinities, but blue-green algae commonly dominated the samples, as they did in those taken by Aramco biologists along the Saudi Arabian coast. Very few animal species were found at salinities higher than 70⁰/₀₀ (Hughes Clarke and Keij, 1973).

Samples taken during the Aramco surveys have extended the known range of salinity tolerance upward for several major groups of marine organisms. Sea grasses and much of the associated biota, including shrimp and a considerable variety of fish, thrive at salinities of at least 62⁰/₀₀ in Dawhat Zalum and many parts of the Gulf of Salwah (Fig 182). The same areas are inhabited by a variety of pelecypods and gastropods and by at least three echinoderms, the starfish *Astropecten phragmorus*, *A. polyacanthus* and *Asterina burtoni*. Alcyonarians of the "sea pen" type occur at salinities of 60⁰/₀₀ in Dawhat Zalum, and true coral reefs are found off Dammam and in Tarut Bay in locations where salinities sometimes exceed 50⁰/₀₀. Pearl oysters are extremely abundant, though of rather small size, at salinities of 56 to 58⁰/₀₀ in the Ras al-Qurayyah area, along with the filamentous green alga *Chaetomorpha linum* (Fig 184), *Avrainvillea amadelpha*, *Sargassum heteromorpha* and an extraordinary variety of sponges. Several species of fish, including large hamour *Epinephelus tauvina* (Fig 183), are abundant at salinities approaching 70⁰/₀₀, and large numbers of healthy fish fry were encountered at salinities over 110⁰/₀₀ in parts of the al-'Uqayr lagoon system. In addition to *Dunaliella*, diatoms, a turbellarian, nematodes, and five species of copepods were found actively reproducing at salinities exceeding 300⁰/₀₀ in the salt lagoon adjacent to Dawhat Zalum. This appears to represent a new record for salinity tolerance by metazoan animals of any kind.

In spite of these findings, however, and in spite of the unexpected diversity of coral reefs and other marine communities found throughout the Aramco study, it is clear that salinity is one of the most important environmental factors limiting the occurrence of marine life in the Gulf. Human activities, such as engineering works or industrial plants, which bring about substantial local or regional salinity increases, are bound to have striking biological effects in the affected areas, and will result in at least local impoverishment of the biota. The extent and magnitude of such effects can be roughly predicted from available data on the distribution of communities and species as a function of salinity, but the accuracy of these predictions will improve only as more detailed data on distribution become available.

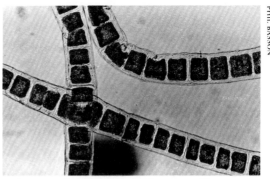

Fig 184. Chaetomorpha linum, *a filamentous green alga which often forms tangled masses reminiscent of coarse cotton-wool.*

193

CTION FOUR

APPENDICES

Section four contains a description of the collection and analysis of samples and data, a glossary of terms used in the text, a bibliography with two further reading lists, and species lists for each biotope.

Description of how samples are collected and studied provides the non-technical reader with some insight into how the information presented in the text was gathered, and also documents the techniques used, so that they can be assessed or repeated by other scientists in future studies.

The glossary presents short definitions of technical terms used in the text as a reference for the reader unfamiliar with biological terms. A more detailed explanation of many of these terms can be found in biological, ecological, or geological texts (e.g. Hedgpeth, 1957; Odum, 1971; Krebs, 1972).

The bibliography includes a listing of all references cited in the text of the book, as well as two lists for further reading. One of these lists contains books or articles of general interest, and the other contains more specialized references.

The last part of the Appendices is a listing of all the plant and animals species found by Aramco biologists. These lists show the great diversity of organisms inhabiting the western Arabian Gulf, and form a base for further scientific research.

Fig 185 (preceding page). The blue angelfish Pomacanthus maculosus *is one of the most common Gulf fishes, and is even found in hypersaline bays at salinities of over 60°/oo. [Jana Island] (Photo by Tom Bobrowski)*

THE COLLECTION AND ANALYSIS OF SAMPLES AND DATA 199
Measuring the physical and chemical environment – quantitative biological sampling methods – estimating species diversity – non-quantitative sampling methods

GLOSSARY 205

WEIGHTS AND MEASURES 213

BIBLIOGRAPHY 214
References cited – further reading (general) – further reading (specific or technical)

THE COLLECTION AND ANALYSIS
OF SAMPLES AND DATA

Although this book is not intended as a technical treatise, the specialist reader will still wish to know how the various kinds of data were obtained. This section may be of interest even for the non-technical reader, however, and provide insight into some of the ways in which scientific information about the sea and its animals and plants is collected.

Except for the intertidal zone and sites next to the shore, a ship is always required to bring the scientist and his equipment to the work site. Equipment for sub-surface sampling is heavy and usually requires the use of some kind of mechanical hoist or winch to lower and raise it. During Aramco studies, such equipment was operated from a variety of small trawlers, tugboats and workboats. In the extensive bays and shallows of the Saudi Arabian coastal zone, however, such deep-draft vessels cannot operate, and work was done from inflatable, outboard-powered craft and small launches. For example, some grab and bottle samples were collected in shallow water using a hydrographic winch and 5.2m outboard launch.

Almost all such sampling devices operate "blind," which has some advantages for statistical purposes but at the same time yields a rather incomplete picture of underwater communities. For many purposes, a first-hand assessment by diving is quicker and more accurate; therefore, all the biotopes down to 30m depth were examined by diving as well as by remote-operated sampling gear.

MEASURING THE PHYSICAL AND CHEMICAL ENVIRONMENT

The physical and chemical properties of sea water, and also of the bottom material in the case of benthic organisms, are of primary importance in determining the occurrence of marine plants and animals. An essential part of any biological sampling program is, therefore, the measurement of these properties.

WATER SAMPLES can be conveniently collected from the surface by bringing a sample up on deck in a bucket. Recovery of water samples from below the surface, without disturbing their chemical or physical condition, is a little more complicated. The basic tool is the oceanographer's water bottle, which is lowered while open to a pre-determined depth by means of a winch and wire, and then closed by dropping a "messenger" weight, which slides along the wire to trip a mechanism which closes the bottle. The bottle with contained sample is then hauled to the surface. Normally a whole series or "cast" of such bottles is arrayed along the vertical wire to obtain simultaneous samples from several different depths. Each bottle, on being closed by a messenger arriving from above, drops another messenger to close the next bottle down the wire. During the Aramco investigations, bottles of the "Van Dorn" design, made from chemically inert plastic material (PVC), have been used whenever sub-surface water samples were required (Fig 186).

The **temperature** of surface or sub-surface water samples was measured using a mercury thermometer accurate to the nearest 0.5°C. Sea temperatures were also measured using a direct reading thermistor accurate to the nearest 0.2°C. This device could be lowered to provide a temperature profile of the upper 30m of water.

The **salinity** of water samples was determined using a hand-held, temperature-compensated refractometer accurate to the nearest whole part per thousand ($1.0\%_{00}$). This device depends on the fact that the refractive index of water changes according to its salt content. Much more accurate field determination of salinity is possible using electronic instruments based on either direct or inductive measurement of the conductivity of the water.

Fig 186. Preparing one of a "cast" of Van Dorn bottles, which will be lowered to obtain water samples at various depths. [aboard Gulf Princess *near Karan Island]*

Fig 187. Water samples are prepared in the field for subsequent laboratory analysis to determine the concentration of dissolved oxygen. [Ju'aymah]

None of these instruments, however, is calibrated for salinities greater than 41⁰/₀₀, and so they are of limited usefulness in the Gulf. Laboratory titration of salinity is another accurate but time-consuming method, and such accuracy was not considered essential for this study.

Two different methods were used, either together or separately, to measure the **oxygen content** of the water. A modified version (Strickland and Parsons, 1972) of the Winkler titration method was used on duplicate 60ml samples "pickled" in the field and subsequently titrated in the laboratory. Alternatively, a galvanic cell type oxygen meter was used for direct oxygen readings in the field. Readings were converted directly into oxygen concentrations using a programmable calculator. The galvanic cell, like the thermistor, could be lowered to a maximum depth of 30m. In general, these two methods gave fairly good agreement when they were used together. The accuracy of both these methods is still under study, but is probably within 0.2mg/l.

Of the various **nutrient salts** in sea water, only phosphate, ammonia and the combined sum of nitrate and nitrite were determined for large numbers of samples. Sea water samples obtained from shore or from sea-going vessels were frozen immediately in liquid nitrogen and maintained in a frozen condition until they could be analyzed. Samples obtained from inflatable craft and small boats, where it was not feasible to carry liquid nitrogen, were placed on ice immediately and frozen within three hours of collection. The colorimetric analyses were performed using either an automatic analyzer or a hand operated, 10cm path spectrophotometer.

Phosphate, nitrate, and nitrite were determined by the methods of Strickland and Parsons (1972); while ammonia was analyzed by the method of Solorzano (1969). Most of the analyses were performed in the Beirut laboratories of Drs Basson and Hardy, and one series was carried out by the Danish Water Quality Institute in Copenhagen. Both laboratories and methods produced similar results.

SEDIMENT SAMPLES for particle size analysis were generally collected by the same coring device used for sampling meiofauna (see below). These samples were subsequently dried and fractionated in a set of standard sieves on a RoTap machine. For purposes of comparing different samples and sampling localities, the resulting size distributions were converted into phi values (Holmes & MacIntyre, 1971).

QUANTITATIVE BIOLOGICAL SAMPLING METHODS

The **meiofauna** of intertidal sediments was sampled by a hand-operated corer with a nominal internal diameter of 5cm. The resulting sand or mud cores were sliced into sections 5cm long. As a rule, the uppermost section (containing sediment that originally lay between the surface and a depth of 5cm) was preserved and analyzed, along with a sub-surface section containing sediment that originally lay between the depths of 20 and 25cm. The samples were fixed at the time of collection in neutral formalin, and subsequently the organisms were stained with rose bengal, identified and counted under the microscope. An attempt was made to obtain samples representative of the different regions of a beach or tidal flat, but elaborate statistical sampling procedures were avoided, since analysis of the large number of samples resulting from such procedures would not have been feasible.

Larger animals or **macrofauna** in intertidal biotopes were sampled quantitatively using metal quadrat frames to mark off areas of 0.01, 0.25 or 1.0m², from which the animals were then collected and/or counted by hand. In some cases sand or mud from the sample areas was passed through a sieve to obtain burrowing animals. A hand corer sampling 0.01m² was also used. The size of the area sampled was selected according to the abundance of the animals being studied, wherever feasible, in such a way that the samples contained, on the average, not less than 20 individuals of the species in question. Samples containing fewer individuals must be collected in inordinate numbers to provide an accurate estimate of the population density. On occasion, sample areas as large as 10m² were marked off and collected to meet this requirement.

Organisms from all kinds of subtidal **soft bottoms** were collected using a "Ponar" grab sampler covering 0.053m² (a square 23cm on a side). The contents of the grab were washed over a sieve with mesh openings 0.5mm square, and all organisms retained in the sieve were fixed for later identification and counting in the laboratory. Organisms occurring at densities less than about 100 individuals per m² are not sampled at all adequately by this device, and where such larger organisms were of especial interest quadrats of 1.0m² were sampled by hand (as in the case of *Brissopsis persica*). In a few cases, core samples of 0.01m² were also taken by diving.

Subtidal **hard bottoms** are extremely difficult to sample quantitatively and for the most part such sampling was not attempted. **Coral communities** were, however, investigated to a limited extent using a method of line transects. In this procedure a 10m length of rope, marked off in 1m segments, was stretched across the reef at pre-determined points. The coral species across which the rope passed were recorded separately for each 1m segment. The aim of this procedure was to obtain a measure of the relative abundance of different coral species in the different reef zones, and some indication of whether one species influences the occurrence of others in its vicinity. This work is still continuing.

The extent to which **grassbeds** cover the bottom of Tarut Bay was estimated by a semi-random sampling procedure. On an aerial photomosaic of the entire bay, five widely separated locations were selected as representing the full range of depths, distances from shore, bottom types and current conditions occurring in the bay. Using each of these locations in turn as a starting point, an underwater transect was run by divers using underwater propulsion vehicles. The presence or absence of grass cover was recorded at ten pre-determined points along each transect. The direction of each transect was chosen at random by throwing dice. Dice were also used to determine the location of each sampling point along the transect. The distance of each point from the preceding one (in terms of the running time at a constant vehicle speed setting) was decided by a separate throw of the dice. The transects themselves were thus of variable length. The time scale was chosen in such a way that the average distance between adjacent sample points was about 60m, and the average length of a transect about 600m. To avoid unconscious observer bias the starting point itself was not sampled. The result of this procedure was a list of 50 sample points. Grass was present at 33 of these, giving an estimate of 66% grass cover for the available, subtidal portion of Tarut Bay.

Fig 188. Aramco biologists collect a core sample from an intertidal mud flat in Tarut Bay.

The **biomass** of grassbeds was investigated at one site in Tarut Bay. First, the number of leaf rosettes was counted in a series of eight 0.01m² sample quadrats. The rosette count ranged from 26 to 102 per sample with a mean of 54.4, or 5,440 rosettes per m². On a subsequent occasion, but at the same location, numbers of grass plants were collected intact and brought back to the laboratory in a fresh condition. Rosettes and rhizomes were separated, blotted free of excess water, placed in pre-weighed sample pans and weighed on an analytical balance to the nearest 0.1mg. The samples were then oven-dried at 65°C for several days, until no further weight loss occurred. These weighings, corrected for the weight of the sample pans, gave the "wet" and "dry" weights of the material. Finally the samples were incinerated at 550°C and the weight of the remaining ash determined. This was then subtracted from the dry weight to obtain "ash free dry weight."

Zooplankton were sampled using tow nets of conventional design, 0.5m in diameter. Usually the nets were towed horizontally about 1m below the water surface, and the volume sampled during the 5 minute tow was recorded by a calibrated flow meter in the mouth of the net. A "coarse" net with mesh openings of 0.57mm and a "fine" net with openings of 0.15mm were used routinely. Other mesh sizes down to 64 microns were used for special purposes. Plankton samples were fixed in formalin as soon as collected. In the laboratory they were diluted to a convenient standard volume and sub-samples of appropriate size were examined under the microscope to identify and count the animals. Many samples were also scanned in their entirety to obtain counts of penaeid shrimp eggs and larvae, which are usually not abundant enough to be counted by sub-sampling.

Phytoplankton samples from surface waters were collected by bucket (1 to 10l) and transferred to plastic carboys. Sub-surface samples were taken in Van Dorn bottles and poured into carboys. The samples were immediately fixed in Lugol's iodine solution and on return to the laboratory were allowed to settle for several weeks. The concentrated plankton was then removed by siphoning and suitable sub-samples were identified and counted using an inverted phase-contrast microscope.

Phytoplankton abundance can also be estimated by measuring the chlorophyll content of a sample, though of course this gives no information about the species composition of the plankton. The method is, however, less time-consuming in the laboratory than counting cells. In this technique, the phytoplankton cells from a water sample (1 or 2l) were collected by passing the sample through a collodion membrane filter with pores 0.45 micron in diameter. The membrane with adhering plankton cells was then quick-frozen in liquid nitrogen, and kept frozen until it could be analyzed. In the laboratory, the membrane with plankton was dissolved in acetone and the chlorophyll concentration determined by its light absorption in a spectrophotometer (Strickland and Parsons, 1972). This technique is particularly valuable in providing an approximate estimate of the photosynthetic productive capacity of a body of water.

ESTIMATING SPECIES DIVERSITY

Laboratory analysis of quantitative biological samples yields, generally speaking, a list of the numbers of individuals of each species of plants and animals found in the sample. To compare community conditions in different occurrences of a biotope, or to compare different biotopes, it is convenient to summarize this information in the form of a diversity index. Several different indices of diversity are used by ecologists; all of them attempt to evaluate one or both of two properties of the community, as reflected in samples taken from it. The number of species encountered in a sample obviously depends on the size of the sample as well as on the number of species present in the community sampled. A useful diversity index must compensate in some way for this effect, to yield an estimate independent of sample size; and ideally such compensation should not depend on any particular (and possibly incorrect) assumption about the relative abundance of different species. The other property of particular interest is sometimes called "species dominance," and reflects the relative abundance of different species within the biotope.

The index used by Aramco biologists is a variation of that proposed by Simpson (1949), and is essentially a measure of the probability that two individual organisms, drawn at random from a biotope or sample of it, belong to different species. If each of the species occurring in a biotope is given an identifying index number i ($i=1, 2, 3, \ldots$. s where s is the total number of species in the biotope) then p_i is the probability that a randomly collected individual will belong to a particular species (the ith species) and $(1-p_i)$ is the probability that it will belong to any other species. The product $p_i(1-p_i)$ then gives the probability that two random draws will yield two different species one of which is the ith species; and the sum of these probabilities for all species gives the overall probability of obtaining two different species by two random draws:

$$D = \sum_{i=1}^{s} p_i(1-p_i)$$

which can also be written in the equivalent form

$$D = 1 - \Sigma p_i^2.$$

This formula applies to a sampling "universe" or entire biotope, however, and requires some modification in order to be applicable to samples of relatively small size. The version used by Aramco biologists applies to finite samples and can be considered as an "unbiased estimator" of the actual value of D for the biotope being sampled. The formula can be written in various ways, but the most convenient is

$$d = \frac{N^2 - \Sigma n_i^2}{N(N-1)}$$

where n_i=the number of individuals of the ith species in the sample, and $N=\Sigma n_i$, in other words N is the total number of individual organisms in the sample. This index has two convenient properties:

1 as an estimate of D it is truly independent of sample size even for small samples (though of course the statistical reliability of the estimate is better the larger the sample); and

2 a combined index for several samples can be calculated from the indices of the individual samples by simply weighting each sample index by the total number of organisms in the sample, in other words

$$\bar{d} = \frac{\Sigma N_j d_j}{\Sigma N_j}$$

These properties are not shared to the same degree by other diversity indices in common use.

NON-QUANTITATIVE SAMPLING METHODS

Quantitative sampling is often time-consuming to carry out in the field, and statistically adequate sampling procedures generally yield large numbers of samples whose analysis is extremely demanding of laboratory work. A single grab sample from the Saudi Arabian coastal zone may contain up to 200 species and 10,000 individual organisms; the analysis of such a sample is a matter of weeks or more. Furthermore, some biotopes and some types of organisms are difficult to sample quantitatively. Even in such cases, however, a great deal of valid information may be obtained by the use of semi-quantitative or non-quantitative methods. For example, the species composition of fish populations, and even some idea of the relative abundance of different species, can be obtained by studying the catches of commercial trawlers, although neither the area of bottom covered, nor the catching efficiency of the gear is known. Aramco biologists have learned much by trips aboard trawlers of the Saudi Arabian commercial fleet, and have used similar gear, of smaller size, to sample shrimp and fish populations in Tarut Bay and other shallow water areas. This was done using a "try net" of 3m width, towed behind an outboard launch. Shrimp post-larvae and juveniles were collected on various bottom types using a "skimmer" trawl consisting of a coarse plankton net (mesh openings 0.75mm) on a rectangular frame, mounted on a sort of sled allowing it to be towed with the lower edge of the net opening 5cm off the bottom.

Another "semi-quantitative" type of equipment used in sampling subtidal soft bottoms is the dredge. Innumerable different designs are available, but the one used by Aramco biologists is a relatively simple version consisting of a heavy sheet steel frame with a non-flexible "bridle" of steel rods and a bag of extremely heavy-duty nylon netting with a finer-meshed inner lining. On both dredge and skimmer, flaps of heavy canvas protect the bag against tearing when rock bottoms are encountered. The dredge used had an opening about 20×45cm and a bag about 1m deep. This was towed over the bottom to sample burrowing animals of good size, such as snails and heart urchins.

Many kinds of specimens have also been collected by hand, both along the shore and during diving operations, and returned to the laboratory for study and identification. Finally, many kinds of animals can readily be identified by sight, without the necessity of collecting specimens. This is especially true of birds and many fish. The presence of these animals in a biotope, and to some extent their numbers as well, have been registered on the basis of such "sight records." Such direct visual observation is also, in many cases, the most valuable source of information on the interrelationships of different species, and on the composition and boundaries of the biological communities.

Fig 189. Visual observations, carefully recorded, are one of the most important tools in the analysis of biological communities. [Karan Island]

204

GLOSSARY

ALGA (pl. ALGAE): general name for a very diverse group of plants, including several phyla and ranging in size from microscopic phytoplankton to large seaweeds. Unlike other plants, algae possess unicellular reproductive structures with no layers of sterile cells. They lack true roots and vascular conducting tissue.

ALCYONARIANS: a subclass (Octocorallia) of Anthozoa distinguished from other anthozoans, such as anemones and stony corals, by possession of 8 pinnate or feathery tentacles. Among the most familiar members are gorgonians, whip corals, sea fans and the precious red coral.

ALLUVIAL: relating to alluvium: clay, silt, sand, gravel or similar material deposited by running water.

AMPHIPODS: a group of small Crustacea (order Amphipoda) sometimes known as scuds. Amphipods are distinguished from the closely related isopods by their laterally compressed body, usually bent into a "C" shape, and by possessing legs of two distinct types. Most of the 4,600 known species are marine, but some inhabit fresh water and a few, such as the sandhoppers or beach-fleas, are semi-terrestrial.

ANAEROBIC: (of organisms) capable of living and metabolizing in the absence of free oxygen; (of chemical reactions, etc.) taking place in the absence of free oxygen.

ANGIOSPERMS: a class (Angiospermae) of vascular plants having seeds in a closed case or ovary.

ANNELIDS: segmented worms; the invertebrate phylum (Annelida) which includes the common earthworm, leeches and many marine or aquatic species that are free-swimming, burrowing or tube-dwelling. The clam-worm or rag-worm is a familiar temperate-zone example (see POLYCHAETE).

ANTHOZOANS: the class (Anthozoa) of coelenterates containing sea anemones and true corals, in which the free-swimming medusa stage is absent and only the polyp stage is represented.

ANTIPATHARIAN: black or thorny coral (order Antipatharia); superficially gorgonian-like Anthozoa with upright, plant-like colonies. Largely found in deep water of tropical seas.

ARTHROPODS: a phylum (Arthropoda) of animals with a segmented body, a hard, jointed "skin" or exoskeleton, and paired, jointed limbs. Over half of all the known animal species are arthropods; and the majority of arthropods are insects.

BENTHOS: a community of organisms living on the bottom of a body of water.

BENTHIC: relating to the benthos.

BIOMASS: the mass of living matter in a sample area or volume.

BIOTA (adj. BIOTIC): the flora and fauna of a region.

BIOTOPE: a defined area of the physical environment with a recognizable community of organisms interconnected with each other through certain feeding and energy pathways (see also p. 13). Also: "a region uniform in environmental conditions and in its populations of animals and plants for which it is the habitat." (Webster, 1973.)

BIVALVE: see PELECYPODS.

BRYOZOANS: moss animals; also known as polyzoans or ectoprocts. A class (Bryozoa) of small, sessile, colonial animals, each individual having a ring of tentacles around the mouth. They superficially resemble coelenterate polyps, but unlike the latter possess a body cavity called a coelom, and an alimentary canal with two openings.

BYSSUS: a tuft of long, tough filaments by which some bivalve mollusks, such as mussels and pearl oysters, attach themselves to solid objects or the bottom.

CALCAREOUS: consisting of or containing calcium carbonate.

CALYX (pl. CALICES): cuplike portion of a coral skeleton which contains an individual polyp.

CARAPACE: a protective "shell" covering part or all of the body, as in many Crustacea and in turtles.

CARID: one of the two main types of shrimp. A diagnostic feature of carid shrimp is the presence of chelae or "pincers" on only the first two pairs of walking legs.

CARNIVOROUS: subsisting or feeding on animal tissues.

CAUDAL: relating to the tail, or hind part of the body.

CEPHALOPODS: a class (Cephalopoda) of mollusks including nautilus, squid, cuttlefish and octopus, and characterized by the possession of long prehensile tentacles surrounding the mouth. Members of the group have a highly developed nervous system, with eyes similar in operation to those of vertebrates.

CHELA (pl. CHELAE, adj. CHELATE): a pincer-like organ or "claw" borne by a limb of an arthropod, such as a crab.

CHITON: a group (class Polyplacophora) of elongated, bilaterally symmetrical marine mollusks with a dorsal shell of 8 calcareous plates. Most chitons are only a few cm long and are found clinging tightly to hard substrates such as rocks. They creep about slowly and feed on algae.

CILIA: small hair-like filaments projecting from a cell, which beat rhythmically and cause movement of water or other fluids. Many Protozoa, flatworms, etc propel themselves by ciliary movement.

CLUPEID: a member of the family (Clupeidae) of herring-like fish with soft fin-rays, a laterally compressed body, and a forked tail. Commonly found in coastal waters and rivers.

COELENTERATES: organisms included in the phylum Cnidaria, such as corals, sea anemones, jellyfish and hydroids.

COMATULIDS: an order of free-swimming stalkless crinoids, sometimes called feather-stars, included in the phylum Echinodermata.

COMMENSALISM (adj. COMMENSAL): a symbiotic relationship between organisms of different species in which one species takes advantage of the food-gathering or "house-building" activities of another, without actually causing it any harm.

COMMUNITY (biological or ecological): a group of organisms of different species populations regularly occurring together in a particular habitat.

CONGLOMERATE: (of rock) composed of rounded fragments varying from small pebbles to large boulders in a cement, as of hardened clay.

COPEPODS: a large subclass (Copepoda) of planktonic, benthic, or parasitic Crustacea found in marine and fresh water habitats. Individuals typically range from less than 1mm to several mm in length. Marine copepods are an important link in many food chains and webs.

COQUINA: soft, whitish limestone formed of broken shells and corals cemented together.

CRINOIDS: a class (Crinoidea) of echinoderms including feather-stars and the stalked sea lilies. Sea lilies were among the most important marine invertebrates during ancient geological times, and modern representatives still inhabit the deep sea.

CRUSTACEANS: a very large and diverse class (Crustacea) of mostly marine arthropods whose most familiar representatives include water-fleas, wood-lice, barnacles, shrimp, crabs and lobsters. All have two pairs of antennae, and breathe by means of gills.

CTENOPHORES: sea walnuts or comb jellies; a small phylum (Ctenophora) of radially symmetrical marine invertebrates resembling jellyfish (see SCYPHOZOA), but having tentacles bearing "lasso-cells," and swimming by means of 8 bands of ciliated, comb-like plates.

DIATOMS: an important class (Bacillariophyceae) of microscopic planktonic or benthic unicellular algae, occurring singly or in colonies. Diatoms have a silica skeleton composed of two parts or valves fitting closely into each other. Diatoms are the most important primary producers in many marine biotopes, forming the base of many food webs.

DINOFLAGELLATE: one of the most important groups (phylum Pyrrophyta) of unicellular, photosynthetic plankton organisms, characterized by possession of two unequal flagella and a characteristic set of brownish photosynthetic pigments. "Red tide" organisms, and several luminescent species are included in this group.

DIURNAL, SEMI-DIURNAL: having a daily, or twice daily cycle respectively.

DORSAL: relating to the back or upper surface of an organism.

ECHIURANS: a phylum (Echiurida or Echiura) of marine worms, related to annelids, often having an extremely long proboscis, or projection of the head. Many species live in sand and mud burrows in shallow water.

ECHINODERMS: the phylum (Echinodermata) of invertebrates which includes starfish (Asteroidea), brittle stars (Ophiuroidea), sea urchins, heart urchins and sand dollars (Echinoidea), sea lilies and feather stars (Crinoidea), and sea cucumbers (Holothurioidea).

Most members are radially symmetrical and characterized by an armor of calcareous ossicles.

ECOLOGY: a branch of science concerned with the interrelationships of organisms with each other and with their environment.

ECOSYSTEM: a complex of several interrelated communities together with their physical environment, having certain properties unique to this level of organization.

FAROUSH: Arabic name for a form of beach rock very widespread in the Arabian Gulf, formed by calcareous cementation of mud, sand or silty sediment. It occupies extensive areas in Tarut Bay and elsewhere, providing a habitat for many organisms.

FAUNA: animals or animal life.

FLAGELLUM (pl. FLAGELLA): a microscopic thread-like or whip-like projection from a cell, whose lashing or beating movements cause water currents (as in sponges) or move the entire cell through the fluid medium (as in micro-algae and many other small organisms). Flagella resemble cilia, but are much longer and generally fewer in number.

FLORA: plants or plant life.

FORAMINIFERANS: an order (Foraminifera) of Protozoa with a calcareous shell usually perforated with small holes. Most members are marine; a few are planktonic but most are benthic. Shells of dead Foraminifera often accumulate in warm seas to form layers of calcareous ooze.

GASTROPODS: a class (Gastropoda) of mollusks with a distinct head, a creeping foot and a single, usually coiled shell, i.e. snails and slugs. In some species, such as nudibranchs (sea slugs) the shell is completely lacking.

GORGONIANS: an order (Gorgonacea) of Octocorallia which includes sea whips, sea fans, and their relatives. The growth form of most gorgonians is plant-like and they are often brightly colored.

HALOPHILE (adj. HALOPHILIC): a salt-loving organism which flourishes or grows best in high concentrations of salt.

HALOPHYTE (adj. HALOPHYTIC): a salt-tolerant plant capable of growing in soil with high salt concentrations.

HERBIVOROUS: feeding on plants.

HERMATYPIC (of coral): reef forming.

HYDROID: hydrozoan polyp, usually colonial (see Fig 151).

HYDROPHIINAE: a subfamily of sea snakes which give birth to live young in the water and do not normally go ashore.

IGNEOUS: rock formed by solidification of molten rock material.

INFAUNA: benthic animals living within, rather than on, the surface of the substrate.

INVERTEBRATE: an animal lacking a vertebral column, i.e. any animal other than a vertebrate. Over 95% of all animal species are invertebrates.

ISOPODS: an order (Isopoda) of small Crustacea, typically with a dorso-ventrally flattened body bearing 7 pairs of similar legs. Most of the more than 4,000 species are marine, but some inhabit fresh water, and a few, known as slaters or wood-lice, are terrestrial (see AMPHIPODS). Many are parasitic on other Crustacea, or on fish.

LITHIFICATION: the process whereby unconsolidated sediments become consolidated into rock.

LITTORAL: the shore zone between high and low water marks; hence SUBLITTORAL, the region below that point.

MACROFAUNA: Large animals.

MEDUSA: the free-swimming or sexual stage in many coelenterates, having the form of a disc-shaped or bell-shaped jellyfish with tentacles around the rim, and a mouth underneath the center.

MEIOFAUNA: microscopic benthic animals inhabiting the interstitial spaces of mud and sand.

MEROPLANKTON: organisms which spend only part of their life cycle as members of planktonic communities, for example the planktonic larval stages of benthic animals such as oysters or shrimp.

METAMORPHIC: rock which has changed its constitution through pressure, heat and/or water, resulting in a more compact, crystalline condition.

METAZOA: all multicellular animals.

MICROFLAGELLATES: microscopic, unicellular organisms possessing at least one mobile, whip-like flagellum. Some members are photosynthetic while others capture food.

MIOCENE: the fourth of five periods of the upper Tertiary era. Approximate time span 5 to 22.5 million years ago.

MUCILAGINOUS: sticky or slimy; containing mucilage.

MYSIS LARVA: larval stage of many decapod Crustacea, which swims by means of the thoracic appendages, while the abdominal appendages are either undeveloped or nonfunctional. (see NAUPLIUS, PROTOZOEA, POST-MYSIS, and Fig 78.)

NAUPLIUS: an early larval stage of many Crustacea, including barnacles and shrimp, which swims by means of its three pairs of appendages.

NEKTON: animals of the water column which have considerable locomotory ability, e.g. most fish, whales and turtles.

NEMATODES: a large class (Nematoda) of invertebrates comprising the roundworms. Members of the group have a smooth, unsegmented body tapering at both ends. There are marine, fresh water and terrestrial nematodes, many of which are parasitic.

NEOGENE: a time period encompassing the Miocene and Pliocene periods; synonymous with upper Tertiary. Approximate time span 1.8 to 22.5 million years ago.

NEUSTON: specialized organisms living on or at the air-water interface of a body of water.

OLIGOCHAETES: a class (Oligochaeta) of segmented worms (Annelida) having a body with few bristles or setae. Members of the class include terrestrial forms such as the common earthworm, and also marine and fresh water species (see POLYCHAETES).

OMNIVOROUS: feeding on both plants and animals.

OPHIUROIDS: class (Ophiuroidea) of echinoderms including brittle stars, serpent stars and basket stars. Members typically have 5 or more arms, which are thin and well marked off from the central disc.

OSTRACODS: a subclass (Ostracoda) of Crustacea sometimes known as mussel-shrimps or clam-shrimps. Most members are about 1mm in length. The body and limbs are enclosed in a bivalved carapace or shell.

PALEOCENE: the earliest period of the upper Tertiary era, between the Cretaceous and the Eocene periods. Approximate time span 55 to 65 million years ago.

PECTORAL: the anterior and posterior paired limbs of vertebrates, including the paired fins of fishes, are called pectoral ("of the breast") and pelvic ("of the hips") respectively.

PELAGIC: inhabiting the open sea; hence SEMI-PELAGIC: inhabiting the open sea near the bottom or shore.

PELECYPODS: "hatchet-footed" bivalves or lamellibranchs; the class (Pelecypoda) of mollusks which includes clams, oysters, mussels, etc. Their most obvious external feature is the possession of a shell consisting of two halves or "valves" hinged together.

PELVIC: see PECTORAL.

PENAEID: one of the two main types of shrimp; more correctly termed "prawns" and distinguishable from "shrimp" or carids by having pincers or chelae on the first three pairs of walking legs, whereas in carids only the first two pairs are chelate.

PERACARIDS: a large superorder (Peracarida) of Crustacea which includes isopods, anisopods, cumaceans, amphipods and mysids. A distinctive feature of the group is the presence of a ventral brood pouch in the female, formed by flaps known as oostegites on certain thoracic appendages.

PERIPHYTON: organisms, including both algae and a variety of sessile animals, that live attached to the surface of submerged plants (and, by extension of the concept, to certain other underwater surfaces).

PHOTOSYNTHESIS: the production of organic matter from carbon dioxide and water by green plants and a few specialized bacteria, using the energy of sunlight. Oxygen is usually released.

PHYLUM (pl. PHYLA): one of the major divisions of the plant and animal kingdoms. At least 8 plant phyla and 17 animal phyla occur in the Gulf.

PHYTOPLANKTON: microscopic plants in the water column.

PLANKTON: plants and animals which, because of their small size and /or limited locomotor capability, live suspended in the water column and drift more or less passively with the ocean currents.

PLATYHELMINTHES: flatworms; a phylum of invertebrates which includes a variety of free-living forms as well as the parasitic tapeworms and flukes.

PLEISTOCENE: the earlier of two epochs of the Quaternary period. Synonymous with Ice Age or glacial period. Approximate time span 10,000 to 1.8 million years ago.

PLIOCENE: the last period of the upper Tertiary era, just before the Pleistocene period. Approximate time span 1.8 to 5 million years ago.

PNEUMATOPHORES: outgrowths of the roots of certain mud-inhabiting plants (e.g. mangroves) which protrude above the substrate and provide oxygen to the buried parts of the root system.

POLYCHAETES: class (Polychaeta) of segmented worms (phylum Annelida), having numerous setae or bristles on paired outgrowths of the body known as parapodia. The 5,300 species are almost all marine and can be divided into errant or free-swimming, and sedentary mostly burrowing species.

POLYP: the sessile form of coelenterates, consisting of a more or less cylindrical stalk attached at the base and with a mouth and tentacles borne on the free end. In the class Anthozoa (sea anemones and corals) only the polyp stage occurs and the free-swimming medusa stage is entirely absent. In Hydrozoa and Scyphozoa an alternation of sessile polyp and free-swimming medusa generations usually occurs.

POST-MYSIS: shrimp developmental stages immediately following the mysis larval stage.

PROTOCHORDATE: non-vertebrate members of the phylum Chordata, including tunicates (sea squirts) and the lancelets *Branchiostoma.*

PROTOZOANS: a phylum (Protozoa) comprising all unicellular animals.

RADIOLARIANS: an order (Radiolaria) of planktonic marine protozoans with a skeleton of siliceous spicules and with radiating thread-like pseudopodia.

RHIZOME: modified subterranean plant stem, which produces shoots above and roots below.

SCARID: parrot fish (family Scaridae) are brilliantly colored wrasse-like fish, whose teeth are modified into a parrot-like beak. They feed on living or dead coral, grinding it in their powerful jaws and so contributing to the formation of coral sand.

SCLERACTINIANS: true or stony corals (order Scleractinia) are anthozoans which secrete a calcareous skeleton and often form large reefs.

SCUTES: external plates of bone or horn.

SCYPHOZOANS: a class (Scyphozoa) of coelenterates which includes familiar jellyfish. The free-swimming medusa is the dominant stage and the polyp stage is either inconspicuous or absent. (see MEDUSA, POLYP.)

SEDIMENTARY ROCK: soft rock such as sandstone or shale, formed of mineral particles transported from their source and deposited elsewhere, or formed partly or wholly from inorganic remains of organisms, as in limestone.

SERPULID: polychaete worms (family Serpulidae) which secrete and live in calcareous tubes, extending a crown of tentacles to feed on plankton.

SESSILE: permanently attached or established, as in the case of many benthic animals such as barnacles.

SILICATE: an important nutrient salt containing silicon and oxygen. Diatoms require it for growth since it forms part of their cell wall. Thus, in areas of seawater where silicate concentrations are low, diatom growth may be inhibited.

SIPUNCULANS: peanut worms; a phylum (Sipunculida or Sipuncula) of marine burrowing worms lacking chaetae or bristles, and with no segmentation of the body.

STOMATOPODS: an order (Stomatopoda) of marine Crustacea with a small flattened carapace, stalked eyes, and five pairs of thoracic limbs bearing inverted pincers. The second pair of these is enlarged for catching prey. Also known as mantis shrimp.

SUBSTRATE: the base upon which an organism lives, such as mud or sand bottom.

SYMBIOSIS: an intimate association or relationship between organisms of different species.

TALUS: a slope formed especially by an accumulation of rock debris.

TAXON (pl. TAXA): any unit used in classifying organisms, e.g. species, genus, family, etc.

TAXONOMY: study of general principles of scientific classification.

TELEOSTS: a superorder (Teleostei) including all present-day bony fish except lung fish and a few surviving primitive types such as the gar-pike and sturgeon.

TINTINNID: free-swimming ciliate Protozoa, usually marine, having a chitinous capsule in which they are anchored.

TROPHIC: involved with energy transfer from one organism to another; as for instance when one species eats another.

TUNICATE: sea-squirt; a subphylum (Urochordata) of animals closely related to vertebrates. Most members are sessile, sac-like animals and feed by filtering sea water through an elaborate pharyngeal net. Certain tunicates (salps and larvaceans) are secondarily adapted to a planktonic existence.

TURBELLARIANS: a class (Turbellaria) of free-living flatworms, including both marine and fresh water species.

VAGILE: freely moving about.

VERTEBRATES: chordates of the subphylum Vertebrata, distinguished by having a true backbone or vertebral column.

ZOOPLANKTON: animal plankton.

ZOOXANTHELLAE: microscopic, photosynthetic algae symbiotic with reef forming corals and certain other animals.

The metric system of weights and measures has been used throughout this book with the following abbreviations:

mm – millimeter   ml – milliliter
cm – centimeter   l – liter
m – meter   g – gram
km – kilometer   kg – kilogram
sq m (or m²) – square meter   kcal – kilocalorie
sq km (or km²) – square kilometer   °C – degrees centigrade

BIBLIOGRAPHY

REFERENCES CITED

Al-Attar, M. H., and Ikenoue, H. 1974. Spawning season of shrimp *Penaeus semisulcatus* in the sea along the coast of Kuwait. Kuwait Institute for Scientific Research Publication MAB 1. VII. 74, 16 pp.

Al-Robaae, K. 1974. *Tursiops aduncus* bottle nose dolphin: a new record for Arab Gulf: with notes on Cetacea of the region. *Bull. Basrah Nat. Hist. Mus.* 1 (1): 7–16.

Badawi, H. K. 1975. On maturation and spawning in some penaeid prawns of the Arabian Gulf. *Mar. Biol.* 32: 1–6.

Boerema, L. K. 1969. The shrimp resources in the Gulf between Iran and the Arabian peninsula. *FAO Fish. Circ.* No. 310, 29 pp.

Boerema, L. K. 1976. Report of the meeting of the *Ad Hoc* Group of the IOFC Special Working Party on stock assessment of shrimp in the Indian Ocean area, to consider the stocks in the Gulf between Iran and the Arabian Peninsula. Doha 26–29 April, 1976. FAO Draft Report.

Brisou, J., Courtois, D., and Denis, F. 1974. Microbiological study of a hypersaline lake in French Somaliland. *Appl. Microbiol.* 27 (5): 819–822.

Caldwell, R. L., and Dingle, H. 1976. Stomatopods. *Sci. Am.* 234 (1): 80–89.

Carr, A. F. 1967. *So Excellent a Fishe.* New York, Natural History Press, 248 pp.

den Hartog, C. 1970, *The Sea-Grasses of the World.* North-Holland Publishing Company, Amsterdam. London, 275 pp.

Ellis, R. W. 1975. An analysis of the state of the shrimp stocks in the Gulf between Iran and the Arabian peninsula. (Provisional Report). IOFC/75/ Inf. 10, 17 pp.

Enomoto, Y. 1971. Oceanographic survey and biological study of shrimp stocks in the waters adjacent to the eastern coast of Kuwait. *Bull. Tokai reg. Fish. Res. Lab.,* No. 66, 74 pp.

FAO, 1973. Report to the government of the People's Democratic Republic of Yemen on marine turtle management, based on the work of H. F. Hirth and S. L. Hollingworth, marine turtle biologists. FAO/UNDP Rept. No. TA 3178, 51 pp.

Farrow, G. E. 1971. Back-reef and lagoonal environments of Aldabra Atoll distinguished by their crustacean burrows; pp. 455–500 in Stoddart, D. R., and Yonge, C. M. (ed.), *Regional Variation in Indian Ocean Coral Reefs.* Symposia of the Zoological Society of London, No. 28.

Forsskål, P. 1775. *Descriptiones animalium,* . . . etc. ed. Carsten Niebuhr. Mölleri, Hauniae, xxxiv + 164 pp., 1 map.

Friedmann, G. M., Amiel, A. J., Braun, M., and Miller, M. 1973. Generation of carbonate particles and laminates in algal mats: Example from sea-marginal hypersaline pool, Gulf of Aqaba, Red Sea. *Bull. Am. Ass. Petrol. Geol.* 57 (3): 541–557.

Gallagher, M. D. 1971. *The Amphibians and Reptiles of Bahrain.* Manama, Bahrain (privately printed), 37 pp.

Hedgpeth, J. W. (ed.) 1957. *Treatise on Marine Ecology and Paleoecology, Vol. 1. Ecology.* Geological Society of America, Memoir 67. 1296 pp.

Hirth, H. F., Klikoff, L. G., and Harper, K. T. 1973. Sea grasses at Khor Umaira, People's Democratic Republic of Yemen with reference to their role in the diet of the Green Turtle, *Chelonia mydas. Fish. Bull.* **71** (4): 1093–1097.

Holme, N. A., and McIntyre, A. D. (ed.) 1971. *Methods for the Study of Marine Benthos* (IBP Handbook No. 16). Blackwell Scientific Publications, Oxford and Edinburgh, 336 pp.

Hughes Clarke, M. W., and Keij, A. J. 1973. Organisms as producers of carbonate sediment and indicators of environment in the southern Persian Gulf; pp. 33–56 in Purser, B. H. (ed.), *The Persian Gulf.* Springer-Verlag, New York. Heidelberg. Berlin.

Kassler, P. 1973. The structural and geomorphic evolution of the Persian Gulf; pp. 11–32 in Purser, B. H. (ed.), *The Persian Gulf.* Springer-Verlag, New York. Heidelberg. Berlin.

Kendall, C. G. St. C., and Skipwith, Sir P. A. d'E. 1968. Recent algal mats of a Persian Gulf lagoon. *J. Sediment. Petrol.* **38**: 1040–1058.

Lewis, A. H., Jones, D. A., Ghamrawi, M., and Khosham, S. 1973. An analysis of the Arabian Gulf shrimp resources landed in Saudi Arabia – 1965–71. *Bull. Mar. Res. Centre, Saudi Arabia,* No. 4, 8 pp.

Odum, E. P. 1971. *Fundamentals of Ecology.* W. B. Saunders Co., Philadelphia, 574 pp.

Por, F. D. 1972. Hydrobiological notes on the high-salinity waters of the Sinai peninsula. *Mar. Biol.* **14**: 111–119.

Price, A. R. G., and Jones, D. A. 1975. Commercial and biological aspects of the Saudi Arabian Gulf shrimp fishery. *Bull Mar. Res. Centre, Saudi Arabia,* No. 6, 24 pp.

Purser, B. H. (ed.) 1973. *The Persian Gulf.* Springer-Verlag, New York. Heidelberg. Berlin, 471 pp.

Simpson, E. H. 1949. Measurement of diversity. *Nature* **163**: 688.

Strickland, J. D. H., and Parsons, T. R. 1972. *A Practical Handbook of Seawater Analysis.* Fisheries Research Board of Canada. Bull. 167 (2nd ed.), 310 pp.

Solorzano, L. 1969. Determination of ammonia in natural waters by the phenylhypochlorite method. *Limnol. Oceanogr.* **14**: 799–801.

Stoddart, D. R. 1969. Ecology and morphology of recent coral reefs. *Biol. Rev.* **44**: 433–498.

Sugden, W. 1963. The hydrology of the Persian Gulf and its significance in respect to evaporite deposition. *Am. J. Sci.* **261**: 741–755.

Webster's New Collegiate Dictionary, 1973. C. and C. Merriam Co., Springfield, Mass., 1536 pp.

Williams, W. D. 1970. Redescription of *Haloniscus searlei* Chilton, 1920 (Isopoda, Oniscoidea, Oniscoidae) from an Australian salt lake. *Crustaceana* **19** (3): 311–319.

Yentsch, C. S. 1963. Primary Production; pp. 157–175 in Barnes, H. (ed.), *Oceanogr. Mar. Biol. Rev.* **1**.

FURTHER READING – GENERAL

Anon., 1957. Pearl harvest . . . in the Persian Gulf. *Aramco World Magazine* **8** (2): 3–5.

Barger, T. J. 1968. Of turtles and terns. *Aramco World Magazine* **19** (3): 16–21.

Carr, A. F. 1967. *So Excellent a Fishe*. New York, Natural History Press, 248 pp.

Dickson, V. 1955. *The Wild Flowers of Kuwait and Bahrain*. George Allen and Unwin, Ltd., London, 144 pp.

Fricke, H. 1973. *The Coral Seas*. G. P. Putnam's Sons, New York and Thames and Hudson, London, 224 pp.

Gasperetti, J. 1973. A preliminary sketch of the snakes of the Arabian peninsula. *Jour. Saudi Arabian Nat. Hist. Soc.* (special issue), 44 pp.

Hardy, A. C. 1956. *The Open Sea: Its Natural History; Part One: The World of Plankton*. New Naturalist series. Collins, London, 336 pp.

Hardy, J. T. 1975. *Science, Technology and the Environment*. W. B. Saunders Co., Philadelphia, 300 pp.

Krebs, C. J. 1972. *Ecology: The Experimental Analysis of Distribution and Abundance*. Harper and Row, New York, 694 pp.

Kuronuma, K. 1974. Arabian Gulf fishery-oceanography survey . . . *Trans. Tokyo Univ. Fish.* No. 1, 118 pp.

Kuronuma, K., and Abe, Y. 1972. *Fishes of Kuwait*. Kuwait Institute for Scientific Research, 123 pp.

Newell, G. E., and Newell, R. C. 1973. *Marine Plankton: A Practical Guide*. Hutchinson Educational Ltd., London, 244 pp.

Perkins, E. J. 1974. *The Biology of Estuaries and Coastal Waters*. Academic Press, London, 678 pp.

Russell-Hunter, W. D. 1970. *Aquatic Productivity: an Introduction to Some Basic Aspects of Biological Oceanography and Limnology*. Collier-Macmillan Ltd., London, 306 pp.

Smith, J. L. B. 1961. *The Sea Fishes of Southern Africa*. Central News Agency, Ltd., South Africa, 573 pp.

Tracey, W. 1966. Pink gold. *Aramco World Magazine* **17** (5): 21–27.

White, A. W., and Barwani, M. A. 1971. *Common Sea Fishes of the Arabian Gulf and Gulf of Oman*. Trucial States Council, Dubai, Vol. 1, 166 pp.

Wickstead, J. H. 1965. *An Introduction to the Study of Tropical Plankton*. Hutchinson and Co. Ltd., London, 160 pp.

FURTHER READING – SPECIFIC OR TECHNICAL

Blegvad, H. 1944. Fishes of the Iranian Gulf; pp. 1–247 in Jessen, K., and Spärck, R. (ed.), *Danish Scientific Investigations in Iran*, Part III, Einar Munksgaard, Copenhagen.

Børgesen, F. 1939. Marine algae from the Iranian Gulf; pp. 47–141 in Jessen, K., and Spärck, R. (ed.), *Danish Scientific Investigations in Iran*, Part I, Einar Munksgaard, Copenhagen.

Bromiley, P. S. 1972. An economic feasibility study of a trawl fishery in the Gulf lying between Iran and the Arabian Peninsula. IOFC/DEV/72/23, 64 pp.

Clark, A. H., (and LeBaron Bowen, R., Jr.), 1949. Echinoderms of Tarut Bay and vicinity, Saudi Arabia with notes on their occurrence. *Amer. Mus. Novit.* No. 1390: 1–20.

Emery, K. O. 1956. Sediments and water of the Persian Gulf. *Bull. Am. Ass. Petrol. Geol.* **40** (10): 2354–2383.

Endlicher, S. L. and Diesing, C. M. 1845. Enumeratio algarum, quas ad oram insulae Karek, sinus Persici, legit Theodorus Kotschy. *Bot. Zeit.*, 3ter Jahrg., pp. 268–269.

Hall, D. N. F. 1962. *Observations on the Taxonomy and Biology of Some Indo-West Pacific Penaeidae (Crustacea, Decapoda)*. Colonial Office Fishery Publication No. 17, 229 pp.

Heding, S. G. 1941. The holothurians of the Iranian Gulf; pp. 113–117 in Jessen, K., and Spärck, R. (ed.), *Danish Scientific Investigations in Iran*, Part II, Einar Munksgaard, Copenhagen.

Hirth, H. F. 1971. Synopsis of biological data on the Green Turtle *Chelonia mydas* (Linnaeus) 1758. *FAO Fish. Synop.* No. 85.

Jones, D. A. 1974. The systematics and ecology of some sand beach isopods (Family Cirolanidae) from the coasts of Saudi Arabia. *Crustaceana* **26** (2): 201–211.

La Violette, P. E., and Frontenac, T. R. 1967. Temperature, salinity and density of the world's seas: Arabian Sea, Persian Gulf and Red Sea. U.S. Naval Oceanographic Office, Washington D.C. Informal Report No. IR 67–49, 118 pp.

"Meteor" Expedition Publications, 1966–   . Results of "Meteor" Expeditions in the Arabian Gulf and Straits of Hormuz in March and April, 1965, recorded in the serial publication "*METEOR*" *Forsch. Ergebnisse*, Gebrüder Borntraeger, Berlin, 1966–   . In progress.

Mortensen, Th., and Gislen, T. 1941. Echinoderms from the Iranian Gulf. Asteroidea, Ophiuroidea, and Echinoidea; pp. 55–112 in Jessen, K., and Spärck, R. (ed.), *Danish Scientific Investigations in Iran*, Part II, Einar Munksgaard, Copenhagen.

Nizamuddin, M. and Gessner, F. 1970. The marine algae of the northern part of the Arabian Sea and of the Persian Gulf. *"METEOR" Forsch. Ergebnisse*, Reihe D, No. 6, pp. 1–42, 27 pls.

Paldi, R. 1968. The Persian (Arabian) Gulf and Gulf of Oman – an annotated bibliography for the years 1859–1965. *FAO Fish Circ.* No. 117, 13 pp.

Peery, K. *et al.* Results of the Persian Gulf – Arabian Sea Oceanographic Surveys 1960–61. U.S. Naval Oceanographic Office Technical Report TR-176, Washington D.C., 239 pp.

Smith, M. 1926. *Monograph of the Sea-Snakes (Hydrophiidae).* The British Museum, London, 130 pp.

Stephensen, K. 1944–49. The Brachyura of the Iranian Gulf; pp. 57–237 in Jessen, K., and Spärck, R. (ed.), *Danish Scientific Investigations in Iran*, Part IV, Einar Munksgaard, Copenhagen.

Stoddart, D. R., and Yonge, C. M. (ed.) 1971. *Regional Variation in Indian Ocean Coral Reefs.* Symposia of the Zoological Society of London, No. 28, Academic Press, London, 584 pp.

Thorson, G. 1941. Studies on the egg masses and larval development of Gastropoda from the Iranian Gulf; pp. 159–238 in Jessen, K., and Spärck, R. (ed.), *Danish Scientific Investigations in Iran*, Part II, Einar Munksgaard, Copenhagen.

Volsøe, H. 1939. The sea snakes of the Iranian Gulf and the Gulf of Oman. With a summary of the biology of the sea snakes; pp. 9–45 in Jessen, K., and Spärck, R. (ed.), *Danish Scientific Investigations in Iran*, Part I, Einar Munksgaard, Copenhagen.

Wesenberg-Lund, E. 1944–49. Polychaetes of the Iranian Gulf; pp. 247–400 in Jessen, K., and Spärck, R. (ed.), *Danish Scientific Investigations in Iran*, Part IV, Einar Munksgaard, Copenhagen.

SPECIES LISTS

Following are lists of plant and animal species collected or observed by Aramco biologists during study of the various biotopes described in this book. Even for the non-specialist, these lists may give an idea of the variety of life forms to be encountered in the Gulf. For the specialist both the actual names listed, and the number of kinds of organisms in different major categories will have particular meaning.

For many important groups these lists contain more than twice as many species as have previously been recorded from the Gulf. In spite of this, the lists are by no means complete or exhaustive. Hopefully they will provide a guide and stimulus to further research which will certainly reveal the presence of many more species not listed here.

The taxonomic categories used to classify the plants and animals encountered in our studies are listed on pp. 220–221, together with the common names of many. The species list for each biotope is presented in two parts: first, a summary of the number of kinds of organisms in each major taxonomic category; and second, a list of the species identified by name or number, arranged according to the same set of taxonomic categories.

Identification of animals and plants has been made as complete as possible but it has not been possible to treat all groups with equal thoroughness, nor to identify all organisms to the species level. Errors will certainly be found in the lists, and we hope that these will be called to our attention.

In many cases it has been possible to recognize different species with certainty, but not yet to determine the correct names to be applied. In such cases a numerical code has been used to enable recognition of the same species in different lists; for instance, "sp. G-266" refers to a species of gastropod mollusk, subsequently determined as belonging to the genus *Acteocina*, and referred to in the lists as "*Acteocina* sp. G-266."

Sometimes only the family is known with certainty, and the species is then referred to by family name, for example "Atyidae sp. G-47." In some groups the species have been numbered consecutively within a family or order, as for example "Capitellidae sp. 7" among polychaetes, or "Cyclopoida sp. 15" among copepods.

In other cases a taxonomic group has not yet been studied in any detail, and is listed as "sp." (singular) or "spp." (plural) according to whether one, or definitely more than one species was encountered.

The species lists for each habitat differ greatly in total numbers of species. The list for "subtidal sand," for instance, includes 637 species, while that for "subtidal rock" includes only 193. Such differences are to some extent "real," that is to say some environments actually do contain more species than others, by virtue of providing a greater variety of ecological niches or ways for organisms to live.

Another reason for differences in the length of species lists, however, is unequal thoroughness in the sampling. Some biotopes are much easier to sample accurately than others; and some have attracted greater interest than others for various reasons. Bias of this kind is definitely present in the data from which the species lists were compiled, and great caution is therefore required when drawing conclusions based on differences in the numbers of species in different lists.

Somewhat more informative comparisons can be made based on the proportions of the total made up by species of a given taxonomic unit. For instance, the proportion of polychaetes, gastropods, etc. often varies from one biotope to another in a systematic way. Even here caution is necessary, however, since almost any sampling equipment has an inherent tendency to collect some types of organisms more efficiently than others.

TAXONOMIC CATEGORIES USED IN THE SPECIES LISTS

Plant Kingdom
Phylum **CYANOPHYTA** (blue-green algae)
Phylum **CHLOROPHYTA** (green algae)
Phylum **EUGLENOPHYTA** (microflagellates)
Phylum **CHRYSOPHYTA** (diatoms, coccolithophores, etc.)
Phylum **PYRROPHYTA** (dinoflagellates)
Phylum **PHAEOPHYTA** (brown algae)
Phylum **RHODOPHYTA** (red algae)
Phylum **ANTHOPHYTA** (flowering plants)

Animal Kingdom
Phylum **PROTOZOA**
       order FORAMINIFERA (foraminiferans)
       order RADIOLARIA (radiolarians)
Phylum **PORIFERA** (sponges)
Phylum **CNIDARIA** (coelenterates)
   class HYDROZOA (hydroids, hydromedusae and siphonophores)
   class SCYPHOZOA (scyphomedusae, i.e. "jellyfish")
   class ANTHOZOA
       order ACTINIARIA (sea anemones)
       order SCLERACTINIA (stony corals)
       order CERIANTHARIA (*Cerianthus)*
       order ANTIPATHARIA (black corals)
     subclass OCTOCORALLIA (alcyonarians, e.g. soft corals and gorgonians)
Phylum **CTENOPHORA** (comb jellies)
Phylum **PLATYHELMINTHES** (flatworms)
   class TURBELLARIA (free-living flatworms)
   class TREMATODA (flukes; all parasitic)
   class CESTODA (tapeworms; all parasitic)
Phylum **RHYNCHOCOELA** (nemertines or "proboscis worms")
Phylum **ASCHELMINTHES**
   class GASTROTRICHA (gastrotrichs; largely meiofauna)
   class ROTIFERA (rotifers)
   class KINORHYNCHA (kinorhynchs; largely meiofauna)
   class NEMATODA (roundworms)
   class ENTOPROCTA (kamptozoans; mostly epibiontic)
Phylum **MOLLUSCA** (mollusks)
   class POLYPLACOPHORA (chitons)
   class GASTROPODA (snails)
   class SCAPHOPODA (tusk shells)
   class PELECYPODA (bivalves)
   class CEPHALOPODA (cephalopods, e.g. squid)
Phylum **ECHIURIDA** (echiurans or "tongue worms")
Phylum **SIPUNCULIDA** (sipunculans or "peanut worms")
Phylum **ANNELIDA** (segmented worms)
   class POLYCHAETA (bristle worms)
   class OLIGOCHAETA (oligochaetes, e.g. earthworms)
   class HIRUDINEA (leeches)

Phylum **ARTHROPODA** (joint-legged animals)
    class ARACHNIDA
        order ACARI (mites)
    class PYCNOGONIDA (sea spiders)
    class CRUSTACEA
        order CLADOCERA (water fleas)
      subclass OSTRACODA (ostracods)
      subclass COPEPODA (copepods)
      subclass BRANCHIURA (fish lice)
      subclass CIRRIPEDIA (barnacles)
      subclass MALACOSTRACA (higher crustacea)
        order LEPTOSTRACA *(Nebalia)*
        order STOMATOPODA (mantis shrimp)
        order EUPHAUSIACEA (krill)
        order DECAPODA (decapods, e.g. shrimp, lobsters and crabs)
       superorder PERACARIDA
       order MYSIDACEA (opossum shrimp)
       order CUMACEA (cumaceans)
       order TANAIDACEA (anisopods)
       order ISOPODA (isopods)
       order AMPHIPODA (amphipods)
    class INSECTA (insects)
        order DIPTERA (flies)
        order COLEOPTERA (beetles)
Phylum **LOPHOPHORATA**
    class PHORONIDA (phoronids)
    class BRYOZOA (moss animals)
    class BRACHIOPODA (lamp shells)
Phylum **ECHINODERMATA**
    class CRINOIDEA (Sea lilies)
    class ASTEROIDEA (starfish)
    class OPHIUROIDEA (serpent stars or brittle stars)
    class ECHINOIDEA (sea urchins)
    class HOLOTHURIOIDEA (sea cucumbers)
Phylum **CHAETOGNATHA** (arrow worms)
Phylum **HEMICHORDATA** (acorn worms)
Phylum **CHORDATA**
   subphylum UROCHORDATA (tunicates)
    class ASCIDIACEA (ascidians)
    class THALIACEA (salps and doliolids)
    class LARVACEA (appendicularians)
   subphylum CEPHALOCHORDATA *(Branchiostoma)*
   subphylum VERTEBRATA
    class ELASMOBRANCHII (sharks, rays, etc.)
    class ACTINOPTERYGII (bony fishes)
        superorder TELEOSTEI ("modern" bony fishes)
    class REPTILIA (reptiles)
    class AVES (birds)
    class MAMMALIA (mammals)

Summary List

Chrysophyta	2+ [1]
Porifera	1+
Actiniaria	2+
Platyhelminthes	2+
Rhynchocoela	2+
Aschelminthes	2+
Gastropoda	48
Scaphopoda	1
Pelecypoda	22
Sipunculida	1+
Polychaeta	33+
Ostracoda	9
Copepoda	2+
Cirripedia	1
Stomatopoda	1
Decapoda	21+
Cumacea	1+
Tanaidacea	1+
Isopoda	13+
Amphipoda	23+
Coleoptera	1
Asteroidea	2
Ophiuroidea	2
Echinoidea	3
Holothurioidea	2+
Cephalochordata	1
Teleostei	8
Reptilia	2
Aves	9
	218+

Species List

phylum **CHRYSOPHYTA**
       diatoms spp.
phylum **PORIFERA**
      sp.
phylum **CNIDARIA**
    class ANTHOZOA
        order Actiniaria
          spp.
phylum **PLATYHELMINTHES**
      spp.
phylum **RHYNCHOCOELA**
      spp.

phylum **ASCHELMINTHES**
    spp.
phylum **MOLLUSCA**
    class GASTROPODA
        Acteon sp.
        Alaba virgata
        Amphithalamus microthyra
        Amphithalamus sp.
        Ancilla castanea
        Ancilla fasciata
        Atys cylindrica
        Brachytoma griffithi
        Brachina? glabella? [2]
        Bulla ampulla
        Cerithium ruppelli
        Cerithium scabridum
        Cythara cylindrica
        Diala sulcifera
        ?Drupa sp.
        Emarginula sp. G-114
        Epitoniidae sp. G-92A
        Eucithara sp. G-75B
        Eucithara sp.
        Eunaticina papilla
        Gibberula mazagonica
        Macrophragma sp. G-116
        Macrophragma sp.
        Mangilia townsendi
        Marginellidae sp. G-123
        Mitrella blanda
        Mitrella cartwrighti
        Murex kusterianus
        Nassarius pullus
        Nassarius stigmarius
        Natica lineata
        Nudibranch sp.
        Oliva bulbosa
        Phasianella sp. G-50B
        Polinices mammilla
        Pyramidellidae sp. G-38
        Pyramidellidae sp. G-49
        Pyrene atrata
        Pyrene spectrum
        Pyrene sp.
        Sinum sp.
        Smaragdia sp.
        Solidula affinis
        Stomatella sp. G-7
        Strombus decorus persicus
        Tornatina sp. G-203
        Turridae sp. G-74B

1 A plus sign (+) has been used to indicate that the number so marked is a minimum value for the number of species encountered. In many cases, species identification of the material is not yet complete. Such samples are listed as "spp." whenever they clearly contain two or more distinct species of a given category. A listing of "spp." thus carries a value of "2+"; several such listings may occur in different subdivisions of one major taxon, giving rise to larger numbers such as "34+" indicating that 34 or more species were found.

2 A question mark (?) has been used to indicate that the name assigned to a particular organism is tentative; i.e. there is some uncertainty as to whether the name used in the lists is correct. Resolution of such uncertainty is usually a matter for museum specialists and the elimination of all uncertainties would take years.

class SCAPHOPODA
  Dentalium octogonum
class PELECYPODA
  Codakia fischeriana
  Divaricella cumingii
  Donacilla sp. P-69
  Dosinia alta
  Ervilia scaliola
  Gafrarium arabicum
  Gastrochaena cuneiformis
  Glycymeris striatularis
  Iacra seychellarum
  Mactra olorina
  Mactra sp.
  Meretrix meretrix
  Notirus sp. P-59B
  Notirus sp. P-68
  Notirus sp.
  Pillucina sp. P-21
  Pitaria erycina
  Solen sp. P-45
  Spondervilia sp. P-191
  Tellinidae sp. P-13
  Timoclea farsiana
  Trachycardium lacunosum
phylum **SIPUNCULIDA**
  sp.

phylum **ANNELIDA**
  class POLYCHAETA
    Arabellidae sp.
    Ariciidae sp. 2
    Capitellidae sp.
    Chaetopteridae sp.
    Chrysopetalidae sp.
    Chrysopetalum sp.
    Cirratulidae sp.
    Dorvilleidae sp.
    Eunicidae sp. 3
    Eunicidae sp. 7
    Eunicidae sp.
    Exogoninae sp.
    Hesionidae sp. 4
    Hesionidae sp.
    Lumbrineridae sp. 3
    Lumbrineridae sp. 4
    Nereidae sp.
    Nereis sp.
    Onuphinae sp.
    Opheliidae sp. 3
    Opheliidae sp.
    Paraonidae sp.
    Pectinariidae sp. 1
    Phyllodocidae sp.
    Polynoidae sp. 3
    Polynoidae spp.
    Sabellidae spp.
    Serpulidae sp. 1
    Sigalionidae sp.
    Spionidae sp.
    Syllidae sp.
    Syllis sp.
    Terebellidae sp.

phylum **ARTHROPODA**
  class CRUSTACEA
    subclass OSTRACODA
      sp. 2
      sp. 10
      sp. 12
      sp. 15
      sp. 18
      sp. 19
      sp. 25
      sp. 31
      sp. 34
    subclass COPEPODA
      Cyclopoida spp.
      Harpacticoida spp.
      spp.
    subclass CIRRIPEDIA
      ?Ascothoracica sp.
    subclass MALACOSTRACA
      order Stomatopoda
        Lysiosquilla sp. 4
      order Decapoda
        Actumnus asper
        Alpheidae sp.
        Alpheus sp. 2
        Callianassa sp. 1
        Diogenidae spp.
        Etisus electra
        Hippolyte sp. 1
        Hippolytidae sp.
        Leucosia? sp. 12
        Matuta planipes
        Menaethius monoceros
        Ocypode saratan
        Palaemonidae sp. 1
        Penaeus latisulcatus
        Philyra platychira
        Philyra scabriuscula
        Philyra sp. 8A
        Portunus emarginatus
        Portunus pelagicus
        Portunus sp. nr. *hastatoides*
        Thalamita poissoni
      superorder Peracarida
      order Cumacea
        sp.
      order Tanaidacea
        sp.
      order Isopoda
        Anthura sp. 4
        Anthura sp.
        Colopisthus sp 3
        Cymothoidae sp. 6
        Eurydice peraticis
        Excirolana orientalis
        Gnathia sp.
        Gnathiidae sp.
        Jaeropsis sp. 20
        Polyexosphaeroma sp. 2

        Parasellidae sp.
        sp. 5
        spp.
        Sphaeromidae sp.
      order Amphipoda
        Ampeliscidae sp. 1
        Ampeliscidae sp. 3
        Ampithoidae sp. 15
        Atylidae sp. 13
        Gammaridae sp.
        Leucothoe sp. 10
        Leucothoe sp. 11
        Pholidae sp. 54
        sp. 1
        sp. 2
        sp. 2A
        sp. 3
        sp. 4
        sp. 9
        sp. 11
        sp. 12
        sp. 14
        sp. 20
        sp. 48
        sp. 51
        sp. 52
        sp. 53
        spp.
        Talitridae sp. 16
  class INSECTA
    order Coleoptera
      Staphylinidae sp.
phylum **ECHINODERMATA**
  class ASTEROIDEA
    Astropecten phragmorus
    Astropecten polyacanthus
  class OPHIUROIDEA
    Amphiura sp.
    Amphiuridae sp.
  class ECHINOIDEA
    Clypeaster humilis
    Echinodiscus auritus
    Metalia townsendi
  class HOLOTHURIOIDEA
    spp.

Sand Beach, Species List – Cont'd

phlyum **CHORDATA**
    subphylum CEPHALOCHORDATA
        Branchiostoma sp.
    subphylum VERTEBRATA
      class ACTINOPTERYGII
        superorder Teleostei
          Gerres oyena
          Gerridae sp.
          Gobiidae sp.
          Lethrinus nebulosus
          Lutjanus sp.
          Sillago sihama
          Stolephoridae sp.
          Upeneus tragula
      class REPTILIA
          Chelonia mydas
          Eretmochelys imbricata
      class AVES
          Ardea cinerea
          Charadrius alexandrinus
          Charadrius hiaticula
          Charadrius leschenaultii
          Haematopus ostralegus
          Hydroprogne tschegrava
          Numenius arquata
          Pluvialis squatarola
          Tringa cinereus

ROCK BEACH

Summary List

Cyanophyta	8
Phaeophyta	9
Rhodophyta	8
Actiniaria	2+
Platyhelminthes	1+
Polyplacophora	1
Gastropoda	24+
Pelecypoda	9
Sipunculida	1
Polychaeta	18+
Pycnogonida	1+
Ostracoda	2+
Copepoda	4
Cirripedia	1+
Stomatopoda	1
Decapoda	17
Mysidacea	1
Tanaidacea	1+
Isopoda	5+
Amphipoda	6
Asteroidea	1
Holothurioidea	1+
Ascidiacea	2+
Teleostei	4+
Aves	3
	131+

Species List

phylum **CYANOPHYTA**
    Calothrix confervicola
    Chroococcus varius
    Lyngbya ceylanica var. *constricta*
    Lyngbya confervoides
    Oscillatoria limosa
    Oscillatoria princeps
    Phormidium jenkelianum
    Spirulina major
phylum **PHAEOPHYTA**
    Colpomenia sinuosa
    Dictyota dichotoma var. *intricata*
    Dictyota divaricata
    Hormophysa triquetra
    Padina gymnospora
    Sargassum angustifolium
    Sargassum boveanum var. *aterrima*
    Sargassum latifolium
    Sphacelaria furcigera

phylum **RHODOPHYTA**
    Acanthophora spicifera
    Amphiroa fragilissima
    Centroceras clavulatum
    Ceramium subverticillatum
    Chondria dasyphylla
    Dasyopsis pilosa
    Gelidiella myrioclada
    Jania rubens
phylum **CNIDARIA**
  class ANTHOZOA
    order Actiniaria
    Anemone spp.
phylum **PLATYHELMINTHES**
    sp.
phylum **MOLLUSCA**
  class POLYPLACOPHORA
    sp. A-1
  class GASTROPODA
    Cerithium caeruleum
    Cerithium morum
    Cypraea grayana
    Diala goniochila
    Diodora funiculata
    Diodora sp. G-104
    Drupa margariticola
    Euchelis asper
    Euchelis bicinctus
    Macrophragma sp. G-116
    Mangilia townsendi
    Monodonta canalifera
    Morula margariticola
    Nodilittorina subnodosa
    Nudibranch spp.
    Onchidium peronii
    Planaxis sulcatus
    Pyrene spectrum
    Pyrene sp.
    Siphonaria rosea
    Thais pseudohippocastaneum
    Thais tissoti
    Trochus erythraeus
    Turbo coronatus
  class PELECYPODA
    Acar plicata
    Brachydontes variabilis
    Gafrarium arabicum
    Isognomon sp. P-146
    Ostraeidae sp.
    Ostraeidae sp. P-142A
    Periglypta? reticulata
    Pinctada sp. P-70
    Saxostraea sp. P-143
phylum **SIPUNCULIDA**
    Aspidosiphon sp.

phylum **ANNELIDA**
  class POLYCHAETA
    Chrysopetalidae sp. 1
    Chrysopetalidae sp.
    Eunicidae sp. 2
    Eunicine sp.
    Exogoninae sp.
    Hesionidae sp.
    Nereidae sp. 8
    Nereis sp.
    Opheliidae sp.
    Perinereis? sp.
    Platynereis sp.
    Sabellidae sp.
    Serpulidae sp. 5
    Serpulidae spp.
    Syllidae sp.
    Syllis sp. 1
    Syllis sp. 3
    Syllis sp.
phylum **ARTHROPODA**
  class PYCNOGONIDA
    spp.
  class CRUSTACEA
    subclass OSTRACODA
      spp.
    subclass COPEPODA
      Alteutha sp. 9
      Euterpina sp. 15
      Harpacticoida sp.
      Porcellidium sp. 10
    subclass CIRRIPEDIA
      sp.

subclass MALACOSTRACA
  order Stomatopoda
    Gonodactylus demanii
  order Decapoda
    Alpheus sp. 2
    Coenobita sp.
    Eriphia sebana smithii
    Grapsus tenuicrustatus
    Hapalocarcinidae sp. 1
    Menaethius monoceros
    Pachycheles sp. 3
    Petrolisthes lamarckii
    Petrolisthes ornatus
    Pilumnus longicornis
    Portunus pelagicus
    Portunus sp. nr. *hastatoides*
    Saron marmoratus
    Schizophrys aspera
    Thalamita admete
    Thalamita crenata
    Xantho exaratus
  superorder Peracarida
  order Mysidacea
    sp. 5
  order Tanaidacea
    sp.
  order Isopoda
    Gnathia sp. 14
    Gnathia sp. 15
    Jaeropsis sp. 20
    Polyexosphaeroma sp. 2
    sp. 5
    sp.
  order Amphipoda
    sp. 1
    sp. 3
    sp. 4
    sp. 7
    sp. 9
    sp. 59
phylum **ECHINODERMATA**
  class ASTEROIDEA
    Asterina burtoni
  class HOLOTHURIOIDEA
    sp.
phylum **CHORDATA**
  subphylum UROCHORDATA
  class ASCIDIACEA
    spp.
  subphylum VERTEBRATA
  superorder Teleostei
    Blenniidae spp.
    Gobiidae spp.
  class AVES
    Arenaria interpres
    Haematopus ostralegus
    Tringa cinereus

TIDAL MUD FLAT

Summary List

Cyanophyta	**2+**
Chrysophyta	**1+**
Anthophyta	**7**
Nematoda	**2+**
Gastropoda	**13**
Pelecypoda	**7**
Echiurida	**1**
Sipunculida	**1+**
Polychaeta	**14+**
Ostracoda	**1+**
Copepoda	**1+**
Decapoda	**12**
Cumacea	**1+**
Tanaidacea	**1+**
Isopoda	**1+**
Amphipoda	**2+**
Aves	**42**
	109+

Species List

phylum **CYANOPHYTA**
    Chrococcus membraninus
    Microcoleus chthonoplastes
    spp.
phylum **CHRYSOPHYTA**
    diatoms spp.
phylum **ANTHOPHYTA**
    Aeluropus lagopoides
    Arthrocnemon macrostachyum
    Avicennia marina
    Bienertia cycloptera
    Cistanche lutea
    Halocnemon strobilaceum
    Phragmites communis
phylum **ASCHELMINTHES**
  class NEMATODA
    spp.
phylum **MOLLUSCA**
  class GASTROPODA
    Cerithidea cingulata
    Cerithiidae sp.
    Cerithium rugosum
    Diodora funiculata
    Fusus townsendi
    Gibberula mazagonica
    Mitrella blanda
    Monilea obscura
    Murex kusterianus
    Nassarius pullus
    Pirinella conica
    Planaxis sulcatus
    Turbonilla sp.

class PELECYPODA
  Dosinia sp.
  Eumarcia opina
  Gafrarium arabicum
  Malleus sp.
  Meretrix meretrix
  Musculus sp. P-61
  Solen sp.
phylum **ECHIURIDA**
  Ikeda taenioides
phylum **SIPUNCULIDA**
  sp.
phylum **ANNELIDA**
  class POLYCHAETA
    Aricia sp. 3
    Capitellidae sp.
    Cirratulidae sp. 4
    Dorvilleidae sp.
    Eunice sp.
    Eunicidae sp.
    Exogoninae sp.
    Maldanidae sp.
    Nereidae sp. 17
    Nereis sp.
    Sabellidae spp.
    Spionidae sp.
    Syllis spp.
    Terebellidae sp.
phylum **ARTHROPODA**
  class CRUSTACEA
    subclass OSTRACODA
      sp.
    subclass COPEPODA
      Harpacticoida sp.
    subclass MALACOSTRACA
      order Decapoda
        Cleistostoma dotilliforme
        Diogenidae sp.
        Eurycarcinus sp.
        Grapsidae sp. 7
        Ilyograpsus paludicola
        Macrophthalmus depressus
        Macrophthalmus grandidieri
        Metopograpsus messor
        Paracleistostoma sp. 9
        Pilumnopeus vauquelini
        Scopimera sp. 3
        Scopimera sp. 10
      superorder Peracarida
      order Cumacea
        sp.
      order Tanaidacea
        sp.
      order Isopoda
        sp.
      order Amphipoda
        sp. 60
        sp.

phylum **CHORDATA**
  subphylum VERTEBRATA
    class AVES
      Accipiter nisus
      Acrocephalus spp.
      Anas acuta
      Anas clypeata
      Anas crecca
      Anas penelope
      Anas platyrhynchos
      Anas sibilatrix
      Aquila pomarina
      Ardea cinerea
      Calidris minuta
      Capella gallinago
      Charadrius alexandrinus
      Charadrius leschenaultii
      Chlidonias spp.
      Circus aeruginosus
      Egretta garzetta
      Egretta gularis
      Falco peregrinus
      Gallinago gallinago
      Himantopus himantopus
      Larus argentatus
      Larus genei
      Larus ridibundus
      Limosa lapponica
      Limosa limosa
      Milvus migrans
      Numenius arquata
      Philomachus pugnax
      Phoenicopterus ruber
      Pluvialis squatarola
      Porzana spp.
      Recurvirostra avosetta
      Tadorna ferruginea
      Tadorna tadorna
      Tringa cinereus
      Tringa nebularia
      Tringa ochropus
      Tringa totanus
      Vanellus vanellus

TIDAL SAND FLAT

Summary List

Cyanophyta	2+
Chrysophyta	2+
Actiniara	2+
Ceriantharia	1
Platyhelminthes	2+
Aschelminthes	6+
Gastropoda	43
Scaphopoda	2
Pelecypoda	34
Echiurida	1
Sipunculida	3+
Polychaeta	39
Pycnogonida	1
Ostracoda	3
Copepoda	2+
Decapoda	15
Mysidacea	1
Cumacea	1
Tanaidacea	2+
Isopoda	3
Amphipoda	5
Asteroidea	1
Ophiuroidea	3
Echinoidea	4
Holothurioidea	1
Ascidiacea	1
Aves	11
	191+

Species List
phylum **CYANOPHYTA**
    spp.
phylum **CHRYSOPHYTA**
    diatoms spp.
phylum **CNIDARIA**
    class ANTHOZOA
        order Actiniaria
        anemone spp.
        order Ceriantharia
        Cerianthus sp.
phylum **PLATYHELMINTHES**
    class TURBELLARIA
        spp.
phylum **ASCHELMINTHES**
    class GASTROTRICHA
        spp.
    class KINORHYNCHA
        spp.
    class NEMATODA
        spp.

phylum **MOLLUSCA**
    class GASTROPODA
        Acteocina persica
        Ancilla castanea
        Ancilla fasciata
        Brachina sp. G-124
        Bulla ampulla
        Calyptraea pellucida
        Cerithidea cingulata
        Cerithiidae sp.
        Cerithium rugosum
        Cerithium scabridum
        Cyclostrematidae sp. G-8A
        Cypraea turdus
        Diala semistriata
        Drillia clevei
        Eucithara sp.
        Eulimidae sp. G-56A
        Eulimidae sp.
        Fusus townsendi
        Mitrella blanda
        Monilea obscura
        Murex scolopax
        Nassarius pullus
        Natica lineata
        Nudibranch spp.
        Omalogyridae sp. G-122
        Omalogyridae sp. G-122B
        Opisthobranch sp.
        Otopleura mitralis
        Pulmonate sp.
        Pyramidellidae sp. G-57A
        Pyramidellidae sp. G-89
        Pyrene sp.
        Retusidae sp. G-46
        Rissoina distans
        Scaliola arenosa
        Setia sp. G-21
        Sinum papillum
        Sinum planulatum
        Solidula affinis
        Strombus decorus persicus
        Triphoridae sp. G-120
        Turritella torulosa
        Umbonium vestiarium
    class SCAPHOPODA
        Dentalium octogonum
        Dentalium politum
    class PELECYPODA
        Arca uropigmelana
        Cardium papyraceum
        Circe intermedia
        Costacallista sp. P-9
        Donacidae sp. P-85
        Eumarcia opina
        Eumarcia? sp. P-87A
        Exotica rhomboides
        Gafrarium arabicum
        Gari occidens

Gari weinkauffi
Glycymeris pectunculus
Loripes fisheriana
Mactra fauroti
Mactra hians
Mactra olorina
Mactra sp. P-163
Meretrix meretrix
Myochamidae sp. P-75
Paphia sulcaria
Parvicardium suezensis
Pillucina sp. P-21
Pillucina sp. P-197
Pseudopythina? sp. P-77A
Pseudopythina sp. P-77B
Septifer bilocularis
Solecurtus australis
Soletellina sp.
Tellina dissimilis
Tellina robusta
Tellinidae sp.
Trachycardium lacunosum
Ungulinidae sp. P-20
Ungulinidae sp.

phylum **ECHIURIDA**
Ikeda taenioides

phylum **SIPUNCULIDA**
Aspidosiphon sp.
Sipunculus sp.
spp.

phylum **ANNELIDA**
class POLYCHAETA
Amphinomidae sp. 2
Ancistrosyllis sp.
Aphroditidae sp.
Arabellidae sp.
Capitellidae sp. 2
Capitellidae sp.
Chrysopetalidae sp. 1
Chrysopetalum sp.
Cirratulidae sp. 1
Cirratulidae sp. 3
Cirratulidae sp.
Dasybranchus sp.
Eunice sp.
Eunicidae sp. 2
Eunicidae sp.
Exogone sp.
Fabricia? sp.
Glyceridae sp. 1
Glyceridae sp. 2
Glyceridae sp.
Hesionidae sp. 1
Hesionidae sp.
Lumbrineridae sp.
Nereidae sp. 17
Nereis sp.
Opheliidae sp.
Paraonidae sp. 2
Platynereis sp.
Polydora colonia
Polydora sp.
Sabellidae sp. 2
Sabellidae spp.
Sigalionidae sp. 6
Syllidae sp. 27
Syllis sp. 2
Syllis sp. 12
Syllis spp.
Terebellidae sp. 1
Terebellidae sp.

phylum **ARTHROPODA**
    class PYCNOGONIDA
            sp.
    class CRUSTACEA
      subclass OSTRACODA
            sp. 7
            sp. 18
            sp. 19
      subclass COPEPODA
            Harpacticoida spp.
      order Decapoda
            Callianassa sp. 2
            Cryptodromia sp. 2
            Diogenidae spp.
            Leucosia ?anatum
            Macrophthalmus grandidieri
            Macrophthalmus telescopicus
            Ocypode saratan
            Philyra sp. 8
            Pilumnopeus vauquelini
            Portunus pelagicus
            Portunus sp. nr. *hastatoides*
            Scopimera scabricauda
            Thalamita admete
            Thalamita poissoni
            Upogebia (Calliadne) sp.
      superorder Peracarida
        order Mysidacea
        sp. 6
        order Cumacea
        sp.
        order Tanaidacea
        spp.
        order Isopoda
          Anthura sp.
          Paracerceis sp.
          sp.
        order Amphipoda
          Ampithoidae sp.
          Leucothoe sp.
          sp. 17
          sp.
          Talitridae sp.
phylum **ECHINODERMATA**
    class ASTEROIDEA
          Astropecten phragmorus
    class OPHIUROIDEA
          Ophiothrix savignyi
          sp.
    class ECHINOIDEA
          Clypeaster humilis
          Echinodiscus auritus
          Metalia sternalis
          Metalia townsendi
    class HOLOTHURIOIDEA
          sp.

phylum **CHORDATA**
    subphylum UROCHORDATA
      class ASCIDIACEA
          sp.
    subphylum VERTEBRATA
      class AVES
          Ardea cinerea
          Calidris minuta
          Charadrius hiaticula
          Egretta gularis
          Falco peregrinus
          Limosa lapponica
          Numenius arquata
          Philomachus pugnax
          Phoenicopterus ruber
          Pluvialis squatarola
          Vanellus vanellus

Summary List

Cyanophyta	2+
Chlorophyta	2
Chrysophyta	2+
Rhodophyta	1
Foraminifera	2+
Porifera	2+
Actiniaria	2
Platyhelminthes	2+
Aschelminthes	2+
Polyplacophora	6
Gastropoda	68+
Pelecypoda	64+
Sipunculida	2
Polychaeta	87+
Acari	1
Ostracoda	5
Copepoda	3
Cirripedia	2
Stomatopoda	1
Decapoda	25
Tanaidacea	2
Isopoda	7
Amphipoda	9
Bryozoa	1
Asteroidea	1
Ophiuroidea	4
Echinoidea	2
Ascidiacea	2+
Teleostei	3
Aves	2
	314+

Species List

phylum **CYANOPHYTA**
    spp.
phylum **CHLOROPHYTA**
    Enteromorpha sp.
    Rhizoclonium kochianum
phylum **CHRYSOPHYTA**
    diatoms spp.
phylum **RHODOPHYTA**
    Chondria dasyphylla
phylum **PROTOZOA**
    order Foraminifera
      spp.
phylum **PORIFERA**
    spp.
phylum **CNIDARIA**
    order Actiniaria
      anemone sp.
      Calliactis sp.
phylum **PLATYHELMINTHES**
    class TURBELLARIA
      spp.

phylum **ASCHELMINTHES**
    class NEMATODA
      spp.
phylum **MOLLUSCA**
    class POLYPLACOPHORA
      sp. A-1
      sp. A-1C
      sp. A-5
      sp. A-5A
      sp. A-6
      sp.
    class GASTROPODA
      Acteocina persiana
      Atyidae sp. G-223
      Cerithidea cingulata
      Cerithiidae spp.
      Cerithium morum
      Cerithium rugosum
      Cerithium scabridum
      Cyclostrema? sp. G-10
      Diala semistriata
      Diodora funiculata
      Drupa margariticola
      Euchelis asper
      Eulimidae sp. G-129
      Finella scabra
      Fusus townsendi
      Macroschisma sp. G-128
      Marginellidae sp. G-123
      Mitra bovei
      Mitrella blanda
      Monilea obscura
      Monilea sp. G-102
      Monodonta canalifera
      Morula margariticola
      Morula sp.
      Murex kusterianus
      Nassarius stigmarius
      Nodilittorina subnodosa
      Nudibranch spp.
      Omalogyridae sp. G-122
      Onchidium peronii
      Peasiella isseli
      Persicula isseli
      Planaxis sulcatus
      Pyramidellidae sp. G-68
      Pyramidellidae sp. G-89
      Pyramidellidae sp. G-255
      Pyramidellidae sp. G-257
      Pyramidellidae sp. G-258
      Pyramidellidae spp.
      Pyrene atrata
      Pyrene phaula
      Pyrene spectrum
      Pyrgulina callista
      Scaliola arenosa
      Setia sp. G-21
      Siphonaria asghar
      Siphonaria kurachiensis

Siphonaria rosea
Stomatia phymotis
Syphopatella walshii
Thais tissoti
Thais pseudohippocastaneum
Tricolia fordiana
Triphora cingulata
Triphoridae sp. G-22B
Triphoridae sp. G-120
Triphoridae sp. G-121
Trochidae sp. G-5B
Trochidae sp. G-13
Trochidae sp.
Trochus erythraeus
Turbo coronatus
Turbo radiatus
Turbonilla materna
Turbonilla sp.
Turritella torulosa
Vermetidae sp. G-213
Vermetidae sp.

class PELECYPODA

Abra sp. P-79
Acar divaricata
Acar plicata
Anomia sp.
Arca uropigmelana
Barbatia decussata
Barbatia lacerata
Barbatia sp. P-90
Beguina gubernaculum
Botula cinnamomea
Brachydontes variabilis
Cardium papyraceum
Chama brassica
Chama sp. P-160
Chama sp.
Chlamys ruschenbergerii
Circe intermedia
Costacallista sp. P-9
Crassostraea sp. P-142
Crassostraea sp. P-162
Cycladichama sp. P-80
Exotica rhomboides
Gastrochaena cuneiformis
Isognomon ephippium
Isognomon sp. P-146
Isognomon sp.
Isognomonidae sp.
Lithophaga lithophaga
Lithophaga sp. 1
Lithophaga sp. P-38
Lithophaga sp. P-38B
Malleus regula
Malleus sp. P-147
Malleus sp. P-150
Malleus sp.
Mantellum sp. P-71
Mantellum sp. P-141

Musculus sp. P-27
Musculus sp. P-61
Musculus spp.
Mytilidae sp.
Mytilus sp.
Notirus sp. P-59
Notirus sp. P-68
Parvicardium suezensis
Petricola hemprichi
Pinctada margaritifera
Pinctada radiata
Pinctada sp. P-70
Pinna sp. P-149
Plicatula imbricata
Plicatula sp. P-83
Plicatula sp. P-144
Plicatula sp. P-145
Rocellaria cymbium
Rocellaria? sp. P-123
Septifer bilocularis
Spondylus exilis
Standella sp. P-135
Trachycardium lacunosum
Trachycardium maculosum
Trapezium sublaevigatum
Ungulinidae sp. P-138
Vulsellidae sp. P-88

phylum **SIPUNCULIDA**

Aspidosiphon sp.
sp.

phylum **ANNELIDA**

class POLYCHAETA

Aphroditidae sp.
Brania sp. 6
Brania sp. 17
Capitellidae sp. 3
Capitellidae sp.
Chrysopetalidae sp. 1
Chrysopetalidae sp. 2
Chrysopetalidae sp.
Cirratulidae sp. 1
Cirratulidae sp. 2
Cirratulidae sp. 3
Cirratulidae sp. 4
Dorvilleidae sp. 1
Dorvilleidae sp.
Eunice sp. 1
Eunice sp. 5
Eunice sp. 6
Eunicidae sp. 2
Eunicidae sp. 3
Eunicine sp. 4
Exogone sp. 4
Exogone sp. 22
Exogone sp. 29
?Fabricia sp. 1
Harmothoe sp. 5
Hesionidae sp. 1
Hesionidae sp. 3

233

Hesionidae sp. 4
Hesionidae sp. 5
Hesionidae sp.
Lumbrineridae sp. 1
Nereidae sp. 1
Nereidae sp. 1A
Nereidae sp. 1B
Nereidae sp. 2
Nereidae sp. 3
Nereidae sp. 4
Nereidae sp. 5
Nereidae sp. 5A
Nereidae sp. 7
Nereidae sp. 8
Nereidae sp. 9
Nereidae sp. 11
Nereidae sp. 12
Nereidae sp.
Nereis sp.
Opheliidae sp. 1
Opheliidae sp. 2
Opheliidae sp.
Paraonidae sp. 1
Paraonis sp. 3
Phyllodocidae sp. 1
Phyllodocidae sp. 2
Phyllodocidae sp.
Platynereis sp. 6
Platynereis sp. 6A
Polydora colonia
Polydora sp. 6
Polydora sp. 7
Polynoidae sp. 1
Polynoidae sp. 4
Sabellidae sp. 2
Sabellidae sp. 3
Sabellidae sp.
Serpulidae sp. 1
Serpulidae sp. 2
Serpulidae sp. 3
Serpulidae sp. 4
Serpulidae sp. 5
Serpulidae sp. 12
Serpulidae sp.
Spionidae sp. 2
Spionidae sp. 4
Spionidae sp.
Syllidae sp. 1 ?
Syllidae sp. 8
Syllidae sp.
Syllis gracilis
Syllis sp. 1
Syllis sp. 2
Syllis sp. 3
Syllis sp. 9
Syllis sp. 11
Syllis sp.
Terebellidae sp. 1
Terebellidae spp.

phylum **ARTHROPODA**
class ARACHNIDA
order Acari
sp. 3
class CRUSTACEA
subclass OSTRACODA
sp. 1
sp. 12
sp. 13
sp. 25
sp. 30
subclass COPEPODA
Euterpina sp. 15
Harpacticoida sp. 2
Notodelphyoida sp. 2
subclass CIRRIPEDIA
Acasta sp.
Balanus amphitrite
order Stomatopoda
Gonodactylus demanii
order Decapoda
Actumnus asper
Alpheidae sp.
Alpheus sp. 2
Arete dorsalis
Charybdis paucidentata
Chlorodiella nigra
Diogenidae spp.
Etisus electra
Eupagurus sp.
Eurycarcinus sp.
Ilyograpsus paludicola
Menaethius monoceros
Metopograpsus messor
Micippa philyra
Pachycheles sp. 3
Petrolisthes lamarckii
Petrolisthes sp.
Pilumnopeus vauquelini
Pilumnus longicornis
Porcellanidae sp.
Portunus pelagicus
Thalamita admete
Xanthidae sp. 12
Xanthidae sp
Xantho exaratus
superorder Peracarida
order Tanaidacea
sp. 3
sp.
order Isopoda
Cirolana sp. 19
Cymothoidae sp. 7
Cymothoidae sp.
Gnathia sp. 1
Gnathia sp.
Paracerceis sp. 1
sp.

order Amphipoda
  Ampithoidae sp. 15
  Atylidae sp. 13
  Leucothoe sp.
  Lysianassa sp. 1
  Lysianassa sp.
  sp. 9
  sp. 11
  sp. 18
  sp.
phylum **LOPHOPHORATA**
  class BRYOZOA
    Bugula? sp.
phylum **ECHINODERMATA**
  class ASTEROIDEA
    Asterina burtoni
  class OPHIUROIDEA
    Amphiura sp.
    Macrophiothrix elongata
    Ophiothrix savignyi
    sp.
  class ECHINOIDEA
    Echinometra mathaei
    Temnopleurus toreumaticus
phylum **CHORDATA**
  subphylum UROCHORDATA
  class ASCIDIACEA
    Microcosmus sp.
    spp.
  subphylum VERTEBRATA
  class ACTINOPTERYGII
    superorder Teleostei
    Blenniidae sp.
    Omobranchus sp.
    sp.
  class AVES
    Arenaria interpres
    Tringa cinereus

TIDAL CREEKS

Summary List

Gastropoda	3
Pelecypoda	1
Decapoda	14
Mysidacea	1+
Amphipoda	1
Teleostei	12
Aves	1
	33+

Species List

phylum **MOLLUSCA**
  class GASTROPODA
    Cerithidea cingulata
    Mitrella blanda
    Monilea obscura
  class PELECYPODA
    Lioconcha picta
phylum **ARTHROPODA**
  subclass MALACOSTRACA
  order Decapoda
    Diogenidae sp.
    Eurycarcinus sp.
    Grapsidae sp.
    Ilyograpsus paludicola
    Macrophthalmus depressus
    Macrophthalmus grandidieri
    Metapenaeus affinis
    Metapenaeus stebbingi
    Metopograpsus messor
    Palaemon (Palaeander) sp. 3
    Paracleistostoma sp.
    Portunus pelagicus
    Scopimera sp. 3
    Scopimera scabricauda
  superorder Peracarida
  order Mysidacea
    sp.
  order Amphipoda
    sp. 57
phylum **CHORDATA**
  subphylum VERTEBRATA
  class ACTINOPTERYGII
  superorder Teleostei
    Acanthopagrus sp.
    Aphanius dispar
    Gerres oyena
    Gerres sp.
    Hemirhamphus far
    Mugil dussumieri
    Mugil sp.
    Nematalosa nasus
    Platycephalus sp.
    Pseudorhombus sp.
    Sardinella sp.
    Therapon jarbua
  class AVES
    Ceryle rudis

Summary List

Chlorophyta	1
Phaeophyta	11+
Rhodophyta	6
Porifera	2+
Hydrozoa	2+
Actiniaria	2+
Scleractinia	5+
Antipatharia	1+
Platyhelminthes	2+
Nematoda	2+
Polyplacophora	1
Gastropoda	30
Pelecypoda	19
Polychaeta	25+
Ostracoda	2+
Copepoda	5+
Cirripedia	2+
Stomatopoda	1
Decapoda	14
Mysidacea	1+
Tanaidacea	2
Isopoda	2
Amphipoda	18
Bryozoa	1+
Asteroidea	1
Ophiuroidea	1
Ascidiacea	1
Elasmobranchii	1
Teleostei	33+
	194+

phylum **PORIFERA**
  spp.
phylum **CNIDARIA**
 class HYDROZOA
  spp.
 class ANTHOZOA
  order Actiniaria
   anemone spp.
  order Scleractinia
   Cyphastrea sp.
   Favia sp.
   Paracyathus sp.
   Platygyra sp.
   Porites sp.
   spp.
   Turbinaria sp.
  order Antipatharia
   sp.
phylum **PLATYHELMINTHES**
  spp.
phylum **ASCHELMINTHES**
 class NEMATODA
  spp.

Species List

phylum **CHLOROPHYTA**
  Enteromorpha clathrata
phylum **PHAEOPHYTA**
  Colpomenia sinuosa
  Dictyota dichotoma **var.** *intricata*
  Dictyota divaricata
  Hormophysa triquetra
  Padina gymnospora
  Pocockiella variegata
  Sargassum angustifolium
  Sargassum binderi
  Sargassum boveanum var. *aterrima*
  Sargassum latifolium
  Sphacelaria furcigera
  sp.
phylum **RHODOPHYTA**
  Ceramium maryae
  Corallinaceae sp.
  Jania rubens
  Lithothamnium sp.
  Polysiphonia sp.
  Spyridia filamentosa

phylum **MOLLUSCA**
    class POLYPLACOPHORA
        sp. A-5B
    class GASTROPODA
        Alaba virgata
        Cerithiidae sp. G-216
        Cerithiopsidae sp. G-253
        Cerithium scabridum
        Cypraea caurica
        Cypraea turdus
        Diala goniochila
        Diala semistriata
        Diniatys dentifer
        Drupa margariticola
        Eulimidae sp.
        Eulimidae sp. G-129
        Mitrella cartwrighti
        Monilea obscura
        Murex kusterianus
        Nudibranch sp.
        Opisthobranch sp.
        Pyrene atrata
        Pyrene phaula
        Pyrene spectrum
        Rissoidae sp.
        Scissurella sp. G-1B
        Stomatellidae sp. G-251
        Thais pseudohippocastaneum
        Tricolia fordiana
        Triphora perversa
        Triphoridae sp. G-23
        Triphoridae sp. G-252
        Trochus erythraeus
    class PELECYPODA
        Abra sp. P-79
        Acar plicata
        Anomiidae sp.
        Brachydontes variabilis
        Cardita ffinchi
        Gastrochaena sp.
        Isognomon sp.
        Lithophaga sp.
        Malleus sp.
        Musculus sp. P-26
        Musculus sp. P-27
        Musculus sp.
        Ostraeidae sp. P-142
        Pinctada margaritifera
        Pinctada radiata
        Pinctada sp. P-3
        Septifer bilocularis
        Spondylus exilis
        Ungulinidae sp.

phylum **ANNELIDA**
    class POLYCHAETA
        Chrysopetalidae sp. 1
        Dorvilleidae sp. 3
        Exogone sp. 4
        Exogone sp. 29
        ?Fabricia sp. 1
        Hesionidae sp. 9
        Hesionidae sp.
        Opheliidae sp. 2
        Opheliidae sp.
        Platynereis sp. 6
        ?Polydora sp. 3
        Nereidae sp. 4
        Nereidae sp. 15 ?
        Nereidae sp. 19
        Nereidae sp.
        Sabellidae sp.
        Serpulidae sp. 1
        Serpulidae sp. 10
        spp.
        Syllidae sp. 8
        Syllidae sp. 25 ?
        Syllidae sp. 28
        Syllidae spp.
        Syllis sp. 1
        Syllis sp. 3
        Syllis sp.
phylum **ARTHROPODA**
    class CRUSTACEA
        subclass OSTRACODA
            sp. 1
            sp. 2
            sp.
        subclass COPEPODA
            Harpacticoida sp. 1
            Harpacticoida sp. 14
            Harpacticoida sp. 22
            Harpacticoida sp.
            Siphonostomata sp.
            sp.
        subclass CIRRIPEDIA
            Balanus spp.
        subclass MALACOSTRACA
        order Stomatopoda
            Gonodactylus demanii
        order Decapoda
            Acanthonychidae sp. 10
            Acanthonyx limbatus
            Alpheidae sp. 4
            Diogenidae spp.
            Hippolytidae sp. 1
            Hippolytidae sp.
            Hippolysmata sp. 5
            Palaemonidae sp. 1
            Petrolisthes lamarckii
            Pilumnus longicornis
            Porcellanella sp. 1
            Saron marmoratus

Synalpheus sp. 1
Xantho exaratus
superorder Peracarida
  order Mysidacea
    sp.
  order Tanaidacea
    Leptochelia ?dubia
    sp. 3
    sp. 4
  order Isopoda
    Cyathura sp. 30
    Paracerceis sp. 1
    Sphaerominae sp.
  order Amphipoda
    Ampeliscidae sp. 3
    Ampithoidae sp. 15
    Caprellidae sp. 1
    sp. 1
    sp. 2
    sp. 9
    sp. 18
    sp. 19 or 15
    sp. 20
    sp. 37
    sp. 42
    sp. 47
    sp. 53
    sp. 58
    sp. 59
    sp. 60
phylum **LOPHOPHORATA**
  class BRYOZOA
    sp.
phylum **ECHINODERMATA**
  class ASTEROIDEA
    Asterina burtoni
  class OPHIUROIDEA
    Ophiothrix savignyi

phylum **CHORDATA**
  subphylum UROCHORDATA
    class ASCIDIACEA
      sp. 7
  subphylum VERTEBRATA
    class ELASMOBRANCHII
      Dasyatis sp.
      Chiloscyllium griseum
    class ACTINOPTERYGII
      superorder Teleostei
        Abudefduf saxatilis
        Acanthopagrus berda
        Acanthopagrus bifasciatus
        Blenniidae sp.
        Chaetodon nigropunctatus
        Ecsenius sp.
        Epinephelus chlorostigma
        Epinephelus coeruleopunctatus
        Epinephelus tauvina
        Gaterin gaterinus
        Gobiidae sp.
        Heniochus acuminatus
        Lutjanus fulviflamma
        Lutjanus johni
        Lutjanus sanguineus
        Lutjanus sp.
        Omobranchus sp.
        Parapercis nebulosus
        Plectorhynchus schotaf
        Pomacanthus maculosus
        Pseudochromidae sp.
        Pseudochromis persicus
        Pterois volitans
        Salarias spp.
        Sargus noct
        Scolopsis ghanam
        Scorpaenopsis sp.
        Siganus oramin
        Spilotichthys pictus
        Syngnathidae spp.
        Thalassoma lunare

SUBTIDAL SAND

Subtidal Sand, Species List – Cont'd

Summary List

Chlorophyta	5
Chrysophyta	2+
Anthophyta	3
Foraminifera	2+
Porifera	2
Hydrozoa	2+
Actiniaria	1
Scleractinia	6
Ceriantharia	1
Octocorallia	2
Platyhelminthes	2+
Rhynchocoela	2+
Aschelminthes	3+
Polyplacophora	8+
Gastropoda	102
Scaphopoda	2
Pelecypoda	54
Sipunculida	3+
Polychaeta	167+
Acari	3+
Pycnogonida	2+
Ostracoda	24+
Copepoda	37+
Leptostraca	1
Stomatopoda	3
Decapoda	66
Mysidacea	2
Cumacea	9+
Tanaidacea	6+
Isopoda	14+
Amphipoda	39+
Bryozoa	1+
Brachiopoda	1
Crinoidea	1
Asteroidea	8
Ophiuroidea	5+
Echinoidea	9
Holothurioidea	3+
Ascidiacea	2+
Cephalochordata	1
Elasmobranchi	3
Teleostei	30
	638+

Species List

phylum **CHLOROPHYTA**
  Acetabularia calyculus
  Avrainvillea amadelpha
  Caulerpa sertularioides
  Chaetomorpha linum
  Dasycladaceae sp.
phylum **CHRYSOPHYTA**
  diatoms spp.

phylum **ANTHOPHYTA**
  Halodule uninervis
  Halophila ovalis
  Halophila stipulacea
phylum **PROTOZOA**
  order Foraminifera
    spp.
phylum **PORIFERA**
  Algea? sp.
  sp.
phylum **CNIDARIA**
  class HYDROZOA
    Hydroid spp.
  class ANTHOZOA
    order Actiniaria
      Anemone sp.
    order Scleractinia
      Heterocyathus sp. 2
      Heterocyathus sp. 3
      Heteropsammia sp. 4
      Heteropsammia sp.
      Paracyathus sp.
      Siderastrea sp. 2
    order Ceriantharia
      Cerianthus membranaceus
    subclass OCTOCORALLIA
      Gorgonian sp.
      Pennatulid sp.
phylum **PLATYHELMINTHES**
  class TURBELLARIA
    spp.
phylum **RHYNCHOCOELA**
    spp.
phylum **ASCHELMINTHES**
  class KINORHYNCHA
    sp.
  class NEMATODA
    spp.
phylum **MOLLUSCA**
  class POLYPLACOPHORA
    Callochiton sp. A-2
    sp. A-1B
    sp. A-1C
    sp. A-3
    sp. A-4
    sp. A-5A
    sp. A-6
    spp.
  class GASTROPODA
    Acteocina sp. G-266
    Acteocina sp. G-266A
    Acteocina spp.
    Ancilla castanea
    Ancilla fasciata
    Ancilla sp. G-254
    Ancilla sp. G-254A
    Atyidae sp. G-47
    Atyidae sp. G-47A
    Atyidae sp. G-271

Atys cylindrica
Atys sp. G-298
Brachina glabella
Caecidae sp. G-274
Caecidae sp. G-274A
Caecidae sp.
Caecum arabicum
Calliostoma sp. G-100
Calyptraea pellucida
Calyptraea sp.
Cerithiopsidae sp. G-221
Clava kochi
Conus eburneus
Cyclostrema sp. G-8B
Cyclostrema quadricarinatum
Cypraea turdus
Diala goniochila
Diala semistriata
Drillia clevei
Drupa margariticola
Epitonium schepmani
Ethalia carneolata
Eulima sp. G-105
Eulimidae sp. 1
Eulimidae sp. 2
Eulimidae sp. 3
Eulimidae sp. 4
Eulimidae sp. 5
Eulimidae sp. G-56B
Eulimidae sp.
Fusus townsendi
Gibberula sp. G-299
Iraqirissoa xanthias
Leptothyra filifera
Liotinaria sp. G-8A
Macroschisma sp. G-128
Mitra clathrus
Monilea obscura
Monilea sp. G-102
Morula sp. G-103
Murex kusterianus
Murex scolopax
Nassarius stigmarius
Natica sp. G-108
Natica sp. G-108A
Neocollonia sp. G-10
Neocollonia sp. G-10B
Nerita albicilla
Nudibranch sp. 4
Nudibranch sp. 5
Nudibranch sp.
Odostomia carinata
Oliva bulbosa
Otopleura mitralis
Philinidae sp. G-80
Pirinella conica
Primovula rhodia
Prosimnia trailli
Pyramidellidae sp. G-38C

Pyramidellidae sp. G-44
Pyramidellidae sp. G-44B
Pyramidellidae sp. G-89A
Pyramidellidae sp. G-112A
Pyramidellidae sp. G-269
Pyrene atrata
Pyrene phaula
Pyrene sp. G-243
Retusidae sp. G-46
Ringicula propinquans
Scaliola bella
Scaliola sp. G-267
Scissurella sp. G-1
Setia sp. G-21
Smaragdia soverbiana
Solidula affinis
Stomatella sp. G-7
Strombus decorus persicus
Strombus fusiformis
Syphopatella walshii
Thais carinifera
Triphoridae sp. G-23
Triphoridae sp. G-120
Trochidae sp. G-5
Trochidae sp. G-5A
Trochidae sp. G-215A
Turbinidae sp. G-10B
Turridae sp. G-33B
Turridae sp. G-33E
Turridae sp. G-51
Turridae sp. G-242
Turritella torulosa
Xenophora caperata
class SCAPHOPODA
Dentalium octogonum
Dentalium politum
class PELECYPODA
Acar plicata
Arcopagia subtruncata
Anomia sp. P-49
Arca sp. P-115A
Barbatia decussata
Cardiidae sp.
Cardita antiquata
Cardita ffinchi
Cardium papyraceum
Chama sp. P-91
Circe scripta
Corbula sulculosa
Costacallista sp. P-9
Crassostraea sp. P-162
Crenella sp. P-120
Dosinia sp. P-16
Ervilia bisculpta
Ervilia scaliola
Exotica rhomboides
Gari maculosa
Glycymeris pectunculus
Glycymeris striatularis

Hiatella sp. P-51
Limatus sp. P-97
Lioconcha picta
Lioconcha sp.
Lucinidae sp.
Mantellum sp. P-71
Mantellum sp.
Musculus sp. P-26
Musculus sp. P-26B
Musculus sp.
Nucula sp. P-92
Pandora unguiculus
Paphia sulcaria
Pinctada margaritifera
Pinctada sp.
Pinna ?strangei
Rocellaria cymbium
Septifer bilocularis
sp. P-54
Spondervilia sp. P-110
Tellidora pellyana
Tellina dissimilis
Tellina sp. P-12 ?
Tellinidae sp. P-13
Tellinidae sp. P-180
Tellinidae sp. P-201
Tellinidae sp. P-202
Timoclea farsiana
Timoclea sp. P-196
Timoclea sp.
Ungulinidae sp.
Veneridae sp. P-200

phylum **SIPUNCULIDA**

Aspidosiphon sp.
sp. 2
spp.

phylum **ANNELIDA**

class POLYCHAETA

Ampharetidae sp. 1
Ampharetidae sp.
Amphictenidae sp.
Amphinomidae sp. 2
Amphinomidae sp.
Ancistrosyllis sp. 2
Arabellidae sp.
Archiannelida sp. 1
Archiannelida sp.
Ariciidae sp. 1
Ariciidae sp. 2
Autolytus sp. 16
Branchiomma sp. 11
Brania sp. 6
Brania sp. 8
Capitellidae sp. 7
Capitellidae sp. 8
Capitellidae sp.
Chaetopterus sp.
Chrysopetalum sp. 1
Chrysopetalum sp. 2

Chrysopetalum spp.
Cirratulidae sp. 1 ?
Cirratulidae sp. 5
Cirratulidae sp. 7
Cirratulidae sp.
Dorvilleidae sp. 1
Dorvilleidae sp. 2
Dorvilleidae sp. 3
Dorvilleidae sp. 6
Dorvilleidae sp. 7
Dorvilleidae sp.
Eunice spp.
Eunicidae sp. 2
Eunicidae sp. 4
Eunicidae sp. 8
Eunicidae sp. 11 or 12
Eusyllis sp. 18
Exogone sp. 4
Exogone sp. 17
Exogone sp. 22
?Fabricia sp. 1
Flabelligeridae sp. 1
Flabelligeridae sp. 2
Flabelligeridae sp. 3
Flabelligeridae sp.
Glyceridae sp. 1
Glyceridae sp. 2
Glyceridae sp. 4
Glyceridae sp.
Goniadidae sp. 1
Goniadidae sp. 2
Goniadidae sp.
Harmothoe sp. 5
Hesionidae sp. 1
Hesionidae sp. 3
Hesionidae sp. 5
Hesionidae sp. 6
Hesionidae sp. 7
Hesionidae sp. 8
Hesionidae sp. 11
Hesionidae spp.
Laonice cerrata
Lumbrineridae sp. 1
Lumbrineridae sp. 2
Lumbrineridae sp.
Magelonidae sp. 1
Magelonidae sp. 2
Magelonidae sp.
Maldanidae sp. 1
Maldanidae sp. 2
Maldanidae sp. 3
Maldanidae sp. 5 ?
Maldanidae sp.
Nephtyidae sp. 1
Nephtyidae sp. 2
Nephtyidae sp.
Nereidae sp. 2
Nereidae sp. 4
Nereidae sp. 13

Nereidae sp. 14
Nereidae sp. 15
Nereidae spp.
Onuphidae sp. 1
Onuphidae sp. 2
Onuphidae sp.
Opheliidae sp. 1
Opheliidae sp. 2
Opheliidae sp. 4
Opheliidae sp. 5
Opheliidae sp. 6
Opheliidae sp.
Paraonidae sp. 5
Paraonidae sp.
Paraonis sp.
Pectinariidae sp. 1
Phyllodocidae sp. 1
Phyllodocidae sp. 2
Phyllodocidae sp. 3
Phyllodocidae sp. 6
Phyllodocidae sp. 10
Phyllodocidae sp. 11
Phyllodocidae sp. 12
Phyllodocidae sp. 13
Phyllodocidae spp.
Pilargidae sp. 1
?Pista cristata
?Polycirrus sp. 7
Polydora colonia
Polynoidae sp. 1
Polynoidae sp. 2
Polynoidae sp. 4
Polynoidae sp.
Polyophthalmus sp.
Prionospio sp. 10
Prionospio sp. 12
Pseudeurythoe hirsuta
Sabellidae sp. 2
Sabellidae sp. 9
Sabellidae sp. 12
Sabellidae spp.
Scalibregmidae sp. 1
Serpulidae sp. 1
Serpulidae sp. 4
Serpulidae sp. 9
Serpulidae sp. 10
Serpulidae sp. 11
Serpulidae spp.
Sigalionidae sp. 1
Sigalionidae sp. 3
Sigalionidae sp. 5
Sigalionidae sp. 6
Spionida sp. 5
Spionidae sp. 4
Spionidae sp. 9
Spionidae sp. 11
Spionidae sp. 13
Spionidae sp. 15
Spionidae sp. 16

Spionidae spp.
Stenelais boa
Stenelais sp.
Syllidae sp. 5
Syllidae sp. 7
Syllidae sp. 8
Syllidae sp. 13
Syllidae sp. 15
Syllidae sp. 16
Syllidae sp. 19
Syllidae sp. 20
Syllidae sp. 21
Syllidae sp. 23
Syllidae sp. 27
Syllidae sp. 28
Syllidae sp. 33
Syllidae spp.
Syllis sp. 2
Syllis sp. 3
Syllis sp. 11
Syllis sp. 12
Syllis sp. 14
Syllis sp. 26
Syllis sp.
Terebellidae sp. 5
Terebellidae sp. 9
Terebellidae sp. 10
Terebellidae sp.
phylum **ARTHROPODA**
class ARACHNIDA
order Acari
sp. 1
sp. 2
sp. 3
sp.
class PYCNOGONIDA
sp. 4
sp. 5
sp.
class CRUSTACEA
subclass OSTRACODA
sp. 1
sp. 2
sp. 3
sp. 5
sp. 6
sp. 7
sp. 8
sp. 9
sp. 11
sp. 12
sp. 14
sp. 15
sp. 17
sp. 18
sp. 21
sp. 22
sp. 23
sp. 24

      sp. 25
      sp. 26
      sp. 27
      sp. 31
      sp. 32
      sp. 33
      spp.
  subclass COPEPODA
    Acartiidae sp.
    Aphanodomus sp.
    Alteutha sp. 9
    Calanoida spp.
    Calanus sp. 2
    Calanus sp. 3
    Candacia sp. 9
    Candacia sp. 10
    Centropagidae sp. 1
    Centropagidae sp. 2
    Corycaeus sp.
    Corycella sp. 10
    Cyclopoida sp. 5
    Cyclopoida sp. 9
    Cyclopoida sp. 14
    Cyclopoida sp. 15
    Cyclopoida spp.
    ?Eucalanus or *Rhincalanus* sp. 6
    Euchaetidae sp. 1
    Euterpina sp. 15
    Euterpina sp.
    Harpacticoida sp. 1
    Harpacticoida sp. 14
    Harpacticoida sp. 16
    Harpacticoida sp. 17
    Harpacticoida spp.
    Harpacticus? sp.
    Oithona sp.
    Oncaea sp.
    Pontellidae sp. 1
    Pontellidae sp. 5
    Pontellidae sp.
    Sapphirina sp.
    Siphonostoma sp. 13
    Temoridae sp. 1
    Tisbidae sp.
    Tortanus sp.
  subclass MALACOSTRACA
    order Leptostraca
    Nebalia sp.
    order Stomatopoda
    Lysiosquilla spp.
    Squilla nepa
    order Decapoda
    Alpheidae sp. 4
    Alpheidae sp.
    Alpheus sp. 2
    Alpheus sp. 5
    Anchistus ?custos
    ?Axius sp. 1
    Callianassa sp.

Charybdis hoplites
Ebalia sp. 1
Ebalia (Lithadia) sp. 11
Ebalia sp. 13
Diogenidae spp.
Dorippe ?facchino
Dromidia unidentata
Goneplacidae sp. 3
?Goneplacidae sp.
Halimede ochtodes
Hippolyte sp. 1
Hippolytidae sp. 6
Hippolytidae sp. 7
Hippolytidae sp. 8
Hippolytidae sp. 9
Hyastenus hilgendorfi
Ixa sp. 5
Lambrus carinatus
Leptochela robusta
Leucosia ?anatum
Leucosiidae sp. 16
Matuta planipes
Menaethius monoceros
Metapenaeopsis mogiensis
Metapenaeopsis stridulans
Metapenaeopsis sp.
Metapenaeus affinis
Metapenaeus stebbingi
Micippa philyra
Myra fugax
Pachycheles sp. 3
Pagurus sp.
Palaemonidae sp. 6
Pandalidae sp. 1
Penaeus japonicus
Penaeus latisulcatus
Penaeus semisulcatus
Periclimenes brevicarpalis
Phalangipus longipes
Philyra platychira
Pilumnopeus vauquelini
Pilumnus longicornis
Pilumnus sp.
Polyonyx sp. 8
Pontoniidae sp. 7
Porcellana sp. 4
Portunus sp. nr. *hastatoides*
Processa sp. 1
Synalpheus sp. 1
Synalpheus sp. 8
Synalpheus sp.
Thalamita admete
Thenus orientalis
Trachypenaeus curvirostris
Trachypenaeus granulosus
Xanthidae sp. 15
Xanthidae sp. 21
Xanthidae sp
Xenophthalmus sp. 2

superorder Peracarida
  order Mysidacea
    sp. 1
    sp. 5
  order Cumacea
    sp. 1
    sp. 2
    sp. 9
    sp. 10
    sp. 11
    sp. 12
    sp. 13
    sp. 15
    sp. 16
    spp.
  order Tanaidacea
    Kalliapseudes sp. 10
    Leptochelia ?dubia
    Leptochelia sp. 9
    Leptochelia sp. 11
    sp. 3
    spp.
    Tanais sp. 2
  order Isopoda
    Arcturidae sp. 28
    Cirolaninae sp.
    Cyathura sp.
    Cymothoidae sp. 34
    Gnathia sp. 14A
    Gnathia sp. 15
    Gnathia sp.
    Gnathiidae sp. 1
    Gnathiidae sp. 14
    ?Idotea sp. 12
    Polyexosphaeroma sp. 2
    Paracerceis sp. 1
    Sphaeromidae sp. 27
    sp. 25
    spp.
  order Amphipoda
    Ampeliscidae sp. 1
    Ampeliscidae sp. 3
    Caprellidae sp. 1
    Caprellidae sp. 3
    Caprellidae sp. 4
    Caprellidae sp. 6
    Caprellidae sp.
    Leucothoe sp. 10
    Lysianassidae sp. 39
    Melita sp. 67
    Pholidae sp. 54
    sp. 2
    sp. 3
    sp. 9
    sp. 11
    sp. 14
    sp. 17
    sp. 19
    sp. 20

    sp. 26
    sp. 28
    sp. 29
    sp. 34
    sp. 35
    sp. 42
    sp. 44
    sp. 46
    sp. 47
    sp. 53 ?
    sp. 58
    sp. 64
    sp. 68
    sp. 69
    sp. 70
    sp. 71
    sp. 72
    sp. 74
    sp. 75
    sp. 76
    spp.
phylum **LOPHOPHORATA**
  class BRYOZOA
    Schizoporella sanguinea
    sp.
  class BRACHIOPODA
    Lingula sp. 1

phylum **ECHINODERMATA**
    class CRINOIDEA
          sp.
    class ASTEROIDEA
        Asterina burtoni
        Astropecten indicus
        Astropecten monacanthus
        Astropecten phragmorus
        Astropecten pugnax
        Luidia hardwicki
        Luidia maculata
        Pentaceraster mammillatus
    class OPHIUROIDEA
        Amphioplus hastatus
        Ophiactis savignyi
        Ophiothela venusta
        Ophiothrix savignyi
        sp. 6
        sp.
    class ECHINOIDEA
        Brissopsis persica
        Clypeaster humilis
        Clypeaster reticulatus
        Echinodiscus auritus
        Lovenia elongata
        Metalia sternalis
        Metalia townsendi
        Temnopleurus toreumaticus
        Temnotrema siamense
    class HOLOTHURIOIDEA
        Holothuria (Halodeima) atra
        sp.
        Synaptidae sp.

phylum **CHORDATA**
    subphylum UROCHORDATA
      class ASCIDIACEA
          spp.
    subphylum CEPHALOCHORDATA
        Branchiostoma sp.
    subphylum VERTEBRATA
      class ELASMOBRANCHII
        Chiloscyllium griseum
        Dasyatis gerrardi
        Rhynchobatus djiddensis
      class ACTINOPTERYGII
        superorder Teleostei
          Acanthopagrus cuvieri
          Argyrops filamentosus
          Argyrops spinifer
          Chelonodon patoca
          Epinephelus tauvina
          Euryglossa orientalis
          ?Gastrophysus sp.
          Gerres oyena
          Gerres sp.
          Gobiidae sp.
          Leiognathus sp.
          Leptosynanceja melanostigma
          Lethrinus lentjan
          Lethrinus miniatus
          Lethrinus nebulosus
          Mulloidichthys auriflamma
          Nemipterus tolu
          Opisthognathus sp.
          Pardachirus marmoratus
          Pegasus natans
          Petroscirtes sp.
          Platycephalus indicus
          Platycephalus tuberculatus
          Pomadasys argenteus
          Pomadasys stridens
          Pseudorhombus arsius
          Pseudorhombus javanicus
          Sillago sihama
          Trichonotus sp.
          Upeneus tragula

Summary List

Chlorophyta	1
Anthophyta	3
Foraminifera	2+
Porifera	1+
Hydrozoa	1+
Actiniaria	2+
Scleractinia	2
Ceriantharia	1
Platyhelminthes	1+
Rhynchocoela	1+
Gastrotricha	1+
Kinorhyncha	1+
Nematoda	2+
Polyplacophora	2
Gastropoda	125
Scaphopoda	4+
Pelecypoda	73
Cephalophoda	1
Sipunculida	4+
Polychaeta	171
Hirudinea	1+
Acari	1+
Pycnogonida	1
Ostracoda	23+
Copepoda	4+
Leptostraca	1
Stomatopoda	1
Decapoda	61
Mysidacea	2+
Cumacea	15+
Tanaidacea	4+
Isopoda	15
Amphipoda	32
Bryozoa	3
Asteroidea	2
Ophiuroidea	4+
Echinoidea	3
Holothurioidea	1+
Ascidiacea	3+
Elasmobranchii	10
Teleostei	23
Reptilia	1
	610+

Species List

phylum **CHLOROPHYTA**
      Acetabularia sp.
phylum **ANTHOPHYTA**
      Halodule uninervis
      Halophila ovalis
      Halophila stipulacea
phylum **PROTOZOA**
    order Foraminifera
      spp.

phylum **PORIFERA**
    sp.
phylum **CNIDARIA**
    class HYDROZOA
      sp.
    class ANTHOZOA
      order Actiniaria
        spp.
      order Scleractinia
        Caryophyllidae sp. 4
        Heteropsammia sp.
      order Ceriantharia
        Cerianthus sp.
phylum **PLATYHELMINTHES**
    sp.
phylum **RHYNCHOCOELA**
    sp.
phylum **ASCHELMINTHES**
    class GASTROTRICHA
      sp.
    class KINORHYNCHA
      sp.
    class NEMATODA
      spp.
phylum **MOLLUSCA**
    class POLYPLACOPHORA
      sp. A-5
      sp. A-6
    class GASTROPODA
      Acteocina omanensis
      Acteocina persiana
      Adeorbis sp. G-247
      Ancilla sp. G-249
      Atyidae sp. G-47
      Atys cylindrica
      Bulla ampulla
      Calyptraea pellucida
      Cerithiidae sp. G-53A
      Cerithiopsidae sp. G-221A
      Cerithium scabridum
      Cerithium sp.
      Clava kochi
      Cyclostrematidae sp. G-8A
      Cylichna sp. G-143
      Diastomidae sp. G-14A
      Diala goniochila
      Diala semistriata
      Diala sulcifera
      Diniatys dentifer
      Diodora funiculata
      Drillia clevei
      Drupa margariticola
      Epitoniidae sp. G-93
      Epitoniidae sp. G-94
      Epitonium goniophora
      Epitonium simplex
      Eulima sp. G-105
      Eulimidae sp. G-26
      Eulimidae sp. G-56B

Eulimidae sp. G-56C
Eulimidae sp. G-244
Finella pupoides
Finella reticulata
Finella sp. G-14A
Fusus townsendi
Gibberula mazagonica
Minolia solanderi
Mitra blanfordi
Mitrella blanda
Mitrella cartwrighti
Mitridae sp. G-90
Monilea obscura
Murex scolopax
Murex sp. G-63
Natica lineata
Odostomia carinata
Odostomia eutropia
Odostomia sp. G-35A
Odostomia? sp. G-36
Odostomia? sp. G-36A
Odostomia? sp. G-36B
Opisthobranch sp. G-48
Opisthobranch sp.
Philinidae sp. G-80
Philinidae sp. G-80A
Pyramidellidae sp. G-34
Pyramidellidae sp. G-34A
Pyramidellidae sp. G-35A
Pyramidellidae sp. G-38B
Pyramidellidae sp. G-44
Pyramidellidae sp. G-44A
Pyramidellidae sp. G-49
Pyramidellidae sp. G-49A
Pyramidellidae sp. G-57
Pyramidellidae sp. G-57B
Pyramidellidae sp. G-68
Pyramidellidae sp. G-89
Pyramidellidae sp. G-112
Pyramidellidae sp. G-293
Pyramidellidae sp.
Pyrgulina callista
Pyrene atrata
Pyrene phaula
Retusidae sp. G-46
Retusidae sp. G-150
Retusidae sp.
Retusa truncatula
Rhinoclavis sp. G-81A
Rhinoclavis sp.
Rhizorus ovulinus
Ringicula propinquans
Rissoidae sp. G-115
Rissoidae sp. G-115A
Rissoidae sp. G-279
Scaliola arenosa
Scaphandridae sp. G-203A
Scaphandridae sp. G-291
Scaphandridae sp. G-291B

Scissurella sp. G-1
Setia sp. G-21
Solidula affinis
Smaragdia soverbiana
Smaragdia sp. G-12A
Smaragdia sp.
sp. G-88
Syrnola mekranica
Tornatina sp. G-203
Tricolia fordiana
Triphoridae sp. G-120
Trochidae sp. G-4B
Trochidae sp. G-5
Trochidae sp. G-13
Trochidae sp. G-215B
Trochus erythraeus
Turbonilla materna
Turbonilla recticostata
Turbonilla sp. G-232
Turbonilla sp. G-234A
Turbonilla sp. G-235
Turbonilla sp. G-235A
Turbonilla sp. G-236
Turbonilla sp. G-237
Turbonilla sp.
Turridae sp. G-33A
Turridae sp. G-33C
Turridae sp. G-51
Turridae sp. G-60A
Turridae sp. G-96
Turridae sp. G-140
Turridae sp. G-296
Turridae sp.
Turritella exoleta
Turritella torulosa
Xenophora caperata
class SCAPHOPODA
Dentaliidae sp. S-3
Dentalium octogonum
Dentalium politum
Dentalium sp. S-1A
spp.
class PELECYPODA
Arca uropigmelana
Arca sp.
Arcopagia subtruncata
Anodontia edentula
Bassima calophylla
Bellucina seminula
Brachytoma griffithi
Cardium papyraceum
Chlamys sp.
Circe corrugata
Circe intermedia
Circe scripta
Costacallista sp. P-9
Divaricella sp. P-46
Dosinia hepatica
Ervilia scaliola

Exotica rhomboides
Fabulina sp. P-12C
Gari sp. P-48
Gari sp. P-48A
Gari weinkauffi
Hiatella sp. P-51
Hiatella sp.
Lucinacea sp. P-21A
Lucinidae sp. P-183
Mactridae sp. P-36
Musculus sp. P-26
Musculus sp. P-26A
Musculus sp. P-47
Nucula sp. P-29
Nucula sp. P-29B
Nucula sp. P-92B
Nuculanidae sp. P-96
Nuculanidae sp. P-100
Nuculidae sp. P-92
Nuculidae sp. P-92A
Pandora unguiculus
Pandoridae sp. P-34A
Paphia? textile?
Parvicardium suezensis
Petrasma pusilla
Pillucina sp. P-21
Pinctada sp. P-3
Pinctada sp. P-3A
Pinctada spp.
Pinna bicolor
Pitar sp. P-62
Saccella sp. P-188
Tellidora pellyana
Tellina capsoides
Tellina robusta
Tellina sp. P-12
Tellinidae sp. P-12A
Tellinidae sp. P-12B
Tellinidae sp. P-13
Tellinidae sp. P-13A
Tellinidae sp. P-13B
Tellinidae sp. P-17A
Tellinidae sp. P-32
Tellinidae sp. P-32A
Tellinidae sp. P-33
Tellinidae sp. P-57
Tellinidae spp.
Timoclea farsiana
Trachycardium lacunosum
Ungulinidae sp. P-20
Ungulinidae sp. P-190
Ungulinidae sp.
Veneridae sp. P-18
Veneridae sp. P-18A
Veneridae sp. P-99
Yoldia sp. P-96
class CEPHALOPHODA
Sepia sp.

phylum **SIPUNCULIDA**
Aspidosiphon sp.
sp. 1
sp 5
sp. 6
sp.
phylum **ANNELIDA**
class POLYCHAETA
Ampharetidae sp.
Amphictenidae sp.
Amphinomidae sp. 3
Amphinomidae sp.
Ancistrosyllis sp. 2
Arabellidae sp.
Ariciidae sp. 2
Ariciidae sp. 5
Ariciidae sp.
Autolytus sp.
Capitella capitata
Capitellida sp. 1
Capitellida sp. 2
Capitellida sp.
Capitellidae sp. 8
Capitellidae sp. 9
Capitellidae sp. 10
Capitellidae sp.
Chrysopetalidae sp. 1
Chrysopetalum sp. 2
Chrysopetalum sp.
Cirratulidae sp. 1
Cirratulidae sp. 2
Cirratulidae sp. 3
Cirratulidae sp. 6
Cirratulidae sp.
?Cossura longocirrata
?Dasybranchus sp. 1
Dorvilleidae sp. 1
Dorvilleidae sp. 8
Dorvilleidae sp.
Eteone sp. 5
Eteone sp.
Euclymene sp.
Eulalia sp.
Eunice sp. 1
Eunice sp. 5
Eunice sp.
Eunicida sp.
Eunicidae sp. 7
Eunicidae sp. 8
Eunicidae sp. 11
Eunicidae sp. 12
Eusyllis sp. 18
Exogone sp. 17
Exogone sp. 22
Exogoninae sp.
Flabelligeridae sp. 1
Flabelligeridae sp. 2
Flabelligeridae sp.
?Fabricia sp. 1

Glyceridae sp. 1
Glyceridae sp. 2
Glyceridae sp. 3
Glyceridae sp.
Goniadidae sp. 1
Goniadidae sp. 2 ?
Harmothoe sp. 5
Hesionidae sp. 1
Hesionidae sp. 2
Hesionidae sp. 3
Hesionidae sp. 5
Hesionidae sp. 7
Hesionidae sp.
Lagisca sp.
Laonice cerrata
Lumbrineridae sp. 2
Lumbrineridae sp. 3
Lumbrineridae sp. 3A
Lumbrineridae sp. 5
Lumbrineridae sp.
Magelonidae sp. 1
Magelonidae sp.
Megalomma sp.
Maldanidae sp. 2
Maldanidae sp. 5
Maldanidae sp. 6
Maldanidae sp.
Melinna sp. 1
Melinna sp. 2
Melinna sp.
Nephtyidae sp. 1
Nephtyidae sp. 2
Nephtyidae sp.
Nephtys sp.
Nereidae sp. 3
Nereidae sp. 9
Nereidae sp. 10
Nereidae sp. 14
Nereidae sp. 15
Nereidae sp. 16
Nereidae sp.
Nereis sp. 1
Nereis sp.
Onuphidae sp.
Opheliidae sp. 1
Opheliidae sp. 2
Opheliidae sp.
Ophryotrocha sp. 4
Paralacydoniidae sp. 1
Paraonidae sp. 2
Paraonidae sp. 4
Paraonidae sp. 5
Paraonidae sp.
Paraonis sp. 6
Paraonis sp.
Pectinaria sp.
Pectinariidae sp. 1
Pectinariidae sp. 2
Phyllodoce sp. 1

Phyllodoce sp. 3
Phyllodocidae sp. 1
Phyllodocidae sp. 2
Phyllodocidae sp. 6
?Pista cristata
Pista sp.
Platynereis sp. 6
Platynereis sp.
Polydora sp. 1
Polydora sp. 2
Polydora sp. 3
Polydora sp. 7
Polydora spp.
Polynoidae sp. 1
Polynoidae sp. 4
Prionospio ?malmgreni
Prionospio sp. 1
Prionospio sp. 10
Prionospio sp. 12
Prionospio sp. 13
Pseudeurythoe hirsuta
Sabellidae sp. 6
Sabellidae sp. 7
Sabellidae sp. 8
Sabellidae sp. 9
Sabellidae sp. 10
Sabellidae sp.
Serpulidae sp. 1
Serpulidae sp. 3
Serpulidae sp. 4
Serpulidae sp. 9
Serpulidae sp. 10
Serpulidae sp.
Sigalionidae sp. 3
Sigalionidae sp. 4
Sigalionidae sp. 6
Sphinteridae sp. 1
Spionida sp. 5
Spionidae sp. 2 ?
Spionidae sp. 4
Spionidae sp. 15
Spionidae sp.
Spirorbis sp. 7
Spirorbis sp.
Sternaspidae sp. 1
Syllidae sp. 8
Syllidae sp. 15
Syllidae sp. 16
Syllidae sp. 19
Syllidae sp. 21
Syllidae sp. 27
Syllidae sp. 28
Syllidae sp.
Syllis sp. 1
Syllis sp. 2
Syllis sp. 12
Syllis sp. 30
Syllis sp.
Terebellidae sp. 5

Terebellidae sp. 8
Terebellidae sp.
class HIRUDINEA
Piscicolidae sp. 1
sp.
phylum **ARTHROPODA**
class ARACHNIDA
order Acari
sp. 3
sp.
class PYCNOGONIDA
sp. 1
class CRUSTACEA
subclass OSTRACODA
sp. 1
sp. 2
sp. 4
sp. 7
sp. 8
sp. 9
sp. 10
sp. 11
sp. 12
sp. 13
sp. 14
sp. 18
sp. 19
sp. 20
sp. 21
sp. 22
sp. 23
sp. 24
sp. 28
sp. 29
sp. 32
sp. 35
sp. 36
spp.
subclass COPEPODA
Corycella sp.
Cyclopoida spp.
Harpacticoida spp.
Macrosetella sp.
subclass MALACOSTRACA
order Leptostraca
Nebalia sp.
order Stomatopoda
Squilla nepa
order Decapoda
Acanthonychidae sp. 10
Achaeus sp.
Actumnus asper
Alpheidae sp. 4
Alpheidae sp.
Alpheus sp. 2
Alpheus sp. 5
Anchistus sp. 1
Charybdis hoplites
Charybdis natator

Cryptopodia sp. 2
Diogenidae sp. 5
Diogenidae spp.
Ebalia sp. 1
Ebalia (Lithadia) sp. 11
Goneplacidae sp. 4
?Goneplacidae sp.
Halimede ochtodes
Hippolyte sp. 1
Hippolytidae sp. 3
Hippolytidae sp. 9
Hippolytidae sp.
Hyastenus hilgendorfi
Lambrus carinatus
Leucosia ?*anatum*
Leucosia sp. 14
Metapenaeopsis mogiensis
Metapenaeopsis stridulans
Metapenaeopsis sp.
Metapenaeus affinis
Metapenaeus stebbingi
Micippa philyra
Myra fugax
Penaeus japonicus
Penaeus latisulcatus
Penaeus semisulcatus
Periclimenes brevicarpalis
Phalangipus longipes
Philyra sp. 8
?*Philyra* sp. ?16
Philyra platychira
Philyra rectangularis
Pilumnus longicornis
?Pinnotheridae sp.
Polyonyx sp. 8
Pontoniidae sp.
Porcellana sp. 4
Porcellanella sp. 1
Portunus hastatoides
Portunus sp. nr. *hastatoides*
Portunus pelagicus
Processa canaliculata
Processidae sp.
Synalpheus sp. 1
Synalpheus sp. 8
Thenus orientalis
Thalamita poissoni
Trachypenaeus curvirostris
Trachypenaeus granulosus
Xanthidae sp. 21
Xanthidae sp.
superorder Peracarida
order Mysidacea
sp. 1
spp.
order Cumacea
sp. 1
sp. 3
sp. 4

sp. 5
sp. 7
sp. 8
sp. 9
sp. 10
sp. 13
sp. 14
sp. 17
sp. 19
sp. 20
sp. 21
sp. 22
spp.
order Tanaidacea
  Kalliapseudes sp. 7
  sp. 6
  sp. 8
  sp.
  Tanais sp. 2
order Isopoda
  Aegidae sp. 17
  Arcturidae sp. 9
  Arcturidae sp. 28
  ?Bopyridae sp. 35
  Gnathia sp. 15
  Gnathia sp.
  Gnathiidae sp. 14
  Idotea sp. 12
  Lironeca sp. 22
  Paracerceis sp. 1
  Sphaeromidae sp. 27
  Sphaeromidae sp.
  sp. 9
  sp. 10
  sp. 30
order Amphipoda
  Ampeliscidae sp. 1
  Ampeliscidae sp. 2
  Ampeliscidae sp. 3
  Caprellidae sp. 3
  Caprellidae sp. 6
  Caprellidae sp.
  Erichthonius sp. 30
  Gammarus sp. 15
  ?Haustoriidae sp. 31
  Leucothoe sp. 10
  Leucothoidae sp.
  Lysianassidae sp. 2
  Lysianassidae sp. 39
  Lysianassidae sp.
  sp. 2
  sp. 2A
  sp. 4
  sp. 9
  sp. 11
  sp. 20
  sp. 26
  sp. 27
  sp. 32

sp. 35
sp. 37
sp. 43
sp. 47
sp. 61
sp. 62
sp. 64
sp. 73
sp. 80
phylum **LOPHOPHORATA**
  class BRYOZOA
    Bugula sp. 12
    Bugula sp.
    sp. 11
phylum **ECHINODERMATA**
  class ASTEROIDEA
    Astropecten phragmorus
    Astropecten polyacanthus
  class OPHIUROIDEA
    Amphioplus seminudus
    Amphiura sp.
    Ophiothrix savignyi
    Paracrocnida persica
    sp.
  class ECHINOIDEA
    Brissopsis persica
    Clypeaster humilis
    Temnopleurus toreumaticus
  class HOLOTHURIOIDEA
    Synaptidae sp.
    sp.

phylum **CHORDATA**
  subphylum UROCHORDATA
    class ASCIDIACEA
        sp. 1
        sp. 2
        sp. 6
        sp.
  subphylum VERTEBRATA
    class ELASMOBRANCHII
        Aetomyleus nichofii
        Carcharhinus ?acutus
        Carcharhinus sp.
        Dasyatis gerrardi
        Dasyatis uarnak
        Mustelus manazo
        Rhynchobatus ancylostoma
        Rhynchobatus djiddensis
        Rhinobatus granulosus
        Taeniura melanospila
  class ACTINOPTERYGII
    superorder Teleostei
        Apogon thurstoni
        Argyrops filamentosus
        Arius thalassinus
        Batrachus grunniens
        Chelonodon patoca
        Gobiidae sp.
        Helotes sexlineatus
        Leptosynanceja melanostigma
        Lutjanus fulviflamma
        Lutjanus sanguineus
        Lutjanus sp.
        Mulloidichthys auriflamma
        Nemipterus tolu
        Opisthognathus sp.
        Pegasus natans
        Platycephalus indicus
        Platycephalus tuberculatus
        Pomadasys stridens
        Pseudorhombus arsius
        Siganus oramin
        Sillago sihama
        Therapon puta
        Upeneus tragula
  class REPTILIA
        Hydrophis spiralis

GRASSBEDS

Summary List

Chrysophyta	2+
Anthophyta	3
Foraminifera	2+
Porifera	1+
Hydrozoa	2+
Actiniaria	2+
Octocorallia	1
Turbellaria	1+
Trematoda	1+
Rhynchocoela	2+
Nematoda	2+
Polyplacophora	1+
Gastropoda	89
Scaphophoda	71
Pelecypoda	2
Cephalopoda	2
Sipunculida	2+
Polychaeta	135
Hirudinea	1+
Pycnogonida	2+
Ostracoda	15+
Copepoda	17+
Branchiura	1+
Cirripedia	1+
Leptostraca	1
Stomatopoda	1
Decapoda	46
Mysidacea	4+
Cumacea	7+
Tanaidacea	4+
Isopoda	11+
Amphipoda	35+
Bryozoa	2+
Asteroidea	4
Ophiuroidea	8+
Echinoidea	5
Holothurioidea	3+
Ascidiacea	2+
Elasmobranchii	6
Teleostei	30+
Reptilia	3
	530+

Species List

phylum **CHRYSOPHYTA**
    diatoms spp.
phylum **ANTHOPHYTA**
      Halodule uninervis
      Halophila ovalis
      Halophila stipulacea
phylum **PROTOZOA**
    order Foraminifera
      spp.
phylum **PORIFERA**
    sp.

phylum **CNIDARIA**
    class HYDROZOA
        spp.
    class ANTHOZOA
        order Actiniaria
          Calliactis sp.
          spp.
        subclass OCTOCORALLIA
          Gorgonian sp.
phylum **PLATYHELMINTHES**
    class TURBELLARIA
        sp.
    class TREMATODA
        sp.
phylum **RHYNCHOCOELA**
    spp.
phylum **ASCHELMINTHES**
    class NEMATODA
        spp.
phylum **MOLLUSCA**
    class POLYPLACOPHORA
        sp. A-1
        sp.
    class GASTROPODA
        Acteocina involuta
        Acteocina persiana
        Aeolidae sp.
        Alaba virgata
        Ancilla castanea
        Atys cylindrica
        Bulla ampulla
        Caecidae sp. G-275
        Calyptraea pellucida
        Cerithiidae sp. G-216
        Cerithiidae sp.
        Cerithium scabridum
        Cerithium sp. G-20
        Cyclostrema quadricarinatum
        Diala goniochila
        Diala semistriata
        Diala sulcifera
        Epitonium replicata
        Eulimidae sp. G-26
        Eulimidae sp. G-26A
        Eulimidae sp.
        Finella pupoides
        Finella reticulata
        Finella scabra
        Gibberula mazagonica
        Hipponidae? sp. G-88
        Marginellidae sp. G-71A
        Marginellidae sp. G-299
        Minolia holdsworthiana
        Mitrella blanda
        Mitrella cartwrighti
        Monilea obscura
        Monilea sp. G-102
        Murex kusterianus
        Murex ponderosa

        Nassarius stigmarius
        Neocollonia sp. G-10
        Notosinister sp. G-23
        Nudibranch sp.
        Odostomia eutropia
        Odostomia sp. G-36
        Olividae sp. G-83A
        Otopleura sp. G-70A
        Pyramidellidae sp. G-34
        Pyramidellidae sp. G-38
        Pyramidellidae sp. G-49A
        Pyramidellidae sp. G-57A
        Pyramidellidae sp. G-87
        Pyrene phaula
        Pyrene spectrum
        Retusa truncatula
        Rhinoclavis fasciatus
        Rissoina distans
        Scaliola arenosa
        Scissurella sp. G-1
        Setia sp. G-21
        Setia sp. G-21A
        Setia sp.
        Smaragdia soverbiana
        Smaragdia sp. G-12
        sp. G-71A
        sp. G-89A
        sp. G-281
        sp. G-285
        Stomatella sp. G-7
        Syphopatella walshii
        Syrnola mekranica
        Thais tissoti
        Torinia faveolata
        Torinia bosschi
        Tricolia fordiana
        Tricolia sp. G-11
        Triphora cingulata
        Triphora incolumnis
        Trochidae sp. G-4
        Trochidae sp. G-5
        Trochidae sp. G-5A
        Trochidae sp. G-13
        Trochus erythraeus
        Turbinidae sp. G-10
        Turbinidae sp. G-10A
        Turbonilla materna
        Turbonilla sp. G-232
        Turbonilla sp. G-232A
        Turbonilla sp. G-234A
        Turbonilla sp. G-235
        Turridae sp. G-33
        Turridae sp. G-33B
        Vermetus sp.
    class SCAPHOPODA
        Dentalium politum
        Dentalium sp. S-1B
    class PELECYPODA
        Anodontia edentula

Anomiidae sp. P-24
Arca sp.
Arcidae sp. P-1
Arcopagia subtruncata
Bellucina seminula
Cardiidae sp.
Cardium papyraceum
Circe scripta
Costacallista sp. P-9
Crenella sp. P-120
Ctena divergens
Ervilia scaliola
Ervilia sp. P-15C
Exotica rhomboides
Gafrarium dispar
Galeommatidae sp. P-19
Gari? sp. P-48
Gari maculosum
Gari weinkauffi
Glycymeris spurcus
Hiatella sp. P-51
Lithophaga sp. P-38
Lucina sp.
Malleus regula
Musculus sp. P-26
Musculus sp. P-26A
Musculus sp. 27
Musculus sp. P-27A
Musculus sp.
Notirus sp. P-59A
Nucula sp. P-29
Pandora unguiculus
Paphia sulcaria
Paphia sp.
Parvicardium suezensis
Pillucina sp. P-21
Pinctada margaritifera
Pinctada radiata
Pinctada sp. P-3
Pinctada sp. P-4
Pinctada sp.
Pinna sp. P-164
Pinna sp.
Pinna strangei
Pteriidae sp.
Septifer bilocularis
sp. P-17
sp. P-181
Standella sp. P-135
Tellidora pellyana
Tellina capsoides
Tellina dissimilis
Tellina robusta
Tellina sp. P-12
Tellinidae sp. P-12A
Tellinidae sp. P-13
Tellinidae sp. P-13B
Tellinidae sp. P-32
Tellinidae sp. P-57

Tellinidae sp. P-57A
Tellinidae sp. P-200
Timoclea farsiana
Timoclea sp.
Ungulinidae sp. P-20
Ungulinidae sp. P-122
Veneridae sp. P-18
Veneridae sp. P-23
Veneridae sp. P-23A
Veneridae sp. P-59
?Veneridae sp.
class CEPHALOPODA
Octopus sp.
Sepia sp.
phylum **SIPUNCULIDA**
Aspidosiphon sp.
spp.
phylum **ANNELIDA**
class POLYCHAETA
Amphinomidae sp. 2
Amphinomidae sp.
Arabellidae sp.
Archiannelida sp.
Aricidea sp. 2
Aricidea sp. 5
Aricidea sp.
Brania sp. 8
Brania sp.
Capitella capitata
Capitellida sp.
Capitellidae sp. 2
Capitellidae sp. 3
Capitellidae sp. 4
Capitellidae sp. 8
Capitellidae spp.
Chrysopetalum sp.
Chrysopetalidae sp. 1
Chrysopetalidae sp.
Cirratulidae sp. 1
Cirratulidae sp. 3
Cirratulidae sp. 4
Cirratulidae sp. 6
Cirratulidae spp.
?*Dasybranchus* sp. 1
Dorvilleidae sp. 1
Dorvilleidae sp. 3
Dorvilleidae sp. 6
Dorvilleidae sp.
Eunice sp. 1
Eunice sp. 5
Eunicidae sp. 2
Eunicidae sp. 3
Eunicidae sp. 4
Eunicidae sp. 7
Eunicidae sp.
Exogoninae sp.
Exogone sp. 4
Exogone sp. 5
Exogone sp. 21

Exogone sp. 22
Flabelligeridae sp. 1
Flabelligeridae sp. 2
Flabelligeridae sp.
Glyceridae sp. 3
Glyceridae sp.
Goniadidae sp. 1
Goniadidae sp.
Hesionidae sp. 1
Hesionidae sp. 2
Hesionidae sp. 5
Hesionidae sp. 7
Hesionidae sp.
Eteone sp. 5
Lumbrineridae sp. 1
Lumbrineridae sp. 2
Lumbrineridae sp. 3
Lumbrineridae sp. 5
Lumbrineridae sp.
Magelonidae sp. 1
Melinna sp 1
Melinna sp.
Nephtyidae sp. 1
Nephtyidae sp.
Nereidae sp. 1
Nereidae sp. 3
Nereidae sp. 4
Nereidae sp. 5
Nereidae sp. 10
Nereidae spp.
Nereis sp.
Onuphidae sp. 1
Onuphidae sp.
Opheliidae sp. 1
Opheliidae sp. 2
Opheliidae sp.
Oweniidae sp.
Paraonidae sp.
Paraonis sp. 3
Pectinaria sp.
Pectinariidae sp. 1
Pectinariidae sp.
Phyllodocidae sp. 1
Phyllodocidae sp. 2
Phyllodocidae sp. 3
Phyllodocidae sp.
Pista sp.
Platynereis sp. 6
Platynereis sp.
Polydora sp. 3
Polynoidae sp. 1
Polynoidae sp.
Polynoidae sp. 4
Polyophthalmus sp.
Pseudeurythoe hirsuta
Sabellidae sp. 1
Sabellidae sp. 2
Sabellidae sp. 3
Sabellidae sp. 4

Sabellidae sp. 10
Sabellidae spp.
Serpulidae sp. 2 or 5
Serpulidae sp. 3 ?
Serpulidae sp. 5
Serpulidae sp. 7
Serpulidae sp.
Sigalionidae sp. 2
Sigalionidae sp.
Spionidae sp. 1
Spionidae sp. 6
Spionidae sp. 9
Spionidae sp. 13
Spionidae sp.
Spirorbis sp. 7
Stenelais boa
Stenelais sp.
Syllidae (Autolytinae) sp.
Syllidae (Exogoninae) sp.
Syllidae sp. 6
Syllidae sp. 8
Syllidae sp. 8A
Syllidae sp. 10
Syllidae sp. 14
Syllidae sp. 15
Syllidae sp. 16
Syllidae sp. 17
Syllidae sp. 19
Syllidae sp. 24
Syllidae sp. 28
Syllidae spp.
Syllis sp. 1
Syllis sp. 9
Syllis sp. 26
Syllis sp.
Terebellidae sp. 3
Terebellidae sp.
class HIRUDINEA
sp.
phylum **ARTHROPODA**
class PYCNOGONIDA
sp. 1
sp. 3
sp.
class CRUSTACEA
subclass OSTRACODA
sp. 1
sp. 2
sp. 3
sp. 4
sp. 6
sp. 12
sp. 13
sp. 14
sp. 15
sp. 18
sp. 21
sp. 23
sp. 24

    sp. 25
    sp. 30
    spp.
subclass COPEPODA
    Calanidae sp.
    Calanoida sp.
    Candacia sp.
    Centropagidae sp. 1
    Cyclopoida sp. 4
    Cyclopoida sp. 9
    Euterpina sp. 15
    Harpacticoida sp. 11
    Harpacticoida sp. 12
    Harpacticoida sp. 13
    Harpacticoida sp. 14
    Harpacticoida sp. 16
    Harpacticoida spp.
    Notodelphyoida sp. 1
    Oithona sp.
    Porcellidium sp. 10
    Scambricornus sp. 3
    Siphonostoma sp.
subclass BRANCHIURA
    sp.
subclass CIRRIPEDIA
    sp.
subclass MALACOSTRACA
    order Leptostraca
        Nebalia sp.
    order Stomatopoda
        Squilla nepa
    order Decapoda
        Acanthonychidae sp. 10
        Acanthonyx limbatus
        Alpheidae sp.
        Alpheus dentipes
        Alpheus sp.
        ?Cryptodromia sp.
        Diogenidae sp.
        Dorippe dorsipes
        Ebalia sp. 1
        Elamena sindensis
        Goneplacidae sp.
        Hippolyte sp. 1
        Hippolytidae sp. 2
        Hippolytidae sp. 3
        Hippolytidae sp. 6
        Hippolytidae sp.
        Hyastenus hilgendorfi
        Ilyograpsus paludicola
        Latreutes sp. 2
        Leucosiidae sp. 9
        Leucosiidae sp. 15
        Leucosiidae sp. 16
        Macrophthalmus telescopicus
        Menaethius monoceros
        Metapenaeus stebbingi
        Micippa philyra
        Palaemonidae sp. 1

        Palaemonidae sp.
        Penaeus semisulcatus
        Periclimenes brevicarpalis
        Philyra sp. 8
        Philyra platychira
        Philyra rectangularis
        Pilumnopeus vauquelini
        Pilumnus longicornis
        Polyonyx sp. 8
        Portunidae sp. 1
        Porcellana sp. 4
        Portunus pelagicus
        Processa sp. 1
        Processidae sp.
        Thalamita poissoni
        Thalamita sp.
        Trachypenaeus curvirostris
        Xanthidae sp. 15
        Xanthidae sp.
superorder Peracarida
    order Mysidacea
        Gastrosaccus sp. 3
        sp. 1
        sp. 2
        sp. 5
        spp.
    order Cumacea
        sp. 1
        sp. 2
        sp. 3
        sp. 4
        sp. 5
        sp. 8
        sp. 10
        spp.
    order Tanaidacea
        Kalliapseudes sp. 7
        Leptochelia sp. 9
        Leptochelia ?dubia
        sp. 3
        sp.
    order Isopoda
        Aegidae sp. 17
        Arcturidae sp. 9
        Arcturidae sp.
        Colopisthus sp. 3
        Cymodoce sp.
        Gnathia sp. 14
        Neastacila sp. 18
        Paracerceis sp. 1
        Polyexosphaeroma sp. 2
        sp. 8
        sp. 13
        sp.
    order Amphipoda
        Ampeliscidae sp. 1
        Ampeliscidae sp. 2
        Ampithoidae sp. 15
        Atylidae sp. 13

Caprellidae sp. 1
Caprellidae sp. 3
Caprellidae sp. 5
Caprellidae sp. 6
Erichthonius sp. 30
?Haustoriidae sp. 31
Leucothoe sp. 10
Lysianassa sp. 1
sp. 1
sp. 2
sp. 3
sp. 4
sp. 7
sp. 9
sp. 11
sp. 17
sp. 19
sp. 20
sp. 22
sp. 24
sp. 25
sp. 26
sp. 27
sp. 37
sp. 38
sp. 43
sp. 44
sp. 45
sp. 55
sp. 56
sp. 64
spp.
phylum **LOPHOPHORATA**
   class BRYOZOA
      spp.
phylum **ECHINODERMATA**
   class ASTEROIDEA
      Asterina burtoni
      Astropecten phragmorus
      Astropecten sp.
      Luidia maculata
   class OPHIUROIDEA
      Amphioplus hastatus
      Amphioplus sp.
      Amphipholis squamata
      Amphiura fasciata
      Amphiuridae sp.
      Ophiothela venusta
      Ophiothrix savignyi
      Ophiura kinbergi
      sp.
   class ECHINOIDEA
      Clypeaster humilis
      Diadema sp.
      Echinodiscus auritus
      Echinometra mathaei
      Temnopleurus toreumaticus

   class HOLOTHURIOIDEA
      Holothuria (Halodeima) atra
      sp.
      Synaptidae sp. 1
      Synaptidae sp.
phylum **CHORDATA**
   subphylum UROCHORDATA
     class ASCIDIACEA
      Botryllus sp.
      sp. 1
      spp.
   subphylum VERTEBRATA
     class ELASMOBRANCHII
      Dasyatis gerrardi
      Dasyatis sephen
      Dasyatis uarnak
      Pristis cuspidatus
      Pristis zysron
      Rhynchobatus djiddensis
     class ACTINOPTERYGII
      superorder Teleostei
        Apogon sp.
        Apogon uninotatus
        Argyrops filamentosus
        Argyrops spinifer
        Arothron stellatus
        Chelonodon patoca
        Crenidens crenidens
        Helotes sexlineatus
        Hippocampus kuda
        Lethrinus sp.
        Lutjanus fulviflamma
        Mulloidichthys auriflamma
        Nemipterus tolu
        Paramonacanthus choirocephalus
        Petroscirtes sp.
        Platycephalus indicus
        Platycephalus sp.
        Plectorhynchus schotaf
        Plotosus anguillaris
        Pomadasyidae sp.
        Pseudorhombus javanicus
        Rhabdosargus globiceps
        Sargus noct
        Siganus oramin
        Siganus sp.
        Stephanolepis sp.
        Syngnathidae spp.
        Synodidae sp.
        Therapon puta
        Upeneus tragula
     class REPTILIA
      Chelonia mydas
      Hydrophis cyanocinctus
      Hydrophis ornatus

Summary List

Cyanophyta	8
Chlorophyta	4
Phaeophyta	6
Rhodophyta	5
Foraminifera	2+
Porifera	2+
Hydrozoa	2+
Actiniaria	2+
Scleractinia	43
Octocorallia	2+
Platyhelminthes	2+
Turbellaria	2+
Trematoda	1+
Rhynchocoela	2+
Nematoda	2+
Polyplacophora	2+
Gastropoda	61+
Pelecypoda	45+
Cephalopoda	1
Sipunculida	2+
Polychaeta	88+
Hirudinea	1+
Acari	1+
Ostracoda	11+
Copepoda	27+
Branchiura	3
Stomatopoda	2
Decapoda	46
Mysidacea	1
Cumacea	4
Tanaidacea	3+
Isopoda	14
Amphipoda	25+
Diptera	2
Coleoptera	2
Bryozoa	2+
Crinoidea	1
Asteroidea	5
Ophiuroidea	9
Echinoidea	6
Holothurioidea	3+
Ascidiacea	2+
Elasmobranchii	8+
Teleostei	73+
Reptilia	2
Aves	6+
	$\overline{543+}$

Species List

phylum **CYANOPHYTA**
- *Calothrix scopulorum*
- *Lyngbya aestuarii*
- *Lyngbya confervoides*
- *Microcoleus* sp.
- *Oscillatoria limosa*
- *Oscillatoria princeps*
- *Phormidium jenkelianum*
- *Spirulina major*

phylum **CHLOROPHYTA**
- *Chaetomorpha linum*
- *Chaetomorpha linum* forma *brachyarthra*
- *Enteromorpha clathrata*
- *Cladophoropsis zollingeri*

phylum **PHAEOPHYTA**
- *Colpomenia sinuosa*
- *Hydroclathrus clathratus*
- *Padina* sp.
- *Pocockiella variegata*
- *Sphacelaria tribuloides*
- *Turbinaria conoides* var. *conoides*

phylum **RHODOPHYTA**
- *Ceramium maryae*
- *Erythrocladia irregularis*
- *Hypnea cornuta*
- *Lithothamnium* sp.
- *Polysiphonia* sp.

phylum **PROTOZOA**
    order Foraminifera
      spp.

phylum **PORIFERA**
    spp.

phylum **CNIDARIA**
    class HYDROZOA
        spp.
    class ANTHOZOA
        Order Actiniaria
        Anemone spp.
        order Scleractinia
          Acanthastrea sp. 1
          Acropora sp. 1
          Acropora sp. 2
          Acropora sp. 3
          Acropora sp.
          Anomastraea sp.
          Coscinaraea sp.
          Culicia sp.
          Cycloseris sp.
          Cyphastrea sp. 7
          Dendrophyllia sp.
          Echinophyllia sp.
          Favia sp. 11
          Favia sp. 12
          Favia sp. 15
          Faviidae sp. 17
          Favites sp.
          ?Goniastrea sp. 9
          Goniastrea sp. 18
          Goniopora sp. 4
          Goniopora sp. 5
          Hydnophora sp. 8
          Leptastrea sp. 4
          Madracis sp.
          Montipora sp. 4
          Paracyathus sp.
          Pavona spp.
          Platygyra sp. 1?
          Platygyra sp. 3
          Platygyra sp. 13
          Plesiastrea sp.
          Pocillopora sp.
          Porites sp. 1
          Porites sp. 2
          Porites sp. 4
          Psammocora sp.
          Siderastrea sp.
          Stylophora sp.
          Tubastrea sp.
          Turbinaria crater 1
          Turbinaria peltata 2
        subclass OCTOCORALLIA
          spp.
phylum **PLATYHELMINTHES**
    class TURBELLARIA
        spp.
    class TREMATODA
        sp.
phylum **RHYNCHOCOELA**
        spp.
phylum **ASCHELMINTHES**
    class NEMATODA
        spp.

phylum **MOLLUSCA**
    class POLYPLACOPHORA
        sp. A-3
        sp. A-3A
        sp.
    class GASTROPODA
        Alaba virgata
        Aplysiidae sp. G-241
        Ancilla castanea
        Cerithiopsidae sp. G-153
        Cerithiopsidae sp. G-153A
        Cerithium columna
        Cerithium echinatum
        Cerithium morum
        Columbellidae sp. G-152
        Conus eburneus
        Conus sumatrensis
        Conus textile
        Cypraea caurica
        Cypraea gracilis notata
        Cypraea lentiginosa
        Cypraea turdus
        Diala goniochila
        Diala sp.
        Drupa margariticola
        Drupa sp.
        Emarginula sp. G-114
        Ergalatax sp. G-103A
        Homalacanthus rota
        Modulus sp. G-205
        Modulus tectum
        Morula sp. G-103
        Muricidae sp.
        Nassarius stigmarius
        Nerita albicilla
        Nudibranch sp. 3
        Nudibranch sp.
        Opisthobranch sp.
        Pyramidellidae sp. G-57
        Pyrene phaula
        Pyrene spectrum?
        Pyrene sp. G-152
        Rhinoclavis fasciatus
        Rhinoclavis kochi
        Rhinoclavis sp.
        Rissoidae sp. G-225
        Rissoina seguenziana
        Scissurella sp. G-1
        Scissurella sp. G-1B
        Scissurella sp.
        Setia sp. G-21
        Setia sp.
        Strombus decorus persicus
        Strombus fusiformis
        Strombus sp.
        Thais pseudohippocastaneum
        Tricolia fordiana
        Triphora incolumnis
        Triphora perversa

Triphoridae sp. G-23
Triphoridae sp. G-120A
Triphoridae sp. G-154
Triphoridae sp. G-174
Trochidae sp. G-13A
Trochidae sp. G-13B
Turbo radiatus
Vermetus sp. G-264
class PELECYPODA
Acar plicata
Anomia sp. P-49
Anomia sp. P-49A
Anomia sp.
Anomiidae sp. P-102
Anomiidae sp. P-102A
Anomiidae sp. P-184
Arca sp. P-112
Arca uropigmelana
Arcidae sp. P-179
Barbatia decussata
Barbatia lacerata
Botula cinnamomea
Chamidae sp. P-91
Chlamys ruschenbergerii
Chlamys sp. P-101
Circe intermedia
Cuspidaria sp. P-106
Dosinia radiata
Erycinacea sp. P-104
Gastrochaena cuneiformis
Glycymeris pectunculus
Hiatella sp. P-51
Hiatella sp.
Isognomon sp.
Isogomonidae sp.
Lithophaga lithophaga
Lithophaga sp. 1
Lithophaga sp. P-38A
Lithophaga sp. P-171
Lithophaga sp.
Lopha cristagalli
Malleidae sp. P-146
Malleus sp. P-103
Musculus sp. P-27
Musculus sp.
Pteria sp. P-126
Pteriidae sp.
Rocellaria sp. 1
Rocellaria sp. P-123
Septifer bilocularis
Spondylus exilis
Spondylus sp.
sp.
Tellinidae sp. P-108
class CEPHALOPODA
Sepia sp.
phylum **SIPUNCULIDA**
Sipunculus sp.
sp.

phylum **ANNELIDA**
class POLYCHAETA
Aricia sp. 3
Ariciidae sp. 4
Brania sp. 6
Brania? sp.
Capitellidae sp. 6
Capitellidae sp. 7
Chrysopetalidae sp. 2
Chrysopetalum sp. 1
Chrysopetalum sp.
?Dasybranchus sp. 1
Dorvilleidae sp. 1
Dorvilleidae sp. 2
Dorvilleidae sp. 3
Dorvilleidae sp. 5
Dorvilleidae sp.
Eunice sp. 1
Eunice sp. 5
?Eunice torquata
Eunicidae sp. 2
Eunicidae sp. 3
Eunicidae sp. 4
Eunicidae sp. 8
Eunicidae sp.
Eusyllis sp. 18
Exogone sp. 4
Exogone sp. 17
Exogone sp. 22
Exogone sp. 29
Euphrosinidae sp. 1
Harmothoe sp. 5
Hesionidae sp. 8
Hesionidae sp.
Lagisca sp.
Lumbrineridae sp. 1
Maldanidae sp. 4
Nereidae sp. 3
Nereidae sp. 4
Nereidae sp. 9
Nereidae sp. 14
Nereidae sp. 15
Nereidae sp. 16
Nereidae sp.
Opheliidae sp. 1
Opheliidae sp. 2
Opheliidae sp. 4
Paraonidae sp. 4
Paraonis sp. 3
Phyllodocidae sp. 1
Phyllodocidae sp. 2
Phyllodocidae sp. 3
Phyllodocidae sp. 10
Phyllodocidae spp.
Pilargidae sp. 1
Polydora colonia
Polydora sp.
Polynoidae sp. 1
Polynoidae sp. 2

Polynoidae sp. 3
Polynoidae sp. 4
Sabellidae spp.
Serpulidae sp. 1
Serpulidae sp. 2
Serpulidae sp. 5
Serpulidae sp. 6
Serpulidae sp. 8
Serpulidae sp. 9
Serpulidae sp. 10
Serpulidae sp.
Sigalionidae sp. 5
Spionidae sp. 11
Spionidae sp. 16
Syllidae sp. 8
Syllidae sp. 15
Syllidae sp. 19
Syllidae sp. 20
Syllidae sp. 24
Syllidae sp. 27
Syllidae sp. 28
Syllidae sp. 31
Syllidae spp.
Syllis sp. 1
Syllis sp. 2
Syllis sp. 3
Syllis sp. 9
Syllis sp. 14
Syllis sp. 26
Syllis sp. 30
Syllis sp.
Syllis variegata
Terebellidae sp. 2
Terebellidae sp.
class HIRUDINEA
sp.
phylum **ARTHROPODA**
class ARACHNIDA
order Acari
sp.
class CRUSTACEA
subclass OSTRACODA
sp. 1
sp. 3
sp. 7
sp. 8
sp. 12
sp. 13
sp. 15
sp. 19
sp. 20
sp. 24
sp. 33
spp.
subclass COPEPODA
Alteutha sp. 9
Alteutha sp.
Calanoida sp. 24
Calanoida sp.

Candacia sp.
Clytemnestra sp.
Cyclopoida sp. 4
Cyclopoida sp. 5
Cyclopoida sp. 9
Cyclopoida sp.
Euterpina sp.
Gigasilus sp. 12
Harpacticoida sp. 3
Harpacticoida sp. 4
Harpacticoida sp. 5
Harpacticoida sp. 11
Harpacticoida sp. 18
Harpacticoida sp. 22
Harpacticus sp.
Oithona sp.
Oncaea sp.
Poecilostoma sp. 11
Porcellidiidae sp. 21
Porcellidium sp. 10
Scambricornus sp. 3
Siphonostomata sp. 3
Siphonostomata sp.
spp.
subclass BRANCHIURA
sp. 1
sp. 2
sp. 3
subclass MALACOSTRACA
order Stomatopoda
Lysiosquilla sp. 3
order Decapoda
Actumnus asper
Alpheidae sp.
Alpheus sp. 2
Alpheus sp. 3
Callianassa sp. 1
Carpilius convexus
Charybdis paucidentata
Chlorodiella nigra
Chlorodopsis sp.
Coenobita sp.
Diogenidae sp.
Dromidia unidentata
Dromiidae sp.
Eriphia sebana smithii
Etisus anaglyptus
Etisus electra
Etisus laevimanus
Galatheidae sp. 1
Goneplacidae sp. 1
Grapsus tenuicrustatus
Hapalocarcinus sp.
Heteropilumnus trichophoroides
Maiidae sp. 10
Menaethiops nodulosa
Ocypode saratan
Pachycheles sp. 3
Palaemonidae sp. 4

261

Palaemonella sp. 6
Panulirus versicolor
Periclimenaeus sp. 5
Pilumnus longicornis
Pinnotheridae sp. 1
Polyonyx sp. 6
Pontonia? sp. 4
Pontoniinae sp.
Porcellanella sp. 1
Porcellanidae sp.
Portunidae sp.
Stegopontonia commensalis
Synalpheus sp. 1
?Synalpheus sp. 8
Tetralia glaberrima
Trapezia cymodoce
Xanthidae sp. 17
Xanthidae sp. 18
Xanthidae sp. 20
superorder Peracarida
order Mysidacea
Gastrosaccus sp. 7
order Cumacea
sp. 4
sp. 6
sp. 10
sp. 12
order Tanaidacea
Leptochelia sp. 9
sp. 3
sp. 5
sp.
order Isopoda
Aegidae sp. 17
Arcturidae sp. 9
Bagatus sp. 11
Bagatus sp. 16
Bopyridae sp. 31
Cirolana sp. 19
Cryptoniscid larva sp.
Cyathura sp. 10
Cymothoidae sp. 6
Cymothoidae sp. 33
Gnathia sp.
Gnathiidae sp. 14
Gnathiidae sp.
sp. 13
order Amphipoda
Ampelisca sp. 50
Ampithoidae sp. 15
Gammaridae sp. 36
Leucothoe sp.
Leucothoidae sp. 10
Leucothoidae sp. 41
Lysianassa sp. 8
Lysianassidae sp. 36
sp. 1
sp. 2
sp. 3

sp. 7
sp. 11
sp. 19
sp. 26
sp. 37
sp. 38
sp. 40
sp. 42
sp. 43
sp. 44
sp. 47
sp. 55
sp. 65
sp. 66
spp.
class INSECTA
order Diptera
Ephydridae sp. 1
Ephydridae sp. 2
order Coleoptera
Carabidae sp.
sp. 1
phylum **LOPHOPHORATA**
class BRYOZOA
sp. 2
sp. 3
spp.
phylum **ECHINODERMATA**
class CRINOIDEA
sp. 1
class ASTEROIDEA
Asterina burtoni
Euretaster cribrosus
Leiaster leachi
Linckia multifora
Pentaceraster mammillatus
class OPHIUROIDEA
Amphiura crispa
Amphiuridae sp.
Macrophiothrix elongata
Ophiactis savignyi
Ophiothela danae
Ophiothrix savignyi
sp. 3
sp. 4
sp. 7
class ECHINOIDEA
Brissopsis persica
Diadema setosum
Echinometra mathaei
Lovenia elongata
Metalia sternalis
Prionocidaris baculosa
class HOLOTHURIOIDEA
sp. 1
sp. 2
spp.
Stichopus sp.

phylum **CHORDATA**
  subphylum UROCHORDATA
    class ASCIDIACEA
       spp.
  subphylum VERTEBRATA
    class ELASMOBRANCHII
       Aetomyleus narinari
       Carcharhinus leucas
       Carcharhinus melanopterus
       Carcharhinus sorrah
       Carcharhinus spp.
       Chiloscyllium griseum
       Galeocerdo cuvieri
       Negaprion brevirostris
    class ACTINOPTERYGII
      superorder Teleostei
       Abudefduf saxatilis
       Acanthopagrus bifasciatus
       Acanthopagrus cuvieri
       Acanthurus sohal
       Amphiprion sp.
       Apogon spp.
       Blenniidae sp.
       Caesio sp.
       Callyodon sp.
       Caranx fulvoguttatus
       Caranx ignobilis?
       Caranx sexfasciatus
       Caranx sp.
       Cephalopholis miniatus
       Cephalopholis rogaa
       Chaetodon melapterus
       Chaetodon nigropunctatus
       Cheilinus sp.
       Cheilodipterus spp.
       Diodon hystrix
       Echeneis naucrates
       Ecsenius sp.
       Epinephelus coeruleopunctatus
       Epinephelus summana
       Epinephelus tauvina
       Gaterin gaterinus
       Gnathanodon speciosus
       Gobiodon citrinus
       Heniochus acuminatus
       Labroides dimidiatus
       ?Leptoscarus sp.
       Lethrinus lentjan
       Lethrinus miniatus
       Lethrinus nebulosus
       Lethrinus sp.
       Lutjanus fulviflamma
       Lutjanus johni
       Lutjanus sanguineus
       Lutjanus sp.
       Ostracion sp.
       Paracaesio sp.
       Parapercis nebulosus
       Pardachirus marmoratus

       Petroscirtes sp.
       Platax sp.
       Plectorhynchus pictus
       Plectorhynchus schotaf
       Pomacanthus imperator
       Pomacanthus maculosus
       Pomacentridae sp.
       Pseudochromidae sp.
       Pseudochromis persicus
       Pterois volitans
       Pygoplites diacanthus
       Rastrelliger kanagurta
       Rhinecanthus aculeatus
       Salarias sp.
       Sargus noct
       Scolopsis ghanam
       Scomberomorus commersoni
       Scorpaenopsis sp.
       Siganus spp.
       Sphyraena japonica?
       Sphyraena jello
       Spilotichthys pictus
       Sufflamen albicaudatum
       Thalassoma lunare
       Trachinotus blochii
       Ulua mentalis
       Zebrasoma xanthurus
    class REPTILIA
       Chelonia mydas
       Eretmochelys imbricata
    class AVES
       Ardea cinerea
       Charadrius spp.
       Phalacrocorax carbo
       Sterna anaethetus
       Sterna bengalensis
       Sterna repressa

Summary List

Cyanophyta	4
Chlorophyta	6
Chrysophyta	9
Pyrrophyta	7
Phaeophyta	7
Rhodophyta	10
Foraminifera	2+
Porifera	2+
Hydrozoa	2+
Actiniaria	3+
Octocorallia	1
Turbellaria	1+
Nematoda	2+
Gastropoda	9+
Pelecypoda	24
Sipunculida	1+
Polychaeta	17+
Ostracoda	4+
Copepoda	9+
Cirripedia	3+
Decapoda	11+
Isopoda	2
Amphipoda	2+
Bryozoa	2+
Brachiopoda	2+
Crinoidea	2+
Ophiuroidea	2+
Echinoidea	3
Holothurioidea	2+
Ascidiacea	2+
Teleostei	25+
	178+

Species List

phylum **CYANOPHYTA**
- *Calothrix scopulorum*
- *Microcoleus chthonoplastes*
- *Lyngbya confervoides*
- *Oscillatoria* spp.

phylum **CHLOROPHYTA**
- *Acetabularia calyculus*
- *Cladophora koiei*
- *Cladophora sericoides*
- *Cladophora* sp.
- *Enteromorpha* sp. (cf. *E. flexuosa*)
- *Trichosolen* sp.

phylum **CHRYSOPHYTA**
- *Coscinodiscus* sp. 1
- *Coscinodiscus* sp. 2
- *Diploneis crabro*
- *Hemiaulus heibergii*
- *Navicula* sp.
- *Navicula vacillans*
- *Nitzschia angularis*
- *Pleurosigma* sp. 1
- *Pleurosigma* sp. 2

phylum **PYRROPHYTA**
- *Ceratium furca*
- *Exuviella* sp.
- *Gymnodinium* sp. 1
- *Gymnodinium* sp. 2
- *Oxytocum* sp.
- *Peridinium* sp.
- *Prorocentrum* sp.

phylum **PHAEOPHYTA**
- *Ectocarpus irregularis*
- *Ectocarpus mitchellae*
- *Ectocarpus* sp.
- *Nemacystus* sp.
- *Sargassum asperifolium*
- *Sargassum tenerrimum*
- *Sphacelaria* sp.

phylum **RHODOPHYTA**
- *Amphiroa fragilissima*
- *Ceramium cruciatum*
- *Ceramium luetzelburgii*
- *Ceramium transversale*
- *Ceramium* sp. (cf. *C. fastigatum*)
- *Dasya ocellata*
- *Erythrotrichia carnea*
- *Polysiphonia broadiae*
- *Polysiphonia kampsaxii*
- *Polysiphonia* sp.

phylum **PROTOZOA**
- order Foraminifera
  - spp.

phylum **PORIFERA**
- spp.

phylum **CNIDARIA**
- class HYDROZOA
  - spp.
- class ANTHOZOA
  - order Actiniaria
    - Anemone spp.
  - order Antipatharia
    - sp.
  - subclass OCTOCORALLIA
    - Gorgonacea sp.

phylum **PLATYHELMINTHES**
- class TURBELLARIA
  - sp.

phylum **ASCHELMINTHES**
- class NEMATODA
  - spp.

phylum **MOLLUSCA**
    class GASTROPODA
        Caecidae sp. G-268
        Diastomidae sp. G-19
        Drupa sp. G-155
        Epitoniidae sp. G-91?
        Epitoniidae sp.
        Eulimidae sp. G-244
        Nudibranch spp.
        Trochidae sp.
    class PELECYPODA
        Anomiidae sp.
        Carditidae sp. P-210
        Hiatella sp. P-51
        Hiatellidae sp. P-51A
        ?Hyotissa sp.
        ?Lopha cristagalli
        Musculus sp. P-27
        Musculus sp. P-98
        Mytilidae sp. P-38
        Mytilidae sp. P-120
        Ostraeidae sp. P-142
        Petrasma pusilla
        Pinctada margaritifera
        Pinctada radiata
        Pinctada sp. P-70
        Plicatula sp.
        Pteria sp.
        Pteriidae sp.
        Septifer bilocularis
        Spondylus exilis
        Spondylidae sp.
        Tellinidae sp. P-32?
        Ungulinidae sp. P-122
        Ungulinidae sp. ?
phylum **SIPUNCULIDA**
        sp.
phylum **ANNELIDA**
    class POLYCHAETA
        Chrysopetalidae sp. 2
        Chrysopetalidae sp.
        Eunicidae sp.
        Harmothoe sp. 5
        Lumbrineridae sp. 1
        Nereidae sp. 4?
        Nereidae spp.
        Phyllodoce sp.
        Polynoidae sp. 4
        Polynoidae spp.
        Serpulidae sp. 5
        Serpulidae sp. 6
        Serpulidae sp.
        Syllis sp. 10
        Syllis sp. 14
        Syllis sp. 30?
        Syllidae spp.

phylum **ARTHROPODA**
    class CRUSTACEA
      subclass OSTRACODA
        sp. 1
        sp. 12
        sp. 27
        sp. 33
        sp.
      subclass COPEPODA
        Calanoida spp.
        ?Clytemnestra sp. 25
        Cyclopoida sp. 4
        Cyclopoida spp.
        Harpacticoida sp. 4
        Harpacticoida sp. 24
        Harpacticoida spp.
        Scambricornus sp.
      subclass CIRRIPEDIA
        Balanus amphitrite
        Balanus tintinnabulum
        Balanus sp.
        sp.
      subclass MALACOSTRACA
        order Decapoda
          Alpheidae sp.
          Hyastenus hilgendorfi
          Heteropilumnus trichophoroides
          Menaethiops nodulosa
          Pilumnus longicornis
          Porcellanella sp.
          Porcellanidae spp.
          Synalpheus sp. 1
          ?Synalpheus sp. 8
          Xanthidae sp. 18?
          Xanthidae spp.
      superorder Peracarida
      order Isopoda
        Cryptoniscus sp.
      sp. 36
      order Amphipoda
      spp.
phylum **LOPHOPHORATA**
    class BRYOZOA
        Bugula sp.
        sp.
    class BRACHIOPODA
        spp.
phylum **ECHINODERMATA**
    class CRINOIDEA
        spp.
    class OPHIUROIDEA
        Ophiothrix savignyi
        spp.
    class ECHINOIDEA
        Echinometra mathaei
        Prionocidaris baculosa
        Diadema setosum
    class HOLOTHURIOIDEA
        spp.

phylum **CHORD'ATA**
  subphylum UROCHORDATA
    class ASCIDIACEA
      spp.
  subphylum VERTEBRATA
    class ACTINOPTERYGII
      superorder Teleostei
        Abudefduf saxatilis
        Abudefduf sp.
        Acanthopagrus berda
        Acanthopagrus bifasciatus
        Apogon spp.
        Arothron stellatus
        Cephalopholis miniatus
        Chaetodon nigropunctatus
        Decapterus sp.
        Epinephelus tauvina
        Gnathanodon speciosus
        Heniochus acuminatus
        Ostracion sp.
        Platax sp.
        Pomacanthus maculosus
        Pseudochromis persicus
        Pterois volitans
        Rachycentron canadus
        Sargus noct
        Scolopsis sp.
        Sphyraena ?japonica
        Sphyraena jello
        Sphyraena obtusata
        Thalassoma lunare

PLANKTON

Summary List

Cyanophyta	16+
Chlorophyta	1
Chrysophyta	161+
Pyrrophyta	14+
Radiolaria	2+
Hydrozoa	10
Scyphyozoa	2+
Ctenophora	4+
Turbellaria	2+
Nematoda	2+
Gastropoda	9+
Pelecypoda	2+
Polychaeta	8+
Cladocera	4
Ostracoda	5
Copepoda	65+
Cirripedia	2+
Stomatopoda	2+
Euphausiacea	1+
Decapoda	7+
Mysidacea	2+
Cumacea	1
Isopoda	2+
Amphipoda	9
Phoronida	1
Bryozoa	1
Brachiopoda	1
Asteroidea	1
Ophiuroidea	1+
Echinoidea	1+
Chaetognatha	7+
Ascidiacea	2+
Thaliacea	2+
Larvacea	3+
Teleostei	2+
	355+

Species List
phylum **CYANOPHYTA**

        Anabaena spp.
        Anabaenopsis spp.
        Borzia spp.
        Calothrix scopulorum
        Lyngbya confervoides
        Lyngbya spp.
        Microcoleus chthonoplastes
        Nostoc spp.
        Oscillatoria intermedia
        Oscillatoria spp.
        Phormidium spp.
        Spirulina spp.
        Synochococcus custos
        Synochococcus elongatus
        Synochococcus spp.
        Trichodesmium sp.

phylum **CHLOROPHYTA**
  Dunaliella salina
phylum **CHRYSOPHYTA**
  Achnanthes brevipes
  Achnanthes hauckia
  Achanthes parvula
  Amphiprora decussata
  Amphora acustucula
  Amphora angusta
  Amphora arenaria
  Amphora areus
  Amphora binodis
  Amphora coffeaformis
  Amphora exigua
  Amphora hyalina
  Amphora laevis
  Amphora laevissima
  Amphora lineolata
  Amphora macilenta
  Amphora ostrearia
  Amphora peragalli var. *balearica*
  Amphora pusio
  Amphora salina
  Amphora spp.
  Amphora steltoforthii
  Amphora sulcata
  Asterionella nitzschioides
  Asterionella spp.
  Auricula insecta
  Auricula spp.
  Bacteriastrum delicatulum
  Bacteriastrum hyatinum
  Bacteriastrum sp.
  Bacteriastrum varians
  Campylodiscus spp.
  Chaetocerus brevis
  Chaetocerus decipiens
  Climacosphenia elongata
  Climacosphenia sp.
  Cocconeis disrupta
  Cocconeis distans
  Cocconeis molesta
  Cocconeis scutellum
  Corethron hystrix
  Coscinodiscus lineatus
  Coscinodiscus spp.
  Cyclotella stytorum
  Cylindrotheca longissima
  Diploneis crabro
  Ditylum brightwellii
  Eucampia sp.
  Grammatophora spp.
  Hautzschia amphioxys
  Hautzschia hyalina
  Hemiaulus heibergi
  Hemiaulus hauckii
  Hemiaulus membranicus
  Hemiaulus sinensis
  Leptocylindrus danicus

Leptocylindrus spp.
Licmophora dalmatica
Licmophora flabellata
Licmophora gracilis
Licmophora juergensii
Licmophora lebilis
Licmophora lyngbyei
Licmophora sp.
Licmophora tenuis
Mastigloia angulata
Mastigloia arabica
Mastigloia decussata
Mastigloia erythraea
Mastigloia quinquecostata
Mastigloia porteriana
Mastigloia smithii
Melosira sp.
Navicula arenaria
Navicula cancellata
Navicula carinifera
Navicula crabro
Navicula crucifera
Navicula forcipata
Navicula fusca
Navicula lanceolata
Navicula liber
Navicula littoralis
Navicula lyra
Navicula marina
Navicula muscaeformis
Navicula palpebralis
Navicula rectangulata
Navicula smithii
Navicula spp.
Navicula suborbicularis
Navicula tuscula
Navicula vacillans
Nitzschia amphioxys
Nitzschia angularis
Nitzschia apiculata
Nitzschia commutata
Nitzschia constricta
Nitzschia distans
Nitzschia hybrida
Nitzschia jelineckii
Nitzschia lanceolata
Nitzschia longissima
Nitzschia lorenziana
Nitzschia media
Nitzschia obtusa
Nitzschia pacifica
Nitzschia pandoriformis
Nitzschia paradoxa
Nitzschia punctata
Nitzschia pungens
Nitzschia recta
Nitzschia rigida
Nitzschia seriata
Nitzschia sigma

Nitzschia socialis
Nitzschia spathulata
Nitzschia spp.
Nitzschiella incerta
Nitzschiella lorenziana
Nitzschiella sp.
Ornithocercus spp.
Orthoneis binotata
Orthoneis fimbriata
Orthoneis sp.
Plagiogramma spp.
Pleurosigma/Gyrosigma angulatum
Pleurosigma/Gyrosigma spp.
Raphoneis amphiceros
Raphoneis surirella
Rhizosolenia alata
Rhizosolenia calcaravis
Rhizosolenia delicatula
Rhizosolenia hebatata
Rhizosolenia imbricata
Rhizosolenia setigera
Rhizosolenia steltoforthii
Rhizosolenia styliformis
Skeletonema costatum
Skeletonema sp.
Stauroneis salina
Stauroneis sp.
Striatella delicatula
Striatella dirrupta
Striatella interrupta
Striatella sp.
Striatella unipunctata
Surirella fastuosa
Surirella gemma
Surirella pandora
Surirella sp.
Synedra crystallina
Synedra gallionii
Thalassiothrix sp.
Thalassionema nitzschioides
Toxonidea insignis
Toxonidea sp.
Trachyneis aspera
Trachysphenia australis
Triceratium spp.
Tropidoneis lepidoptera

Plankton, Species List – Cont'd

phylum **PYRROPHYTA**
    Ceratium furca
    Ceratium pulchellum
    Ceratium spp.
    Dinoastridium spp.
    Dinophysis spp.
    Exuviella spp.
    Gonyaulax spp.
    Glenodinium spp.
    Gymnodinium spp.
    Mastoneis biformis
    Oxytocum spp.
    Peridinium spp.
    Prorocentrum micans
    Prorocentrum spp.
phylum **PROTOZOA**
  order Radiolaria
    spp.
phylum **CNIDARIA**
  class HYDROZOA
    Aequorea sp.
    Aglanta sp.
    Anthomedusa sp.
    Eirene sp.
    Eleutheria sp.
    Lensia sp.
    Leptomedusa sp.
    Liriope tetraphyllum
    ?Monophie sp.
    Siphonophora spp.
  class SCYPHOZOA
    Rhizostoma sp.
    spp.
phylum **CTENOPHORA**
    Beroe sp.
    Lobata sp.
    Mnemiopsis sp.
    Pleurobrachia sp.
    spp.
phylum **PLATYHELMINTHES**
  class TURBELLARIA
    ?Paraproporus sp.
    spp.
phylum **ASCHELMINTHES**
  class NEMATODA
    spp.
phylum **MOLLUSCA**
  class GASTROPODA
    Atlanta sp.
    Atlantidae sp.
    Creseis sp.
    Heteropoda sp.
    Hyalocilis striata
    Limacina inflata
    Limacina trochiformis
    Pteropoda spp.
    Veliger larvae spp.
  class PELECYPODA
    Veliger larvae spp.

phylum **ANNELIDA**
   class POLYCHAETA
        Chrysopetalid larvae
        Nereidae sp. 18 (epitokes)
        Nereidae spp. (epitokes)
        Serpulid larvae
        Spionid larvae
        Syllidae sp. 27 (epitokes)
        Syllidae spp. (epitokes)
        Trochophore larvae
phylum **ARTHROPODA**
   class CRUSTACEA
      order Cladocera
        Evadne sp.
        Evadne tergestina
        Penilia avirostris
        Podon sp.
      subclass OSTRACODA
        ?Cypridina sp.
        sp. 2
        sp. 15
        sp. 17
        ?Xestoleberis sp.
      subclass COPEPODA
        Acartia erythraea
        Acartia longiremis
        Acartia sp.
        Acartia tonsa
        Acartiidae sp.
        Aegisthus sp.
        Calanidae sp. 2
        Calanidae sp. 4
        Calanidae sp. 5
        Calanidae sp. 6
        Calanidae sp.
        Calanoida spp.
        Calanopia elliptica
        Calanus minor
        Calanus sp. 3
        Candacia armata
        Candacia simplex
        Candacia sp. 1
        Centropages sp. 1
        Centropages sp. 2
        Centropages typicus
        Centropages violaceus
        Centropagidae sp.
        Chyridus sp.
        Clausocalanus sp.
        Clytemnestra sp.
        Copilia mirabilis
        Copilia sp.
        Corycaeus rostratus
        Corycaeus spp.
        Eucalanus crassus
        Eucalanus elongatus
        Euterpina acutifrons
        Euterpina spp.
        Labidocera acutifrons
        Labidocera croyeri
        Labidocera minutum
        Lucicutia ovalis
        Macrosetella gracilis
        Macrosetella sp. 7
        Macrosetella sp.
        Microsetella rosea
        Microsetella sp.
        Monstrilloida sp.
        Oithona nana
        Oithona plumifera
        Oithona spp.
        Oncaea spp.
        Paracalanus parvus
        Paracalanus sp.
        Pontella sp.
        Pontellidae sp. 1
        Pontellidae sp. 2
        Pontellidae sp.
        Pontellopsis regalis
        Pontellopsis strenua
        Porcellidium sp.
        Sapphirina sp.
        Temora discaudata
        Temora sp.
        Temora stylifera
        Temoridae sp. 1
        Temoridae sp. 2
        Tisbidae sp.
        Tortanus murrayi
      subclass CIRRIPEDIA
        larvae
      subclass MALACOSTRACA
        order Stomatopoda
          larvae
        order Euphausiacea
          sp.
        order Decapoda
          larvae
          Leptochela robusta
          Lucifer sp.
          Penaeid larvae
          Penaeus latisulcatus (larvae)
          Penaeus semisulcatus (larvae)
          Solenocera sp. (larvae)
     superorder Peracarida
        order Mysidacea
          spp.
        order Cumacea
          sp. 2
        order Isopoda
          Cryptoniscid larvae
          Gnathia sp. 15
        order Amphipoda
          ?Haustoriidae sp. 31
          Hyperia sp. 2
          Hyperiidae sp. 3
          Hyperiidae sp.
          Lysianassa sp. 8

Plankton, Species List – Cont'd

        Oxycephalus sp. 1
        sp. 1
        sp. 2
        sp. 33
phylum **LOPHOPHORATA**
    class PHORONIDA
        larvae
    class BRYOZOA
        larvae
    class BRACHIOPODA
        larvae
phylum **ECHINODERMATA**
    class ASTEROIDEA
        larvae
    class OPHIUROIDEA
        larvae
    class ECHINOIDEA
        larvae
phylum **CHAETOGNATHA**
        Krohnitta spp.
        Krohnitta subtilis
        Sagitta enflata
        Sagitta ferox
        Sagitta friderici
        Sagitta helenae
        Sagitta spp.
phylum **CHORDATA**
    subphylum UROCHORDATA˙
    class ASCIDIACEA
        larvae
    class THALIACEA
        Doliolum spp.
    class LARVACEA
        Fritillaria sp.
        Oikopleura longicauda
        Oikopleura sp.
    subphylum VERTEBRATA
    class ACTINOPTERYGII
        superorder Teleostei
            eggs
            larvae

OPEN WATER ANIMALS

Summary List

Cephalopoda	1
Elasmobranchii	12
Teleostei	39+
Reptilia	3
Aves	21
Cetacea	7+
	83+

Species List

phylum **MOLLUSCA**
    class CEPHALOPODA
        ?Loligo sp.
phylum **CHORDATA**
    subphylum VERTEBRATA
    class ELASMOBRANCHII
        Aetobatis narinari
        Carcharhinus leucas
        Carcharhinus maculipinnis
        Carcharhinus ?melanopterus
        Carcharhinus ?menisorrah
        Carcharhinus ?sorrah
        Carcharhinus spp.
        Galeocerdo cuvieri
        Mobula diabolus
        Myliobatis nichofii
        Negaprion brevirostris
        Sphyrna spp.
    class ACTINOPTERYGII
        superorder Teleostei
        Acanthopagrus cuvieri
        Allanetta forsskali
        Atule kalla
        Belonidae spp.
        Carangidae spp.
        Caranx fulvoguttatus
        Caranx ?ignobilis
        Caranx sexfasciatus
        Caranx spp.
        Chirocentrus dorab
        Coryphaena hippurus
        Cypselurus oligolepis
        Decapterus sp.
        Echeneis naucrates
        Euthynnus affinis
        Gnathanodon speciosus
        Hemirhamphus far
        Istiophorus gladius
        Nematalosa nasus
        Parexocoetus mento
        Rachycentron canadus
        Rastrelliger kanagurta
        Sardinella spp.
        Scomberoides commersonianus
        Scomberoides ?tol
        Scomberomorus commersoni
        Scomberomorus guttatus

Open Water Animals, Species List – Cont'd

          Scombridae spp.
          Seriola sp.
          Sphyraena ?japonica
          Sphyraena jello
          Sphyraena obtusata
          Stolephorus spp.
          Thunnus obesus
          Trachinotus blochii
          Ulua mentalis
class REPTILIA
          Chelonia mydas
          Eretmochelys imbricata
          Pelamis platurus
class AVES
          Anas acuta
          Anas clypeata
          Anas crecca
          Anas penelope
          Anas platyrhynchos
          Aythya ferina
          Aythya fuligula
          Fulica atra
          Larus argentatus
          Larus genei
          Larus ichthyaetus
          Larus ridibundus
          Pandion haliaetus
          Phalacrocorax carbo
          Phalaropus ?lobatus
          Podiceps nigricollis
          Stercorarius parasiticus
          Sterna anaethetus
          Sterna bengalensis
          Sterna repressa
          Tachybaptus ruficollis
class MAMMALIA
      order Cetacea
          Balaenoptera spp.
          dolphins spp.
          Orcinus orca
          Sotalia lentiginosa
          Tursiops aduncus

HYPERSALINE (300⁰/₀₀) BIOTOPE

Summary List

Cyanophyta	12
Chlorophyta	1
Chrysophyta	22+
Pyrrophyta	1
Turbellaria	1+
Nematoda	2+
Copepoda	4
Coleoptera	1+
	44+

Species List

phylum **CYANOPHYTA**
          Anabaena sp.
          Anabaenopsis sp.
          Oscillatoria limosa
          Oscillatoria nigro-viridis
          Oscillatoria sp. 1
          Oscillatoria sp. 2
          Spirulina labryinthiformis
          Spirulina subtilissima
          Spirulina sp. 1
          Spirulina sp. 2
          Synochococcus custos
          Synochococcus elongatus
phylum **CHLOROPHYTA**
          Dunaliella salina
phylum **CHRYSOPHYTA**
          Amphora coffeaformis
          Amphora exigua
          Amphora laevissima
          Amphora lineolata
          Amphora macilenta
          Amphora pusio
          Amphora salina
          Amphora sulcata
          Amphora sp.
          Cylindrotheca longissima
          Mastigloia porteriana
          Mastigloia smithii
          Navicula arenaria
          Navicula sp. 1
          Navicula suborbicularis
          Nitzschia commutata
          Nitzschia hybrida
          Nitzschia rigida
          Nitzschia sp.
          Nitzschiella lorenziana
          Pleurosigma/Gyrosigma sp.
          "Small pennate diatoms"
phylum **PYRROPHYTA**
          Gymnodinium sp.
phylum **PLATYHELMINTHES**
      class TURBELLARIA
          sp.

Hypersaline Biotope, Species List – Cont'd

phylum **ASCHELMINTHES**
    class NEMATODA
        spp.
phylum **ARTHROPODA**
    class CRUSTACEA
      subclass COPEPODA
          Cyclopoida sp. 16
          Cyclopoida sp. 17
          Cyclopoida sp. 18
          Harpacticoida sp. 26
    class INSECTA
        order Coleoptera
        larvae

INDEX OF
SCIENTIFIC NAMES
AND
SUBJECT INDEX

INDEX OF SCIENTIFIC NAMES

All scientific names of animals and plants which are given in this book (except in the appendices) will be found in this index. Further information will often be found by looking up the common names in the Subject Index. Specific and generic names are shown in *italics*, names of higher taxa are in **bold print**. References in roman print (21) are to the main text or footnotes on that page, references in italics *(21)* are to the figure or figure legend of that number.

SUBJECT INDEX

This is an index of general subjects (e.g. biotope, reef), common names of animals and plants (e.g. shark, alga) and place names. Reference in roman print (21) are to the main text or footnotes on that page, references in italics(21) are to the figure or figure legend of that number.